Oceanography:
Exploring Earth's
Final Wilderness

Harold J. Tobin, Ph.D.

THE
GREAT
COURSES®

PUBLISHED BY:

THE GREAT COURSES
Corporate Headquarters
4840 Westfields Boulevard, Suite 500
Chantilly, Virginia 20151-2299
Phone: 1-800-832-2412
Fax: 703-378-3819
www.thegreatcourses.com

Harold J. Tobin, Ph.D.

Professor of Geoscience
University of Wisconsin–Madison

Professor Harold J. Tobin is Professor of Geoscience at the University of Wisconsin–Madison. He received his B.S. in Geology and Geophysics from Yale University in 1987 and his Ph.D. in Earth Sciences from the University of California, Santa Cruz in 1995. After postdoctoral research at Stanford University, he held a faculty position at the New Mexico Institute of Mining and Technology for 9 years before joining the faculty at UW–Madison in 2006.

Professor Tobin's research specialty is in marine geology and geophysics, especially the geology of deep-sea trenches and the processes of earthquake faulting beneath the ocean. He is a veteran of 10 oceangoing research expeditions and has spent nearly a year and a half of his life at sea, cumulatively, in locations ranging from the equatorial Pacific off the coasts of Panama, Costa Rica, Colombia, and Ecuador; the northeastern Pacific off Oregon, Washington, and Vancouver Island; the Atlantic near the island of Barbados; and off the Pacific coast of Japan. His seagoing work has also included dives to more than a mile below the surface in the submarine *Alvin*. Since 2004, he has been Co-Chief Scientist for the Integrated Ocean Drilling Program's Nankai Trough Seismogenic Zone Experiment (NanTroSEIZE), an ongoing U.S.-Japanese collaboration on the causes of submarine earthquakes and tsunami that is the largest scientific ocean-drilling project in history.

Professor Tobin has published more than 40 papers and articles in scholarly journals, including *Science, Nature, Geology, Journal of Geophysical Research*, and *Oceanography*. He has authored more than 100 abstracts for national and international conferences, and he has also contributed a chapter to the *Encyclopedia of Solid Earth Geophysics*. His work has been featured on television programs such as The History Channel's *Modern Marvels* and the Discovery Channel's Science Channel special *Exploring Time*, as well as in numerous magazine and newspaper articles.

In 2000, Professor Tobin received NASA's Lyndon B. Johnson Space Center Group Achievement Award for contributions to the astronaut training program. In 2003, he was selected as a Japan Society for the Promotion of Science Fellow. He has been selected twice by scientific organizations as a traveling speaker, giving both public and scholarly presentations across North America: first as a 2005–2006 Joint Oceanographic Institutions Distinguished Lecturer and later as a 2010–2011 Speaker for the EarthScope project of the National Science Foundation. In 2009, he received an award for Best Instructor (University Housing Award) from the students of UW–Madison. In 2007, he was elected as a Fellow of the Geological Society of America. ■

Table of Contents

Table of Contents

Oceanography: Exploring Earth's Final Wilderness

Scope:

Earth's single, truly unique, defining feature is the ocean of salty water that covers most of its solid surface to a depth of thousands of meters. For nearly all of the 4.6-billion-year history of the planet, the ocean has existed and has been essential to life, climate, and even to the planet's geological evolution through plate tectonics. This course explores all of these topics and more.

The global ocean is a rich and incredibly diverse environment that has cradled the original development and evolution of life. The ocean continues to control the climate and distribution of heat energy on the planet and hosts vast resources, yet its watery mysteries have only begun to be explored in full. It remains a great research frontier, and the science of oceanography is still a true adventure. It is therefore an extraordinarily rich and varied topic, incorporating all the physical, chemical, geological, and biological sciences in the study of Earth's single vast ocean. In this course, we explore all of these disciplines to understand how they illuminate the ocean and its inhabitants. The overarching theme of the course is the inextricable linkage between the ocean's water, heat, light, chemistry, biology, and geologic and atmospheric processes. It is impossible to understand any one of these topics without considering all of them.

The course begins with an exploration of the physical environment of the ocean and how we have come to know it. Ocean exploration began with Polynesians, Phoenicians, Vikings, and other early traders and settlers who had to solve problems in navigation and mapmaking to achieve their goals. In modern times, exploration technology maps the seabed using sound waves and the surface using satellites. Therefore, we now know that the ocean basins—the containers for the sea—are the result of plate tectonic processes of seafloor spreading at mid-ocean ridges that create the oceanic crust. The plains give way to the shoaling sea floor of the continental slopes and shelves—locations where sediment detritus that is shed off the ever-eroding land is deposited in voluminous accumulation. Along the edges of some of the ocean basins, deep-sea trenches mark the location at which the destruction of the ocean floor is recycled back into Earth's interior. All of these regions, from the shallowest sunlit waters to the deepest trenches, are habitats for the amazing diversity of organisms that populate every conceivable niche.

Next, we turn to the physical ocean itself—1.3 billion cubic kilometers of water, the properties of which shape life and climate on Earth. All of it has very similar chemistry because currents keep it well mixed, and it remains in a narrow range of temperature. These stable conditions originally allowed life to evolve and exist predominantly in the ocean; life on land is a relatively new development. Light penetrates the upper few hundred meters, and bottom-linked communities—such as coral reefs and kelp forests—as well as open-water plankton are the photosynthesizers and the foundation of the food webs. Darkness reigns below that, and the near-limitless open-water mass supports a diverse ecosystem of pelagic organisms, many of which have no hard parts to their bodies and are virtually transparent. These communities depend on the scavenging of food that rains down constantly from sunlit waters above—as do most of the organisms of the cold, dark, deep sea floor. Perhaps the most fascinating of all bottom communities, however, are those of the hydrothermal hot-spring vents, where life is based on chemical energy rather than sunlight and where key symbiotic relationships feed ecosystems that may be a window into the origin of all life. The adaptations and life strategies of creatures ranging from submicroscopic picoplankton bacteria to fish, invertebrates, and marine mammals interweave to utilize all available energy throughout the entire ocean volume.

All of the water that composes the ocean is constantly in motion. Ocean waves are generated by the drag of wind blowing over water and can travel as swells thousands of miles from where they are generated. Tsunami and rogue waves are special classes of destructive waves, each capable of traveling long distances across the ocean to strike with little warning. In a sense, tides are the longest waves; they result from the gravitational attraction of the Sun and Moon on the ocean's water, modified by the irregular shapes of the sea floor and coastlines.

On longer timescales, the atmosphere and ocean are intimately linked in their motions, driven by the uneven distribution of heat and modified by the Coriolis effect on all movement as Earth rotates on its axis. Together, these 2 phenomena are responsible for both prevailing wind patterns and all the major systems of surface currents in the world, such as the Gulf Stream and the Canary Current. In contrast to the shallow currents, the bulk of the deep water in the ocean moves slowly in great convection systems driven by gravity and the density of saltwater, mixing the ocean on timescales of thousands of years. All these water movements control the conditions for biological productivity.

In the modern era, human activity is beginning to cause major changes in the ocean as a whole for the first time. Intensive fishing is removing predators and prey alike, altering ecosystems. Most of the added heat in the climate system trapped by greenhouse gas is in the ocean, and the sea level is now rising; that rise is expected to accelerate in the coming decades, affecting estuarine habitats, beaches, barrier islands, and wetlands. Sea-level rise combines with human construction activity to extensively modify the natural deposition and erosion processes on coastlines, causing the loss of beaches and natural barriers in many areas. The extra carbon dioxide added to the atmosphere is exchanged with the ocean, making it more acidic, which adversely affects organisms like coral and phytoplankton. Petroleum and natural gas increasingly come from offshore production, and although society depends on these resources, it is also concerned about impacts from oil spills. Finally, the introduction of pollutants into the sea affects coastal regions in particular but, increasingly, the entire ocean as well.

With these pressures on the ocean environment, the rest of the 21st century is undoubtedly going to be marked by growing pressure on its ecosystems, requiring more active stewardship to maintain the health of the entire planet's life-support system. As the course comes to a close, we return to the theme of linkages among all the physical and biological systems in the ocean—and how the study of oceanography weaves them together. ∎

Soft-Bodied Life in the Dark, Open Depths
Lecture 19

T he vast volume of the open ocean is the pelagic zone, dimly lit and very poorly understood until recently. Beneath the sunlit euphotic zone, the dark water mass supports a diverse ecosystem of pelagic organisms, many of which have no hard parts to their bodies and are virtually transparent. Until submersibles became available, these organisms were almost entirely unknown to science. The basis of the pelagic food web is mainly detritus raining down from surface waters. In the darkness, bioluminescence is an important means of both attracting prey and confusing predators.

Life in the Deep Pelagic

- A great deal of life in the ocean, from the surface to great depths, is composed of organisms with no hard parts on their bodies. Except for the surface dwellers, these organisms were barely known to science until recent decades because they are difficult to sample and leave only a small trace in the form of sediments or fossils.

- Below the pelagic photic zone and the pelagic euphotic zone in the open-ocean environment—from about 200 down to 1000 meters— is a region that oceanographers call the **mesopelagic zone**, the middle pelagic zone. This is the transitional region that's disphotic in terms of light and is sometimes called the twilight zone.

- From 1000 meters all the way down to just above the bottom where the benthic realms exist is the deep pelagic, which is also called the bathypelagic or the abyssopelagic. This is the completely aphotic, or completely dark, deep water of the ocean.

- The most familiar of the gelatinous organisms, the jellyfish, are in a phylum of organisms called Cnidaria—the same phylum as sessile organisms, which live on the bottom of the ocean and stay in one place like anemones and corals.

- All Cnidaria have stinging cells called cnidocytes, which are sometimes called **nematocysts**. They also share a symmetrical body plan with a simple, single orifice that is used for both the intake of food and the expulsion of wastes. Cnidaria are largely carnivorous, and they generally eat crustaceans and fish.

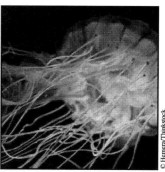

© Hemera/Thinkstock.

A jellyfish is a single organism that is multicellular and has specialized cells that create the head and carapace, for example.

- A jellyfish is a single organism that is multicellular and has specialized cells. For example, the head, or carapace, of a jellyfish is made of a material called **mesoglea**, which is the jellylike substance secreted by the organism that helps it float.

- Cnidocytes, or nematocysts, are the tiny, toxin-containing harpoons that Cnidaria have. They are subcellular structures that are used to capture and stun or kill prey.

- Jellyfish stings vary from being mild to deadly. Box jellyfish called the sea wasp inhabits waters near Australia and is perhaps the most lethal of jellies to humans.

Types of Jellylike Organisms

- There is a vast array of jellylike organisms besides the true jellyfish, and many have only recently been discovered or understood by biology in any significant way.

- **Siphonophores** are closely related to the true jellyfish. They are also Cnidaria, but they're a colonial invertebrate organism. Jellyfish do not self-propel in any organized sense, but siphonophores do.

- Siphonophores are made up of individual, separate organisms—called zooids. They're so tightly symbiotic that they cannot live independently from one another.

- Within one siphonophore colony, there's a central stem and 2 types of zooids: the nectophores, which are the propulsion but can't consume food, and the polyps, which can't swim but can feed. The nectophores are similar to jellyfish; the polyps are similar to anemones.

© Hemera/Thinkstock.

The pulsing motion a jellyfish makes is not so much for propulsion as for sweeping water, along with food particles, toward the mouth.

- All siphonophores have this same strange body plan: The nectophores and polyps bud from the same organism along a central organizing stem. They also all have the ability to coordinate swimming and feeding. Perhaps these organisms provide a clue to how chordates and vertebrates first evolved.

- The Portuguese man-of-war is not an ordinary jellyfish but a siphonophore colony, too. This organism is found mainly in tropical waters and is a true plankton in the sense that it is a drifter—despite its large size.

- Another type of jelly is a **ctenophore**, which is also known as a comb jelly and sometimes colloquially as a sea walnut. Ctenophores have a jellylike, no-hard-parts structure, but they are not in the Cnidaria. They have no stingers, but they do have cilia on some of their cells that slowly propel them through the water.

- Another type of jelly is a **salp**, which is a colony of simple chordates called tunicates. It's not Cnidaria, but it's not like a siphonophore either. They form long chains, but they can live individually as well. They feed largely on phytoplankton.

- One more unusual jellylike creature is called a pteropod, which is a mollusk—closely related to such organisms as snails and slugs. Most pteropods don't have shells, but they all have a single pod, or foot, that gives them their name and propels them through the water.

Submersibles in the Deep Pelagic

- Many newly discovered vertebrate and invertebrate organisms—as well as highly specialized fish such as anglerfish, viperfish, and saccopharynx—populate this world in a surprising diversity.

- Until true deep-submergence vehicles, or submersibles, became available to science beginning in the 1960s, the deep pelagic life was almost entirely unknown to science—except what little had been discovered by dragging plankton nets through the water.

- Deep submersibles became available to science with the development of the submarine *Alvin*, which went into operation in 1964 and was the first submarine available for deep diving to beyond hundreds of feet to thousands of feet in the ocean. The original *Alvin* is still in operation today.

- There are other deep submergence vehicles in the world too, but not very many. There's a French submersible called *Nautile*, and there are 2 Russian submersibles, *MIR 1* and *MIR 2*. There's a Japanese submersible called *Shinkai 6500*, which is the deepest-diving manned submersible in the world.

- The *Johnson SeaLink II* can reach a depth of about 900 meters and has been one of the vehicles that has photographed and sampled many of the organisms in the mesopelagic zone.

- Modern work is increasingly being carried out by remotely operated vehicles (ROVs), or so-called robot subs, than with submarines carrying people to the ocean floor. They're much less expensive and, in fact, less dangerous to operate.

- The trend in science, as well as in offshore petroleum industries, is to use ROVs in much larger numbers. Examples of ROVs used for scientific research are Jason, which is operated by the Woods Hole Oceanographic Institute, and Ventana, which is operated by the Monterey Bay Aquarium Research Institute.

- ROVs, among many other oceanographic tools, played a huge role in what was called the Census of Marine Life, a decade-long, $650 million global research effort that lasted from 2000 to 2010. Approximately 2700 scientists went on 540 expeditions, during which more than 6000 new species were discovered, including entirely new ecosystems and communities.

- About 250,000 marine species were confirmed—excluding microbes—but there are probably 750,000 more that remain to be described. In addition, it is estimated that 1 billion types of microbes exist in the ocean.

The Deep Pelagic Food Web

- At the surface of the ocean, phytoplankton form the base of the food web. Zooplankton feed directly on the phytoplankton, and various higher-trophic-level consumers feed on zooplankton, or directly on phytoplankton—or both—and build up the familiar food webs.

- In the deep pelagic zone, there is no photosynthesis and, therefore, no phytoplankton. The basis of the food web in the deep pelagic is mainly detritus raining down from the surface waters and filtering down through the water and then being scavenged up by various organisms.

- A few examples of such scavengers are copepods and amphipods (in the same family as krill). These 2 types of zooplankton are the new mainstays of the food web in the deep pelagic because they scoop up detritus and then are eaten by larger organisms like fish.

- There are deep pelagic nekton, which are active swimmers that consume detritus scavengers in the deep pelagic. They include numerous species of cephalopods, which have a head that's divided into a number of tentacles.

- For the most part, these cephalopods, or mollusks, are different kinds of squid. Squid swim in groups and prey on small fish. Mesopelagic squid are transparent and are nearly jellylike cephalopods.

- The deep pelagic zone also includes some of the largest invertebrates that live on the planet in the form of giant squids and even what are called colossal squids. Giant squids stay in the deep zone and never come anywhere near the surface.

- Deep pelagic organisms have some interesting adaptations to the water depth. For example, many of them are colored a deep red. No red light penetrates that deep, so any red animal actually appears to be black even in the partially photic zone.

- Deep pelagic fish feed on copepods, krill, and other small fish. Deep pelagic fish are some of the strangest forms that we see on the planet, but they share some common characteristics.

- In the deep pelagic zone, the fish tend to be small because there's not a lot to live on. They also tend to have very large mouths and needlelike teeth. Many of them barely swim; instead, they keep their metabolism low and wait to lure prey.

- In fact, many of these fish use a specific adaptation called **bioluminescence**, which is the ability to generate light, and special organs called **photophores** to lure prey. Anglerfish and lanternfish use photophores as lures. These fish look scary until you realize how tiny they are.

- In the disphotic and aphotic zone, bioluminescence is an important mechanism for survival. The purposes of bioluminescence are to communicate with one's own species, to confuse predators and as a form of camouflage, and to attract prey.

- There are a wide variety of microbes, invertebrates, and fish that produce bioluminescence, which is created by a chemical reaction called chemiluminescence, the combination of the vividly named enzymes luciferin and luciferase.

Important Terms

bioluminescence: The process of production of light by an organism, used for camouflage, defense, and attraction of prey and mates.

ctenophore: Very common pelagic gelatinous organism, also known as comb jellies.

mesoglea: Translucent, jellylike gel that makes up the bulk of organisms like jellyfish.

mesopelagic zone: The dimly lit region of the water column; also called the disphotic zone or the twilight zone.

nematocysts: Also known as cnidocytes, the stinging cells of many jellyfish and other cnidarians.

photophores: The organs that produce light in bioluminescent organisms.

salp: A tubular, gelatinous animal that lives either as an individual or as a colony that is common in equatorial waters.

siphonophore: An order of Cnidaria that are colonial animals; one example is the Portuguese man-of-war.

Suggested Reading

Nouvian, *The Deep*.

Prager, *Sex, Drugs, and Sea Slime*.

Questions to Consider

1. Do you think a colonial organism like a siphonophore is one animal or a community working together? How about an ant colony? Or the collection of cells that make up a dolphin? What basis do you use to draw a distinction?

2. How many different uses can you list for bioluminescence in organisms that live in the aphotic zone?

Soft-Bodied Life in the Dark, Open Depths
Lecture 19—Transcript

We're going to continue our exploration of the pelagic world, the open ocean world by moving up in scale a little bit from the plankton forms that we looked at the last time. We're going to focus in this lecture on the great massive life in the ocean actually that exists from the surface to great depths that exists with virtually no hard parts at all, no skeletons, no shells, the jelly-like organisms that fill up the sea in every depth range from the surface to the bottom of the aphotic zone. Now, except for the surface dwellers, the ones that you can actually see from a boat or something like that, these organisms as a whole, this whole class of organisms was little known to science until very recently and we'll see what that is in a few minutes.

But basically, you know they're very hard to sample and they leave little trace in the sediments in the form of fossils or even in modern sediments, just in the form of their dead bodies, because they're so soft and they're basically such delicate organism. There's been an explosion in our understanding of these various kinds of soft-bodied, jelly-like organism over the past couple of decades. We're going to explore them in this lecture as well as some of the predators that live deep in the water column that live off of these organisms.

In this lecture as I said, I'm going to focus on the majority of the ocean environment, the deep pelagic zone or the middle and deep pelagic zones that are mostly beneath the surface waters themselves. Let me go back and remind us of a few basic definitions. You know at the surface water, there's the pelagic photic zone or sometimes the pelagic euphotic zone, the well-lit surface waters that we're familiar with. As we go below those in the open ocean environment, then from about 200 or so down to 1000 meters is a region that oceanographers will call the mesopelagic zone, the middle pelagic zone. This is the transitional region that's disphotic in terms of our light. Sometimes it's actually the twilight zone, yes that's the name of it and the word twilight zone originally came from oceanography. It's the zone where many of the organisms are living in the mid-water column where there's a little bit of light, but not much.

But, from 1000 meters then down, all the way down to just above the bottom where we enter sort of benthic realms, is what we will just call the deep pelagic. Now, there's specialized terms like bathypelagic or abyssopelagic, but for our purposes we'll group it all together and just call it the deep pelagic zone. The key is though that this is the totally aphotic dark deep water of the ocean.

We're going to look at a whole range of different organisms, all gelatinous, all mostly unfamiliar. But, perhaps the most familiar one is in this whole class of organisms are the jellyfish. Everybody's aware of what jellyfish look like and we've seen their beautiful forms in different videos and we've perhaps even encountered them at the beach. Perhaps, we've even been unfortunate enough to have been stung by one now and then. We'll start with the jellyfish and then we'll look at some of the creatures that are similar but are much less well-known to us.

The jellyfish themselves are in a whole phylum of organisms that are called Cnidaria and these are basically the same phylum actually as some organisms that we call sessile, ones that live on the bottom and stay in one place, like anemones and corals, and we'll see the ways in which the same types of cells and the same types of structures have adapted back and forth between the swimming or open water jellyfish versus the sessile organisms. But, all the Cnidaria share a couple of key things. One is that they all have the stinging cells called cnidocytes, sometimes called nematocysts, and so the cnid is shared between the name of the organism and this particular actual structure in it. Those are the stinging cells we'll look at in just a second.

They also share a symmetrical body plan, so they're sort of circular in plan with a symmetry all the way around and they're very simple body plan structures. They have a simple, single orifice that's for both intake of food and then expulsion of wastes. Basically of the Cnidaria are largely carnivorous. They have these stinging cells for a reason and that's to capture prey and the generally eat crustaceans and fish and small fish and things like that. Despite their appearance as sort of a very simple organism, yes they are predators and carnivores.

Jellyfish we're familiar with are Cnidaria that have these cnidocytes that are tiny, sort of subcellular structures that are basically harpoon-like barbs that can be shot out of the cell at extremely high velocity and extremely high accelerations when something is sensed that can trigger those nematocysts. They're used to capture and stun or kill prey because they contain stinging toxins and they range from sort of just an annoyance to other organisms and annoyance to us if we touch them, in fact, not even an annoyance. If you touch certain kinds of coral polyps you just feel that. It feels a little bit rubbery or strange without actually hurting, but that's actually the nematocysts.

But these nematocysts shoot into the skin or organs of other organisms and can stun and kill and help capture those prey. Among the most deadly of jellyfish are actually a jellyfish called the sea wasp, one class of what are called box jellyfish. They inhabit the waters near Australia and New Guinea and are probably the most lethal of jellies to humans, one of the most lethal organisms that exist in the ocean. A sting from the sea wasp can put you in the hospital for a long time and potentially cause heart failure and death. The toxins that the nematocysts produce though are specific to different specific individual organisms and so some things that are very toxic to one reef fish will be not toxic at all, for example, to us or have only very low toxicity. There are chemical pathways that are specific to different organisms.

There's a vast array of other jelly-like organisms besides the basic jellyfish or the true jellyfish. Many are really only recently described or discovered or really understood to biology in any significant way. We're going to look at a sample of a few of these and the most closely related are the siphonophores that I'll discuss in a moment and then we'll talk about a number of different organisms that you may've never even heard of, like ctenophores and salps and pteropods. Let's see what some of these organisms do and how they make their living in the ocean.

The first one I want to talk about, as I said, is a siphonophore. These are actually closely related to the true jellyfish. They are also Cnidaria, but they're a different type because they're actually a colonial organism. A jellyfish is a single organism, in a sense, that is multicellular and has specialized cells, for example the ones that create the head, the large carapace of the jellyfish that's made of a material that's called mesoglea, which is the jelly-like substance itself secreted by the organism to create that kind of float and then can be manipulated by the rhythmic motion of the muscles.

By the way, you might be interested to know that although jellyfish seem to swim through the water in this rhythmic way and they do, they move through the water over short distances. It turns out that biological study has shown that the pulsing motion that the jellyfish makes is not so much for propulsion as actually for sweeping water along with the particles of food in the zooplankton and things like that that are in it towards the mouth. Actually the propulsion is more of a byproduct of the actual sweeping of water towards the mouth as opposed to the main reason that a jellyfish does that.

But in any case, the jellyfish then are really not self-propelling in any sort of organized sense, but the other siphonophores are. In fact, the siphonophores really cross the boundary between plankton and nekton because many of them are of a large enough size that they can swim in an organized way through the water. As I said, they're colonial invertebrate animals. They're colonial Cnidaria and what does that mean?

They're made up of individual organisms that are actually separate. They're called zooids and each one is distinctly an individual animal; however, they're so tightly symbiotic with each other that they cannot live independently from one another. They have to form a colony in order to survive. Interestingly the zooids are the same species, the same genus, the same organism, but they specialize into different body plans or different body forms that form the colony. Within one siphonophore colony, for example, there's a central stem and then there are 2 types of zooids, the nectophores, which are the propulsion zooids, they can't actually consume any food whatsoever, but they can pulse water so they can again help the organism move. The nectophore is actually the same type of zooid that is similar to what are called the medusa of the jellyfish meaning the swimming, propelling part of the jellyfish.

The second type of zooid though in a colonial siphonophore is called a polyp. Now, the polyps can't do any swimming motions whatsoever, but they can feed. They have the mouth parts that allow them to feed on the prey that is captured by the siphonophore. The nectophores and polyps have to work together. One can't feed itself, one can't move itself or sweep water through itself. They're totally independent. The polyps are like the anemones, so anemones have the body structure essentially of the polyp zooids; remember they're related to the siphonophores. The nectophore is related to the jellyfish. The siphonophores are some combination of the 2 living as a purely colonial organism.

Very strange, it makes you raise sort of the question in your mind that well what is the definition of one siphonophore? Is it the individual zooid or is it the entire colony? In a sense, the way sometimes people talk about an ant colony being a single organism even though it has many thousands or tens of thousands of individual ants. We could say the same about the siphonophore because there are many different species and types of siphonophore with many different body plans. They all share this characteristic of being organized colonial. They grow from an original single zooid so one zooid of a siphonophore grows this stem and they buds the individual polyps and nectophores. It really is one organism and yet not one organism at the same time.

The fact that it has a central stem and cord makes this activity through specialized body parts that actually feed, for example, the polyps, feeding all of the nectophores, is perhaps some kind of clue to the original evolution of the chordates and vertebrates; remember that the chordates are all the organisms that have some kind of central nervous system like a spinal cord whether they have bones or not. These are not vertebrates or chordates; these are a prechordate type of organism, but perhaps they're somehow included in the steps of the evolution of those organisms.

One type of jellyfish that you may think of is not a jellyfish at all actually in the sense of being a true jellyfish, but is really a siphonophore. That's the Portuguese man-of-war, the famous jelly that has the giant float of jelly that is inflated with some air, a kind of a gas bladder that gets blown around by the wind and the surface of the ocean and trails these very long, up to 10 or even 15 liters long, tentacles down into the water covered with stinging cells that can capture prey and then pass the prey or sweep the prey back towards the mouth that's near the top of the organism. A Portuguese man-of-war is also a siphonophore colony and not a single jellyfish. They're plankton because they drift through the ocean, but their large size really kind of defies what we think of as plankton. They're one of the largest organisms that we can think of as a true drifter or plankton form.

Another type of jelly that you probably have not heard of at all is a ctenophore, also known as the comb jellies, and sometimes colloquially as sea walnuts, but a ctenophore is a different organism. It also shares this jelly-like, no hard parts, kind of structure. It's not in the Cnidaria. It has no stingers. There are no nematocysts so they're a different class of organism. They're also all carnivores. They're also invertebrates and they're planktonic. They basically float in the water, but they can get to quite a large size. They're macroscopic. They can get to at least centimeters or even tens of centimeters in size. They have cilia on some of their cells to slowly propel themselves. They can move through the water a little bit especially moving up and down a little bit in the water column to follow their prey, which is the zooplankton and phytoplankton as well.

These very transparent, delicate creatures, very beautiful creatures when seen in their native habitat in the open water, make these complex structures that have various kinds of big sails, wings, or even sort of balloon-like structures made essentially of a kind of a mucus that they spinout to filter and trap small food particles or organisms from the water and sweep them back into their gut where they can be digested. Another type of jelly, again basically very poorly known until they could start to be observed in their native habitat deep in the water, are the salps. A salp is a colony, it's another colonial organism, but it's not Cnidaria; it's not like a siphonophore exactly. It's a colony, a very simple tunicate chordates. Tunicates are just a term for one particular group of chordates. Again chordates are a phylum of the kingdom of animals overall. The chordates include all of us vertebrates, but also a number of marine invertebrates.

All of these are purely marine organisms or all the tunicates in the sea are purely marine organisms. Individually they can actually live as individual sort of bell-shaped organisms that can swim short distances through the water. They feed largely on phytoplankton, sweeping them through their bell or the cavity of their body and digesting them. But they also form very long chains together to basically give them some stability in the water and ability to move long distances in an organized way by all clumping together and in a colonial sense beating their propulsion systems together simultaneously.

One more unusual, let's just say, jelly-like creature in the ocean are the ones called pteropods. Now the pteropods are even different from all the ones that I've described because they're a mollusk so they're in a different phylum within the animal kingdom. These are mollusks; that means that they're related relatively closely to snails and slugs and organisms like that. Most of them don't have shells, although a few do secrete a hard shell, but many of the pteropods are completely soft parts. The single pod or foot that gives it its name, along with the gastropods like the snails and slugs, has evolved the pteropods into kind of a transparent, almost wing-like structure, very broad again, very delicate and beautiful. They use this transparent pod to basically beat its wing and fly through the water to sweep it through regions of plankton. They also cast out sort of a mucus like net and spin a web of material or a net of material that's sticky enough to catch plankton on it and reel it in and digest all the food that they've trapped in that way.

We've looked at all these different organisms from the deep pelagic zone and I want to stop now and take a look at how we know about all these organism. As I said, many of these things live in either the twilight region or the completely dark zone of the deep pelagic and were very poorly known until recently. For a long time the only way to sample this zone was to drag a plankton net through the water, just as we described in a previous lecture. Those plankton nets would fill up with plankton and they would also of course capture many of these organism, the ctenophores and pteropods and so on, but their structures are so soft and delicate as to be completely destroyed just by the action of dragging the plankton net through the water. So a plankton net tow would always have many different individual organism, including fish and things like that described, and then usually the description was just jelly. There was a certain amount, a certain mass in each plankton net of what was just described as jelly.

That was actually the bodies of many dozens or hundreds of individual organisms of many different species, but completely unrecognizable and indescribable by biologists until quite recently, and in fact still true when you use a plankton net. But instead, the way we've learned about most of these organisms is through the use of deep submersibles, deep submergence vehicles. These became available to science really beginning in the 1960s with the development of the submarine called *Alvin*. I've showed you pictures of *Alvin* before. *Alvin* went into operation in 1964 and was literally the first sub that was available for deep diving to beyond hundreds of feet to thousands of feet, in fact thousands of meters even in the ocean. There's only been one *Alvin*.

When you see all the pictures of *Alvin* in *National Geographic* articles and things like that, it's the same *Alvin*. Now, every single part of *Alvin*, since 1964, has literally been replaced at one time or another, including the actual spherical 6-inch thick, now titanium, originally steel, hull of the submarine. All of the porthole windows and the hatches and things like that. Everything has been replaced, but it's one *Alvin* and it's still in operation today, just now in a transition to a new hull and ultimately, hopefully a replacement for *Alvin* that will keep deep submergence research going on to this depth with human beings going to the bottom of the ocean for many years and even decades to come. *Alvin* has made a phenomenal number of discoveries and literally thousands of scientific papers and thousands of individual species have been described based on direct observation using *Alvin*.

There are other deep submergence vehicles in the world too, but not very many. There's a French one called Nautile. There are 2 Russian ones, MIR 1 and 2, which played a role in some of the great videos you've seen from the Titanic and other places. There's a Japanese one called Shinkai 6500, which is rated to a diving depth of 6500 meters, hence the name. That's the deepest diving manned submersible in the world. The Johnson Sea-Links I and II have been real workhorses of studying the twilight zone of the ocean, the mesopelagic zone. It can go to about 1000 meters or so, 900 meters to 1000 meters, and has been one of the vehicles that has photographed and sampled many, many of these organisms and allowed entire ecosystems of soft-bodied organisms to be described in the mid-water.

Modern work today is increasingly being carried out by the ROVs or remotely operated vehicles, so-called robot subs. Now, they're not really true robots in the sense that they don't operate independently using their own computer brain. They're tethered back to a ship with a cable that feeds video back and carries electrical signals so that an operator on the ship, using joysticks, literally can drive the ROV around, illuminate and take video and pictures of different things and use even these robotic style arms or these manipulator arms to take samples or do other things in the water or on the sea floor.

They don't carry people to the bottom of the ocean so they're much less expensive to operate and in fact less dangerous to operate. The trend in the science, as well as actually off-shore industries, is to use ROV in much larger numbers. A couple of the well-known for science include Jason, which is operated by Woods Hole Oceanographic Institute as well as the ROVs operated by the Monterrey Bay Aquarium Research Institute, the Ventana and the new one Doc Ricketts, named after the famous character from Steinbeck's *Cannery Row.*

Dozens and dozens of ROVs are employed by the offshore petroleum industry to do the work on the sea floor that they need to do to keep their industry operating. Many of us in the news saw ROV images from the sea floor during the deep water Horizon oil spill disaster and were kind of amazed by the degree to which we could have a 24-hour a day camera on the seabed seeing what was going on, seeing the horrific things that were going on in that case at the sea floor. ROVs, among many, many other tools for oceanographers played a huge role in what was called the Census of Marine Life, this decade long 650 million dollar global research effort that lasted from 2000 to 2010.

Many of the organisms that I've just mentioned were described and cataloged as part of this Census of Marine Life. Several thousand scientists undertook more than 540 expeditions to see and discovered more than 6000 new species, many of them again these soft part animals in the water and on the bottom of the world's oceans from the Arctic zone all the way to the tropics. There are presently, based on the Census of Marine Life estimates at the end of that operation, something like 250,000 confirmed marine species. Now that's species of all types in the ocean, excluding the microbes though, but there are probably 750,000 more that remain to be described. They estimate about a million species in the ocean of nonmicrobial life and they estimate actually that there are 1 billion types of microbes, 1 billion species of microbes must be in the ocean, not individuals of microbes, but 1 billion types, most of which have never been described and never had their DNA sequenced or anything like that.

Let's take a look at the food web as a whole of the deep pelagic zone. We've talked about the planktonic organisms and now we've talked about some of the larger, but soft-bodied organism that live down there. We can go up from that scale. Now at the surface you have a food web that's essentially the base of the food web is the phytoplankton. Then zooplankton feed directly on the phytoplankton and then various larger higher trophic level consumers feed on zooplankton or directly on phytoplankton or both and build up the familiar food webs. In the deep pelagic zone, below a thousand meters or so, down there in the darkness, there is of course no photosynthesis and therefore there are not phytoplankton, at least not living and making food, making carbohydrates in that zone.

The basis of the deep pelagic food web is actually detritus raining down from the surface waters and filtering down through the water and being scavenged up by all of these different organisms, many of the ones that I just described and also the zooplankton that are living down there scavenging phytoplankton and then being consumed in turn by different larger organisms than that. Some of the zooplankton that we've already mentioned before, this particular very beautiful copepod is an Arctic deepwater variety that lives at 1000 meters, 600 to 1000 meters in the Arctic Ocean. We also have many organisms called amphipods, they're in the same sort of family as krill, that I've already discussed and they're a very, very common zooplankton. Those are basically the new mainstays of the deep pelagic food web, the copepods and the amphipods as these small organisms that scoop up all the detritus and then in turn are eaten by larger organisms like fish.

There's a deep pelagic nekton, meaning a deep pelagic set of active swimmers and they consume all these detritus scavengers. Basically we're going to spend a lot more time talking about nektonic organism in the next lecture, but just to introduce some of these deep pelagic ones initially they include a lot of cephalopods, which are the squids and octopus and cuttlefish and things like that. A cephalopod is called that because cephalo means head, pod again is foot, so it has a head that's divided into a number of tentacles and for the most part these mollusks, these cephalopods, in the mid-water, are basically different kinds of squid. We even have transparent, very clear, almost jelly-like cephalopods in the mesopelagic zone and in the deep pelagic zone as well.

The deep pelagic zone also includes some of the largest invertebrates, in fact the largest invertebrates that live on the planet, in the form of giant squids and even what are called the colossal squids, which are a different species, but similar in body plan to the giant squids and equally large, in fact perhaps even a little bit heavier. The giant squids are an organism that has been known to exist from tales of mariners and from their partly digested remains found in sperm whale bellies and things like that over many, many years, and even centuries. But, a living giant squid was never photographed until 2004 when a Japanese group put a deep marine camera down and baited it and, in fact, captured a photograph of a giant squid. They stay in the deep zone and never come anywhere near the surface in ordinary life. They're occasionally caught in fishing nets and are brought either nearly dead to the surface and so a number of samples and examples of dead giant and colossal squids have been found.

But, they can be, in fact, up to 15 meters or 50 feet in length. This New Zealand specimen shown in the photograph had an eye, once it was dissected, that was the largest eye of any species on earth, 27 centimeters in diameter, something like that, even after it had shriveled up a little bit in depth, probably 40 centimeters in diameter, huge, bigger than a dinner plate when it was alive. The squid are feeding on all kinds of fish down there and of course in turn they're providing food for sperm whales as we'll look at in the whales lecture a bit later on.

The deepwater pelagic organisms have some interesting adaptations to the water depth, one thing; many of them are colored a deep red. No red light gets that deep so any red animal actually appears to be black even in the twilight zone, even in the partially photic zone. So you see all kinds of examples of deepwater red organisms, giant squid, these red shrimp, many jellies and octopus are all red in color. We're going to deal with the fish largely in the next lecture, but let me introduce a few of the deep pelagic fish as we close in this one. They feed on the copepods and the krill and other small fish in fact. The deep pelagic fish are some of the strangest forms that we see on the planet, but they share some common characteristics.

In this zone, they tend to be small. There's not a lot to live on. They keep a very small and low metabolism going. They don't have a very large body mass to support. They tend to have very large mouths and these needle-like teeth and very sort of monstrous frightening forms that we've all seen maybe in some of these television deepwater blue planet type specials and things like that. Many of them barely swim at all. They keep their metabolism very low and wait to lure prey. In fact, many of them lure prey using a very specific adaptation, which is bioluminescence, the ability to generate light, like a firefly and use special organs called photophores as lures.

If we look at an image of the angler fish, for example, they have this photophore lure that is blinking or brightly lit and it hopefully attracts other organisms that think maybe they want to see what's going on over there, I see some food, but then they're captured by the angler fish with its giant teeth. Now these things look pretty giant and frightening until you realize that the angler fish is really only about less than 2 inches in length typically. These are tiny organisms. They may be monsters of the deep, but they wouldn't be very scary if you actually encountered one yourself. Some of them, of course, get a bit bigger. Many of these things like lantern fish and viper fish have really very large mouths to gulp in these soft organism or other organisms that they encounter and basically spend a long time digesting them because a meal doesn't come along very often.

In the disphotic and aphotic zone, bioluminescence is an important mechanism for survival and it has multiple purposes. Bioluminescence is to communicate with your own species so you can find a mate for example or find other of your same kind. But, also it's to confuse predators and as a form of camouflage and even as we just saw to attract prey. There are a wide variety of microbes, invertebrates, and fish to produce bioluminescence. All of it is by something called chemiluminescence.

It's a chemical reaction that produces the light in the photophores and it's the combination of these vividly enzymes luciferin and luciferase that when combined produce light in some devilish way I suppose. One of the most remarkable bioluminescent organism is the firefly squid, which light up brightly with complicated patterns of blue and green light, which are the most common types of light that can be produced by bioluminescent organisms. When they're caught they produce an absolutely amazing firefly squid show in the nets and on the docks.

We've examined this planktonic basis of the grazing and light-based food web of the euphotic zone and also now of the detrital food web of the deep pelagic world. We've examined all of these really mysterious sort and previously unknown forms of the soft organisms that represent a whole bunch of different major phyla of the animal kingdom, not just simply one type like jellyfish, but all the siphonophores and the tunicates and the cephalopods, all representing different soft-bodied adaptations to this deep marine world without walls. In the next lecture, we'll take up the really major groups of the nekton. Maybe the more familiar ones in this sense, the active swimmers of the sea, the fish, the mollusks, and the mammals, reptiles, and birds following after that.

Swimming—The Many Fish in the Sea
Lecture 20

Nekton are all the actively swimming organisms in the ocean, ranging from fish to invertebrates to mammals and birds; nekton have evolved many specific adaptations to succeed in their marine habitats. Squid, octopus, and nautilus are mollusks, which are invertebrates with remarkable adaptations and apparent intelligence. The most successful nekton families are the bony fish, which are uniquely well adapted to their environment—particularly through having evolved the oxygen exchange system of gills.

Active Swimmers

- There are certain characteristics that are shared by most of the marine organisms that are rapid or powerful swimmers. Those basic functions are streamlined in shape and energy efficient, effective propulsion.

- From car and airplane-wing design, we know that a teardrop shape is aerodynamic. It's the shape that in a wind tunnel produces the least drag and the least turbulence.

- A phenomenon called vortex shedding involves the creation of vortices, which take some of the energy out of the flow, behind an object embedded in a streaming fluid. It's a fundamental problem of turbulence and drag in flow in any medium. The teardrop shape inhibits vortex shedding.

- Water is much thicker and more viscous than air, so it is extremely important to minimize drag in water because drag in water is many times greater than drag in air.

- There are certain body shapes for organisms that do the best job of minimizing drag. Drag is minimized when the ratio of the width to the length in terms of the profile, or cross-section, of a given body moving through liquid is about 0.2 to 0.25.

- The body shapes that have been evolved by many different marine organisms come very close to the mathematical calculation of what the optimal body plan is. Organisms like swordfish, tuna, and dolphins are at somewhere around 0.25 to 0.28, and they are the strongest swimmers in the sea as a result. The shape of a blue whale is very close to optimal at 0.21.

- In general, the different organisms that swim actively through the water provide an example of convergent evolution because these different organisms started out as very different types of creatures with very different types of body plans and, yet, evolved to these streamlined shapes.

- The hydrodynamic shapes all emerged from the ancient jawless fish, which evolved into some of the modern fish. A shark, for example, has a very streamlined shape, including fins that have evolved to control it and to enable it to swim in the water.

- In the ocean, the ichthyosaur—a marine reptile of the Mesozoic Era—evolved a similar shape, with a flipper system, from the legs of reptiles that evolved on land. In addition, the flippers of dolphins and whales evolved from land-based organisms that have legs. Birds such as penguins have evolved a flipper that was a wing that is currently useless for flight but is fantastic for swimming.

Categories of Active Swimmers: Invertebrates

- The category of active swimmers that is the most adapted over the longest period of time in the ocean is the invertebrates. The larger invertebrates, for the most part, are represented by the **cephalopods**—mollusks that actively swim. Cephalopods include squids, octopuses, and nautiluses.

The ink that is produced by squids is used to confuse predators and prey as an escape mechanism.

- All cephalopods have a body plan that includes a single foot that protrudes directly off of the head of the organism and is divided into multiple parts, or tentacles. Cephalopods move around by jetting water from their bodies. They feed very efficiently by using their tentacles to capture prey, move it into their mouth, and then move it into their gut.

- The chambered nautilus is an interesting cephalopod because it makes a shell, which makes it look like a snail. It has a spiraling shell that is famous in both mythology and in the fossil record. These were very prevalent organisms in the Paleozoic Era before fish took over as the main organisms of the ocean.

Categories of Active Swimmers: Vertebrates

- The most numerous species of **nekton** in the ocean, by far, are fish in terms of number of different species and overall adaptation success to all niches. In fact, fish are the most numerous vertebrates on the planet.

- There are 30,000 species (and still counting) of fish. There are more species of fish, in fact, and individuals of fish overall than all other vertebrates on the planet combined, including all the land vertebrates.

- Fish dominate the nekton because of the fact that they are adapted to virtually every niche in the ocean and virtually every habitat that's available in the ocean. Fish exist in all the zones of the ocean, but they are much more numerous in coastal areas and in surface waters of the ocean.

- There are a few distinguishing features that all fish have in common, including the existence of fins for various types of locomotion among several different species and the existence of gills for respiration.

- There are 3 major types of fish: jawless fish, cartilaginous fish, and bony fish. The cartilaginous fish are in the class **Chondrichthyes**, and the bony fish are in the class **Osteichthyes**.

- Cartilaginous fish are evolutionarily the oldest group of fish. They've been around for practically all of the 450 million years that fish have been on the planet. They evolved first in the ocean, before the bony fish did.

- The Chondrichthyes include rays, skates, and sharks. As the name cartilaginous implies, they have no true bone in their skeleton; they only have cartilage making up their skeletal materials. Their skeleton is fairly rigid, but it is more flexible than mineralized bone, which is what bony fish and other bony vertebrates, such as human beings, have.

- Even sharks' scales are basically cartilaginous. Shark teeth are modified scales that include dentine, a substance similar to what makes the teeth of human beings hard. All their scales have dentine, which is why they are so rough. Most sharks bear live young, which is different from bony fish but similar to mammals.

- Despite their relatively early evolution, sharks have developed some phenomenally acute senses, including some senses that are unfamiliar to humans.

  - Sharks have excellent vision, even in very dim light.

  - They also have a sense of smell and taste that's highly developed and includes their entire bodies.

  - Sharks have pit organs, which are chemical receptor cells that are distributed over their entire body.

  - They can also sense very weak electrical signals through a set of organs, which allows them to detect minute currents for use in orientation and predation.

- The vast majority of sharks have no interest in predation on human beings, and in fact, shark attacks are very rare. Great white sharks and mako sharks are the ones that can be dangerous to people. We are much more dangerous to sharks than they are to us because of overfishing and overconsumption.

- There are more than 450 species of Chondrichthyes, which include rays and skates. Most of them are basically benthic organisms, living near the sea floor in both shallow water and deep water.

- The largest Chondrichthyes are the manta rays, which are actually plankton feeders. Others are carnivorous and eat small seafloor organisms. Some have a tail with a barbed stinger, and others can produce electric shock—both of which are used as a defense against predators, not to intentionally cause harm.

- The bony fish are the most numerous fish by far. They evolved later than sharks and other cartilaginous fish, but they've radiated throughout the ocean and now represent at least 27,000 different species—probably with many more to be discovered.

- They're exquisitely well adapted for a wide range of marine habitats. Bony fish developed bony skeletons several hundred million years ago, and all land vertebrates evolved initially from bony fish.

- Examples of bony fish include salmon, tuna, halibut, flounder, herring, sea horses, and other familiar species.

Adaptations of Fish

- Bony fish have a variety of body shapes: Some are adapted in a streamlined torpedo shape for fast swimming while others are flat with a large dorsal area. In addition, others are laterally flat—thin looking but wide—for maneuverability in reefs, and many open-ocean fish are rounder to maintain buoyancy as they float along the surface.

© Comstock Images/Getty Images/Comstock/Thinkstock.

A sea horse, which is a type of bony fish, has a body plan that formed as a result of adaptation to its habitat.

- Some key adaptations of fish include having a streamlined in shape, propulsion, buoyancy (maintenance of level), gas exchange, osmoregulation (saltiness), and feeding and defense, which includes schooling behavior and bioluminescence.

- Fish are negatively buoyant and, therefore, sink; their bodies are denser than seawater, so they need to adapt. Cartilaginous fish have no specific adaptation to this except that they must remain in motion, so they glide as though they're in flight to maintain their height in the water. Their fins are like airplane wings.

- By contrast, most bony fish have **swim bladders** beneath their spinal column that are gas-filled chambers that can be delicately controlled to maintain neutral buoyancy. Abyssal species have developed oil-filled buoyancy chambers instead.

- A second adaptation is **osmoregulation**. All saltwater fish have body tissues that are less saline than the seawater around them, so they need to find strategies to maintain internal salinity. Because fish are hypotonic, they have the problem of constant water loss through their skin and scale structure. To offset that, fish are constantly excreting salt through their gills and even through their cells by active transport, forcing osmosis.

- Fish also need oxygen and need to expel carbon dioxide—just like humans do. Gills are the organs that they breathe with, and a gill is simply a way to put a very large surface area of a thin cellular membrane where their bloodstream can flow through gill membranes and exchange gases with dissolved oxygen in the water.

- Primitive fish like eels swim through the water in a sinuous motion, allowing them to swim like a snake crawls on the ground. However, this isn't a very efficient way to get around. By contrast, most bony fish have an inflexible and highly muscular body, which allows them to move straight while their tail moves back and forth.

- The schooling behavior of fish allows them to efficiently work together to appear much larger and, therefore, more intimidating to predators. The interesting things about a school of fish is that all the fish seem to turn as one. To carry out schooling behavior, fish have a lateral-line organ system, which includes pressure sensors that feel tiny motions in the water.

Important Terms

cephalopod: Mollusks including squid, octopus, cuttlefish, and nautilus that are characterized by bilateral symmetry, a prominent head exhibiting many tentacles.

Chondrichthyes: The taxonomic class comprised of all cartilaginous fish, such as sharks and skates.

nekton: All organisms that actively swim in the ocean (e.g., fish, marine mammals, cephalopods, and more).

osmoregulation: Biological process of controlling internal salinity and other chemical balances for optimum metabolism.

Osteichthyes: The taxonomic class comprised of all bony fish.

swim bladder: Gas-filled chambers many fish have beneath their spine to maintain buoyancy in the water.

Suggested Reading

Garrison, *Essentials of Oceanography*, chap. 14.

Videler, *Fish Swimming*.

Questions to Consider

1. Why don't biologists classify organisms by similar function of their anatomy rather than evolutionary lineage?

2. Does a fish's lateral-line system represent a true "sixth sense" compared to our familiar 5 or just a different application of one of them? What about the electrical signals that sharks can sense?

Swimming—The Many Fish in the Sea
Lecture 20—Transcript

In the last lecture as we looked at the organisms that live in the deepwater pelagic zones, we started to make the transition between the plankton, the free-floaters, and drifters, and the nekton or the swimmers in the ocean. In this lecture and the next, I'd like to take that to the really truly active swimmers that are populating the seas and are often at a much higher trophic level and consuming many of the other different organisms in the ocean. We're going to take up all the animals that actively swim through the water, the nektonic organisms and that's going to include invertebrates, we'll revisit the mollusks, like the squid and the nautilus. We'll look at crustaceans and then we'll talk about the vertebrate organisms that are in the ocean, fish and eels. And in the next lecture, mammals like whales and seals, reptiles and birds that actually swim through the water.

The first question we want to ask then is, in general what does it take to be a good swimmer in the ocean. We know that there are certain characteristics that are shared by most of the marine organisms that are rapid or powerful swimmers. Those basic functions or those basic characteristics are, first of all, streamlined in shape and second energy efficient and effective propulsion. So we'll look at both of those over the course of this lecture. We're all familiar with the idea that there is a certain shape that's aerodynamic, if you think of cars and airplane design and things like that or wind design, you know that a kind of a teardrop shape is the one that is called aerodynamic and that's for a very good reason. It's the shape that in a wind tunnel produces the least drag and the least turbulence. Now teardrop shape meaning kind of rounded at the front, not too sharp an edge, but kind of an open curve and then a long tapering form to a tapered back.

Why is that a good shape from the point of view of avoiding aerodynamic drag? The rounded front basically separates the flow lines of the air around the particular shape that's moving through it. But, when that air separates then, if it has a blunt or a round back so that it's a flat body or a flat object or a spherical object, then the separation occurs and just as we sort of saw with capillary waves on the surface of the water, there's a zone behind it where the air is a little bit stiller. In fact, where because of the separation of those flow lines, there's a pocket of very low pressure air and. in fact as we'll see, water in behind that object. That area is a region that generates turbulence, the fluid medium, the air, water swirls in behind it, creates vortices, and those vortices basically take some of the energy out of the flow, direct it back in other directions and dissipate it as heat ultimately.

This phenomenon called vortex shedding or the creation of vortices behind an object embedded in a streaming fluid is a problem. It's a fundamental problem of turbulence and drag in flow in any medium. What you want to do with anything you want to make aerodynamic is minimize that vortex shedding. That teardrop shape basically just conforms the shape of the object to the shape of the airflow that's broken at the front of the object and therefore comes back along the taper to the rear of the object. It inhibits vortex shedding and that's exactly what inhibits drag in either the organism or the object.

I talked about it being aerodynamic, but of course water is much, much thicker and more viscous than air. So the importance of minimizing drag in the water if you're a swimmer or if you're a submarine for that matter moving through the water, it's even more important than it is in the air. Drag in water is many, many times greater than drag in the air. These same shapes that we consider aerodynamic are also hydrodynamic are shapes that are effective for minimizing turbulence and drag in the water.

It turns out that studies in wind tunnels and in water tanks and things like that of what it would take to minimize hydrodynamic drag show that there's certain body shapes that work very well and that do the best job of minimizing that drag. We can express them first of all in terms of a shape that's a teardrop or torpedo shape in the ocean or in the water, but also in terms of a ratio of the length to the width in terms of the profile or cross section of a given object or body. That length to width ratio is optimized in terms of minimizing the drag based on different thicknesses of the profile when the width to length ratio is about 0.2 to 0.25 or so. The width is just a fifth to a quarter of the length of the body that's moving through the liquid or fluid medium.

It turns out then that if we actually look at the body shapes that have been evolved to by many different marine organisms. They come very close to this theoretical or sort of mathematical, physical calculation of what the optimal body plan is. Organisms like swordfish and tuna and dolphins are at somewhere around 0.25 to 0.28 or so in terms of their width to length ratio, very good shapes for minimizing drag. In fact, these are the strongest swimmers in the sea, the ones that move the fastest in order to capture their prey. So they have a great sort of evolutionary pressure or evolutionary incentive, in some sense, to have gotten to this shape. That's, in fact, the shape they've gotten to.

The most efficient shape of all perhaps is the largest organism, the one that needs to move through the water at high speeds in parts of the water by the greatest amount and that's the blue whale. As the blue whale moves through the water, its body shape is at about 0.21 or its body shape ratio is at about 0.21, optimized for that thickness and size of the whale to swim most efficiently through the water and use the least energy to overcome drag and move through the water overall. This is a really, really vivid example of something we call convergent evolution.

In general, actually the different organisms that swim through the water, especially the ones that swim actively and vigorously through the water are a beautiful example of this process because we have many different organisms that started out as very different types of creatures with very different types of body plans and yet evolved to these streamlined shapes. That's shapes that come very close to optimizing the exact same shape for maximum avoidance of drag and maximum hydrodynamic benefit. The adaptation of this streamlined shape for swimming has emerged multiple times. If you think of the original organism that all the different large lineages evolved from, they're basically all an ancient jawless fish. Ultimately that jawless fish in the ocean evolved into some of the modern fish and a shark, for example, has a very streamlined shape, very close to that optimum. It also has fins that have evolved to control it and swim in the water.

If you think of other organisms that actually moved onto the land and continued to evolve, they may also obtain the same shapes. You might think of a land reptile that evolved on land. There was the period of the dinosaurs and then in the ocean there was the ichthyosaur, marine reptile of the Mesozoic period, but an ichthyosaur evolved a similar shape. It involved a flipper system that evolved from the legs of those reptiles on land. If you think of the mammals that inhabit the ocean, the dolphins and whales, as we'll see, are all evolved from land-based organisms that have legs. They're all from various land mammals and ungulates and things like that. Yet those legs evolved into flippers, similarly with seals and sea lions and such organisms. Even birds, a penguin has evolved a flipper that is of course a wing initially or evolved from a wing, but is utterly useless for flight at this time, but is fantastic for swimming. The shape of a penguin swimming through the water, again approximate the same kind of body plan as does the shape of that dolphin, that whale, and even that ichthyosaur.

These are a fantastic example of things that evolved in different directions to solve the same problem and therefore evolved to very similar shapes. This is the reason of course why we don't classify animals based on anatomical shape because then we would group them into the same groups somehow. But, their DNA and their evolutionary history is utterly different among these different organisms.

Okay well let's look at some of the different categories of organisms that actively swim through the water. The earliest, the most adapted over the longest period of time in the ocean is certainly the invertebrates. In the larger invertebrates, for the most part, are represented by the cephalopods, certainly as the most successful group of invertebrates. Those are mollusks. They're mollusks that actively swim so that includes the squid, octopus, and what's called the nautilus, I'll show you in just a second. All of them, as I described a little bit in the last lecture, are called cephalopods because they have this body plan that includes these tentacles or this sort of foot that is coming directly off of the head of the organism. They have a very decentralized nervous system that includes parts of what we might think of as a brain sort of distributed throughout each of the individual tentacles or feet as well as into a nervous system that includes the head.

They have a body or mantle that they primarily move around by jetting water out of jets, so they're basically jet-propelled. They don't swim in the sense that fin fish do or eels do, but they're jet-propelled in the water. They feed very efficiently by using of course those tentacles to capture prey and move it into their mouth and move it into their gut. They have lots of other interesting adaptations like the ink that are produced by squids and octopus to confuse prey and predators and many other adaptations like that. They make them extremely efficient swimmers.

One of the interesting things about the squid are that they actually swim in another example of convergent evolution, in large schools in many cases, and they swim in a way that is very streamlined and, in fact, gives them torpedo shapes that are also similar to the hydrodynamic shapes of larger fish and things like that. They were long thought to be sort of relatively slow-moving creatures and there are a lot of bottom dwellers we'll talk about in another lecture, but the mid-water squid in particular are very rapid swimmers, very active predators, and very successful organisms over a very long period of time in the history of the ocean.

The chambered nautilus is an interesting one because it's a cephalopod that actually makes it shell so it comes out looking something like a snail. It has a spiraling shell, the famous nautilus shell of both mythology and of the fossil record. These were very prevalent organisms back in the Paleozoic period of the ocean before many of the fish really took over as the main organisms of the ocean. There are still nautiluses present today though as this one swimming in the waters off Palau in the South Pacific shows. It shows that jetting or pulsing of water just like its close relatives the squid that just happen to not have that shell.

The most numerous nektonic species in the ocean by far are the fish in terms of number of different species and overall sort of adaptation success to all niches. In fact, the fish are the most numerous vertebrates of all on the whole planet in terms of sheer numbers and of species. There's 30,000 species and still counting of fish. There are more species of fish, in fact, and individuals of fish overall than all other vertebrates on the planet combined, including all the land vertebrates as well as us.

Fish dominate the nekton really because of the fact that they are adapted to virtually every niche in the ocean and virtually every habitat that's available in the ocean. They're in all the zones of the ocean, pelagic and neritic, surface to deep, benthic, everywhere. They're certainly much more numerous in the areas of very high productivity of the bases of the food chain, the phytoplankton and zooplankton that go along with them. They're most numerous by far in coastal areas and in surface waters of the ocean.

We're going to take a look at some different features of different species and types of fish, but of course what all fish have in common in particular are the existence of fins or the evolution of fins for locomotion that are very well adapted to the particular types of locomotion that a particular fish species needs to do whether it's long distance high speed travel like a tuna or a swordfish or navigation in the complicated structures of reef like a parrot fish or an angel fish or something like that. They also have gills for respiration. All fish share the body structure known as gills.

There are 3 major types of fish. The first is the jawless fish, the hagfish and lampreys. We're going to talk about them a little bit in a later lecture on benthic organisms and then the other 2, the main 2 types that we'll consider in this lecture are the cartilaginous fish and the bony fish. The cartilaginous fish called the chondrichthyes and the bony fish called osteichthyes. You can remember osteichthyes because they're bony and it's like osteoporosis and osteopath, words like that that make you think of bone. Then you'll just have to remember chondrichthyes based on the fact that they're different from the bony fish and therefore cartilaginous.

Let's take a look at the cartilaginous fish then because these are the oldest group of fish evolutionarily. They've been around for basically all of the 450 million years that fish have been on the planet, evolved first in the ocean, before the bony fish did. Now the chondrichthyes or cartilaginous fish include the rays, the skates, and the sharks. Those are the main categories of them. They have, as the name implies, they have no true bone in their skeleton. They only have cartilage making up all of their actual, sort of skeletal materials. It's certainly a fairly rigid, but still pliable and flexible to a much greater extent than mineralized bone and it's mineralized bone that's the distinction when we talk about bony fish or other bony vertebrates, such as ourselves. We're mineralized too.

Now, even sharks scales are basically cartilaginous. The scales actually include dentine, a substance similar to what makes your teeth hard and that's why actually sharkskin is so rough and often causes abrasion and can even be used as sort of a form of sandpaper because it has this relatively hard material that's still, again not the same as actual bone. Sharks teeth are very sharp. They're bone though, they are cartilaginous material, but they include more of that, they actually modified scales and include some of that dentine as well. So sharks teeth are fossilized and some of the few parts that actually remain of the sharks after they're fossilized.

They have that capability that you've probably heard where they come in rows in the shark and can be regenerated more or less at will as they get lost. Of course, sharks feed by grabbing on large bites of mostly larger organisms or bigger fish, marine mammals, and things like that using these serrated rows of teeth to pull off big hunks of flesh, which is probably why they're so frightening to us in fact. Most sharks actually bear live young, different from the bony fish and similar to the mammals, although they're not mammals of course.

Now sharks have some incredible senses and despite their relatively early adaptation or their early evolution, they've developed some phenomenally acute senses including some senses that are really pretty unfamiliar to us. First of all, sharks clearly have excellent vision even in very dim light. They swim and chase prey in the dimly lit waters of the deep euphotic zone or the disphotic zone, so they have to be able to see things and sea movement from very large distances through the water and they can. They also have a sense of smell and taste that's really highly developed and actually includes not just their sort of noses or snouts, but literally their entire bodies.

They have these organs that are called pit organs, which are little receptor cells, chemical receptors that are distributed over, not just their face, but their entire body. They essentially taste or smell the water and can sense various kinds of chemical signatures, smell traces of prey that they're interested in down to parts per billion levels, really very tiny levels. They can sense the direction of gradients of those chemicals, for example, through use of these organs that are distributed over their body to allow them to swim to and home in on an organism in the water. They have an even more of an amazing sense that is completely different from anything familiar to us. They have an actual sense of electricity in a way.

They can sense very weak electrical signals or electrical currents through a set of organs that are called the ampullae of Lorenzini, what a wonderful name. This person Lorenzini described these first in 1678. You can see them as actual sort of pores or tiny holes distributed mostly on the snouts of sharks and rays and skates. Those have small fluid sacks in them that are basically sensitive to electrical gradients or electrical voltages. So they can detect minute currents that are perhaps related to even the motion of ocean currents in Earth's magnetic field that can generate a weak electrical current and perhaps they use them for orientation or the electrical signal associated with just the body, the metabolism of other organisms, perhaps prey. These electroreceptors are a whole sense that's completely unfamiliar to us here on the land, but are a major part of shark orientation as well as predation.

Sharks really kind of get a pretty bad name actually. We're afraid of sharks. There are a few sharks that actually are known to attack human beings occasionally. They certainly don't make human beings a major part of their food, but great white sharks and mako sharks are ones that can be dangerous to people, perhaps because we thrash around in the water like a very sick swimmer. We're not very effective, we're not very efficient swimmers so we perhaps look like an organism that's in distress even when we're swimming well. The vast majority of sharks have no interest in predation on human beings and, in fact, shark attacks are very rare. We are much more dangerous to the sharks than they are to us because unfortunately the world has a taste of shark meat and in Asia, shark fin soup, and shark populations are being decimated rapidly by over fishing and over consumption as well as in some cases just by killing them as a potential hazard to life.

Many of the sharks are completely docile. Maybe one interesting one is the whale shark, the largest living fish or the largest fish that exists in the ocean approaches the size of many of the whales. They can be as much as 15 meters in length. They weigh several tons and they are entirely filter feeders. They don't eat anything. They don't predate on anything large in the ocean. They open their large mouths and they just vacuum up lots of seawater, sort of the way a baleen whale does, but they filter it through their gills and they have some structures in their gills that are called gill rakes, these protrusions across the gills that basically catch all the zooplankton and phytoplankton that's filtering through those gills.

They have to filter these at a prodigious rate to get literally many hundreds of kilograms of food per day. They actually filter more than half a million cubic gallons of water per hour through their gills in order to feed. You can swim with the whale sharks; they're utterly harmless to human beings.

Other chondrichthyes include the rays and skates. There are more than 450 species of all of these. Most of them are basically benthic organisms, and we'll look at them again when we talk about benthic habitats, living near the sea floor in both shallow water and deepwater. Again, the largest of them, the manta rays, the very beautiful rays with their flat body plan that seem to fly through the water are actually plankton feeders feeding in a similar way to the whale sharks. Others are carnivorous and do eat small organisms, seafloor organisms, many of the invertebrates and things like that. Some in a defensive way, not as in an attacking way on predators have a tail with either a barbed stinger or even can produce electric shock as you know and there are some skates that if you step on you'll get a nasty sting from them, but only because the skate is basically trying to avoid being stepped on.

Okay so the bony fish are the most numerous fish by far. They evolved later than the sharks and the other cartilaginous fish, but they've radiated throughout the ocean and now represent at least 27,000 different species of bony fish, probably with many more to be discovered. As I said, they're exquisitely well-adapted for the wide range of marine habitats. They've adapted to a myriad of different forms. All land vertebrates, everything that lives on the land that has a spinal column evolved initially from bony fish. We're all the product of evolution from these bony fish.

There's a wide variety of examples, halibut, flounder, herring, seahorses, a range of body plans and that's that result of adaptation as I said. Some are adapted in a streamlined torpedo shape for fast swimming. Others are flat with a large dorsal area, both eyes on top like flounder and halibut because they're bottom scavengers and basically swim only around the bottom eating what's in the mud, other ones are laterally flat, reef fish that are very thin looking, but high and that's good for maneuverability in and among all the corals of the reef and things like that. Other open ocean fish are rounder to maintain buoyancy as they float along the surface. There's just a wide variety of different forms all basically adapted to particular habitats and environments.

Some of those key adaptations are streamlined in shape, we've already talked about. We'll talk about propulsion in just a second and also buoyancy or the maintenance of level because fish need to be buoyant. Gas exchange, they need oxygen, osmoregulation, they have to deal with saltiness and then feeding in defense which involves schooling behavior and also the bioluminescence that I mentioned in the last lecture.

Let's look at a few of these different adaptations in a little bit more detail. First of all, you know fish sink. They're negatively buoyant. They have bones, they have body parts that are heavier than water. They're denser than seawater so they would sink. They basically have to adapt to that. Now cartilaginous fish have no specific adaptation to this except that they must remain in motion. You've probably heard that a shark needs to continue swimming at all times and that's exactly what they do. They glide as though they're in flight. Their fins are shaped like airplane wings to provide lift and so they must maintain their height in the water by continuously swimming or they would simply settle to the bottom.

By contrast, most bony fish, the teleosts as they're called, which are most of the osteichthyes have swim bladders beneath their spinal columns so these are little gas filled chambers that can be delicately controlled by their metabolism muscles to compress them and squeeze the gas out, organs to release a little bit of gas from their respiratory functions into these chambers to maintain neutral buoyancy. The fish can maintain buoyancy levels so they don't have to swim at all and can stay at the same height. Some of the very deep living fish that live at high pressures in the abyssal realm actually developed instead of gas-filled chambers they've developed oil field buoyancy chambers or fatty tissues that are lighter than water and so can maintain the level in the same sort of way as the gas bladders that most fish have.

A second adaptation is osmoregulation. All saltwater fish actually have body tissues that are less saline than the seawater around them, about half the salinity of the seawater around them so instead of 35 per mil about 18 per mil. So, they need to find strategies to maintain that internal salinity which is just simply a balance that has evolved as an optimal salinity for the kind of metabolic processes that their cells are carrying out all the time. Since fish are hypotonic in this way, basically water wants to osmos out to equilibrate with the surrounding seawater all the time so this problem of constant water loss through their skin and scale structure. In order to offset that, the fish are constantly excreting salt as well. In their bloodstream and through their kidney-like organs they excrete very high concentrations of salt so their urine is essentially very high concentrated brine or saltiness. They also employ active transport meaning forces osmosis by biological processes pushing salt out through the membranes in their gills and then excreting salt through the gills as well.

Fish also need to breathe right. They're consumers and they need to respire. So how does a fish breathe? They obviously don't breathe the air like us, but they still need oxygen and they need to get rid of carbon dioxide just like we do. Gills of course are the organs that they breathe with and a gill is simply basically a way to put a very large surface area of a thin cellular membrane where their bloodstream can flow through these, what are called gill membranes inside the gill arches, and exchange gases with dissolved oxygen in the water.

The water carries a certain amount of dissolve O_2, dissolved oxygen, and the blood flows through gill membranes one way, the water flows passed it in the gills the other direction, and exchange oxygen. There's very, very large surface areas in this sort of manifold structure of the gills. In fact a mackerel that needs a lot of oxygen swim a lot, has a high metabolism, has a gill surface area inside its gills that's 10 times the whole surface area of the rest of its body. Actually we're the strange ones because it turns out that being evolved from marine organisms, we have to have a watery coating inside our lungs and we have to get the oxygen that's in the air actually into solution in that watery system in our lungs and then exchange it with the internal membranes.

We talked about body shape and movement and the primitive fish like eels swim through the water in a sinuous motion. They are sort of elongate, but they don't have that optimal shape and they sinuously move through the water. This allows them to swim like a snake would swim or crawl along the ground even. But, it isn't actually a very efficient way to get around and eels are not long distance swimmers in general. Most teleost fish, most bony fish by contrast have that torpedo body plan, but also have an inflexible and highly muscular body so they can flap very hard in a hinged tail area so the body basically stays moving straight while the tail moves back and forth. You can see that in the flopping of fish on a ship's deck and that's an extremely efficient way to move forward because it keeps the body shape moving through the water in just the right profile to minimize turbulence while still allowing those powerful muscles to flap the fin back and forth and move the fish quickly.

The last thing I want to discuss in this lecture is schooling behavior of fish. Now fish have a very efficient means of basically working together to appear much larger and therefore more intimidating perhaps to predators and that is schooling of course. They school for safety. The interesting things about a fish school and we can see in this beautiful video of fish schooling behaviors, they seem to all turn as one. In fact, there's no lead fish like many flocking birds, but all the fish simply move in a way that seems almost like kind of a group mind. In order to actually carry out this schooling behavior they employ a set of organs that we don't even have.

As we watch this video you can see the dolphins actually exploiting the fish schooling behavior, the fish's natural tendency to school by herding them into a very tightly packed school and the dolphins will then feed on them. We'll get to dolphins a little bit in the next lecture. Let's take a look at the lateral line structure that is the key to this schooling behavior, in fact, to a lot of fish behavior. Along the sides of a fish's body, on both sides, there's a line of special cells that are special nerve sensors. These are an organ system that we don't share.

They're tiny pressure sensors, much like the pressure sensors I described at the bottom of the ocean for tsunami, but in the fish they sense minute movements of the water adjacent to the fish that puts a little bit of pressure on those cells and sends a signal up to their brains through the nerve endings in lateral line organs. What those do is they sense the movements of every fish around it in such a way that through the lateral line organ information they are coordinating their activity with all the fish that surround them on both sides. So the school seems to move as one because every fish is sensing the motion of every other fish in that school, these tiny, tiny motions that we would have no way of sensing ourselves.

We've taken a look very briefly and we could go on for a long time, we could have an entire course just about the interesting marine biology of the nekton. We've looked at least at the most familiar sea creatures; these invertebrates like squid and all the different kinds of fish from sharks to tuna to seahorses and we've seen that they're the most numerous and varied and exquisitely adapted animals on the planet. Fish are the most successful of the nekton, but of course there's a lot more than fish out there in the sea. In the next lecture, we're going to look at the other active swimmers of the ocean and large organisms that really use the ocean as their fundamental habitat and lifestyle and that includes the birds, the reptiles, and the mammals of the sea.

Marine Birds, Reptiles, and Mammals
Lecture 21

P erhaps the most intriguing of the open-ocean dwellers are the marine mammals: whales, dolphins, seals, sea lions, and manatees. Many spend all or most of their life in the open ocean. Marine mammals—Cetacea (whales and dolphins), Sirenia (manatees), and Carnivora (seals, sea lions, and walruses)—evolved from land-dwelling mammals and include the largest animals ever to have lived on Earth. Toothed whales use echolocation to find prey, and baleen whales—the largest of the animals—filter feed exclusively on some of the smallest zooplankton, krill.

Marine Birds

- We might not think of birds as marine organisms at all, but what they share with the marine reptiles and mammals is a total adaptation to the life at sea. The ones that we think of as true sea birds are birds that cannot live without the ocean as a large part of their habitat—for virtually everything except nesting.

- Seabirds run the spectrum of extremes in terms of flight from extreme fliers like albatross, who are adapted to fly long distances, to flightless birds like penguins, who are adapted to swim and feed exclusively under water.

- Flightlessness means that penguins can be very differently shaped from virtually all other birds: They can be large, which means they have a lot of fatty insulation and stubby appendages that keep them warm. They can also maintain neutral buoyancy by a combination of having fatty insulation as well as greasy feathers that are laden with insulating fat.

- Penguins are adapted to dive deep in the ocean with phenomenal ability. Emperor penguins, the largest of the penguins, are known to dive to depths of 265 meters and stay submerged for as long as 10 minutes or more.

- A few species of penguins really are almost entirely seabirds, spending 2 uninterrupted years at sea in between individual breeding episodes and then arriving on land or on ice shelves to breed.

Common Characteristics of Seabirds

- Most seabirds live in the Southern Hemisphere, which is also known as the ocean hemisphere because there's not much land and lots of very large areas of open ocean.

- There are a number of different types of seabirds. Gulls and pelicans are familiar shorebirds, and they exclusively feed on fish and invertebrates of the sea.

- The true seabirds are the pelagic birds called **tubenoses**, which include the albatross and sooty shearwaters that specifically travel across open areas of the ocean and are exquisitely good fliers.

- All tubenoses share the ability, by way of the tube in their nose, to sample the airflow and tell them about their speed. These tubes also include special salt-excreting glands that concentrate the salt in their bodies—because they have no access to freshwater—and flow the brine out over their beaks.

- Virtually all marine birds live a fairly long time, have few offspring, and mate monogamously for life on remote rocks and islands where their nests are mostly undisturbed.

- The largest seabird is the wandering albatross of seafaring lore. They have wingspans of up to 3.6 meters (12 feet), yet they only weigh about 10 kilograms (22 pounds). They have a very delicate bone structure and an optimized wing shape for soaring: They barely flap their wings at all.

- One tagged albatross traveled 500 miles over the course of a day at an average speed of more than 35 miles per hour. They use the actual updrafts created by the rise and fall of the waves to keep them aloft.

- Wandering albatross only go ashore to breed on remote islands. They will spend many months at sea and bring food back to their offspring. They are able to find these remote locations because they have a magnetic sensing ability in their bodies that is similar to the capabilities sharks have.

© iStockphoto/Thinkstock.

Sea turtles, like birds, come ashore to lay eggs, but they spend virtually all of their life history in the ocean.

- Another example of a tubenose is the sooty shearwater—a Southern Hemisphere bird as well. Sooty shearwaters are perhaps the most amazing long-distance fliers in the ocean. Tagged birds have been found to fly incredible distances—as much as 950 kilometers (500 miles) in a single day. They are not very large, but they can dive to great depths (68 meters or more) for fishing.

Marine Reptiles

- Related in some ways to birds through their common relationship to the dinosaurs and other even earlier organisms are the marine reptiles. Although reptiles are mostly land-dwelling organisms, each main group of present-day reptiles has some marine species: turtles, lizards and snakes, and crocodiles.

- All reptiles breathe air. None of them are aquatic in the sense of having gills, but they have special salt glands that excrete excess salt from their bodies—another example of convergent evolution.

As reptiles, lizards have evolved special salt glands that excrete excess salt from their bodies.

- There are 8 different species of sea turtles. Like birds, they come ashore to lay eggs but at very infrequent intervals—such as every 2, 3, or 4 years. They spend virtually all of their lifetime in the ocean. In fact, sea turtles return to the original spot on the same beach that they were born on to lay eggs with an incredible sense of navigation.

- Sea turtles are a bit different from land-based turtles and tortoises. They can't retract their heads and limbs into their shell. The shell serves as protection from predators, but their fins are always out. They swim through the water with relatively slow, gentle propulsion.

- All of the major sea turtle species are threatened by human beings, and some are very much in danger. They all feed in shallow water on algae, sea grass, and plants, so they hug coastline areas and low-shelf regions where there is plenty of vegetative material for them to feed on.

Marine Mammals

- The 3 different groups of marine mammals are **Sirenia** (manatees and their relatives), Carnivora (seals and sea lions), and **Cetacea** (whales and dolphins). Each group evolved independently from land mammals that moved into the sea, and all have lost the ability to live totally on land.

- All of these are mammals, which implies that they have live young and feed them with milk. They all breathe air, so during the entire time spent at sea, they breathe air through their blowholes, nostrils, or other organs.

- All marine mammals have the streamlined body shape of high-energy, high-activity swimmers. They also have slippery skin or hair that has developed special oils to both retain heat and retain a slippery, smooth profile.

- All marine mammals are internally heated; they're warm-blooded organisms. They have to maintain a high endothermic body heat, so they need a high metabolic rate. Therefore, they need to consume a lot of food and burn a lot of food as well as be well insulated with fatty tissue. Their large size retains heat because they have a good surface-to-volume ratio.

- Marine mammals have unusual respiratory systems that efficiently use oxygen. Many of the marine mammals have special biochemistry that's optimized to retain and use oxygen during deep, prolonged dives.

- Gases collapse under high pressure, and marine mammals accommodate that by allowing their lungs to collapse after they've taken oxygen into their bloodstream—or while they're taking oxygen in. In fact, the pressure helps drive the dissolved oxygen into the bloodstream.

- Marine mammals also have very strong osmotic adaptations to living in salt water. There's little to no intake of seawater; they don't drink water for the most part. Instead, they get their freshwater directly from food tissue and also from the metabolism of carbohydrates.

Marine Mammals: Sirenia

- The manatees and the dugongs of Indonesia are virtually the only examples of Sirenia. There are only 4 species of these organisms on the planet, and all of them are herbivorous marine mammals—the only herbivorous ones.

- Sirenia graze on sea grass. They're closely related to the land-based grazers, including elephants and water buffalo. Calling them sea cows is not much of a stretch: They are organisms that have adapted to being in the water, so they have no legs. Both manatees and dugongs are currently endangered species.

- Steller sea cows have been extinct since 1768, but they were even larger than manatees—up to 30 feet in length and weighing 20,000 pounds. Seal hunters found them to be pretty easy pickings because they didn't move very fast, so they were hunted for their meat.

Marine Mammals: Carnivora

- The **pinnipeds** and **fissipeds** are of the order Carnivora, which include dogs, cats, bears, and weasels. The pinnipeds are the seals, sea lions, and walruses; the fissipeds are the sea otters. All of these are relatively recent arrivals in an evolutionary sense in the ocean.

- The pinnipeds live mostly in marine environments; they spend almost all of their time in the water, but they come on land to mate and to birth their young.

In the same way people form images with their eyes, dolphins form images of their watery surroundings using sonar.

- The difference between seals and sea lions is that seals have no external ear parts whatsoever—a more streamlined shape. They swim with a fused set of hind limbs that's essentially a single flipper and don't swim with their forelimbs at all. Conversely, sea lions have external ears. Their hind limbs are still partially separated, and their front flippers are also used for swimming actively.

- Walruses are the largest of the pinnipeds and the most massive. They live mostly in very cold-water environments where their massive size is an advantage to maintaining body heat.

- The largest of the seals and the most interesting is the elephant seals because they spend a lot of time on land.

- Sea otters are the geologically most recent newcomers to the ocean, and they're the only marine fissipeds. They can be found in the kelp forests of California, in large numbers in the Pacific Northwest, as well as in many other places around the Pacific.

Marine Mammals: Cetacea

- Cetacea include whales, dolphins, and porpoises. They are the large organisms that spend their entire life cycle at sea and don't come out for giving birth to live young. They evolved from early ungulates, so their closest land relatives are sheep and horses.

- The order of Cetacea can be broken down into 2 categories: Odontoceti, the toothed whales, and Mysticeti, the baleen whales.

- The toothed whales are the top predators of many fish and invertebrates in the ocean. They exist, for the most part, at a very high trophic level. The dolphins, porpoises, orca, beluga, and narwhal are all examples of toothed whales.

- Odontocetes have small to moderate sizes relative to mysticetes. The sperm whale is the largest of the toothed whales. They're all extremely skillful, fast-moving predators.

- All odontocetes share echolocation. They use very sophisticated combinations of clicks in the form of rising and falling tones—a sophisticated sonar. We suspect that dolphins and whales are very intelligent organisms.

- There's evidence that the sonar is not just used to locate prey, but it is used to stun their prey with extremely loud bursts of sound energy up to 230 decibels. Their large, convoluted brains may be used to process these audio tools.

- Baleen whales, mysticetes, don't have teeth. Instead, they have a horn-like, fibrous material that hangs down inside their mouth called **baleen**. As a result, they feed mainly at the surface, taking in great amounts of water that can be strained for small organisms.

- The baleen whales use sound as well. In fact, they are famous for their whale song. They emit low-frequency but loud sounds that can be heard over long distances—perhaps thousands of miles across the open ocean.

Important Terms

baleen: Horn-like fibrous plates used by Mysticeti whales to strain plankton from seawater.

Cetacea: Taxonomic group of marine mammals descended from land ungulates that includes dolphins, porpoises, and whales.

fissipeds: Marine mammal group including sea otters; in the same order as dogs, cats, bears, and weasels.

pinnipeds: Marine mammal group including seals, sea lions, and walruses; in the same order as dogs, cats, bears, and weasels.

Sirenia: Taxonomic group of marine mammals that includes manatees and dugongs.

tubenose: Taxonomic group of far-traveling marine birds including albatrosses, shearwaters, and petrels.

Suggested Reading

Berta, Sumich, and Kovacs, *Marine Mammals*.

Schreiber and Burger, *Biology of Marine Birds*.

Questions to Consider

1. Do any birds live exclusively at sea?

2. Most marine mammals are quite large organisms; there are no tiny ones similar to mice, for example. Why might it be difficult for a small marine mammal to exist?

Marine Birds, Reptiles, and Mammals
Lecture 21—Transcript

Now it's time to turn our attention to the poster children of the ocean, the big marine mammals, the reptiles like sea turtles, the marine birds like penguins and things like that. All of the organisms that are familiar to us all from television specials and trips to ocean aquariums and things like that. We'll take a look at how they make their living in the ocean as well as how some of their adaptations relate to what we've seen already with fish and other organisms and what they share and what they don't share with all the other really large-scale organisms that live in the sea. We'll look at all these different ocean dwellers, but first let's talk about the birds.

We might not think of birds as marine organisms at all, but what they share with the marine reptiles actually and also with the mammals is a total adaptation to the life at sea. The ones that we think of as true sea birds are birds that cannot live without the ocean as their total food source for example and as a large part of their habitat from virtually everything except for nesting itself. All the sea birds breed on land, but all the true sea birds, at least, do feed at sea and they're all specifically adapted to the marine environment in a variety of ways that I'd like to describe.

Let me give you just a few examples. First of all, we can think of sea birds that run the spectrum of extremes in terms of flight from extreme fliers like the albatross and Arctic terns and sooty shearwaters , I'll describe to you in a minute, that fly great distances and are very at home in the open ocean and in fact pelagic environment, all the way to totally flightless birds like penguins who have adapted to life in the sea by adapting their wings to be optimized for swimming and not for flight, and not just their wings actually as we'll see in just a moment.

In fact, penguins are adapted to swim and feed exclusively under water and these adaptations take a number of different forms and this is just a reminder of the kind of converging evolution I talked about in the last lecture. First of all, flightlessness, the fact that they've abandoned their requirement of flying means their body can be very differently shaped from virtually all other birds. They can be large first of all. They can have a lot of mass and have a lot of fatty insulation, sort of like a seal or a sea lion does and so that can keep them warm in cold water and in cold environments like in the Antarctic overwintering and things like that. They can also have stubby appendages also to keep warm. Very importantly, they can maintain neutral buoyancy just as the fish do that we talked about in the last lecture.

In the case of the penguins, they maintain it by a combination of this fatty insulation, fat deposits in their bodies, as well as greasy feathers that are laden with a lot of insulating fat as well. When a penguin swims through the water it can maintain neutral buoyancy, just as a fish can do. Penguins are adapted to phenomenal abilities to dive deep in the ocean. Emperor penguins, the largest of penguins, are known to dive to depths of 265 meters or more and stay submerged for as much as 10 minutes. Few species of penguins really are almost entirely seabirds. They spend 2 uninterrupted years at sea in between individual breeding episodes and then just come on land or on the ice shelves to breed.

Of course, we know that penguins are Southern Hemisphere organisms. They live only in the Southern Hemispheres, no penguins in Alaska. There are penguin species that live as far north though as the Galapagos, they're tropical penguins actually living near the equator, but the majority live in high southern latitudes, New Zealand and South America and certainly in Antarctica where we've seen so many nature films about penguins and penguin lifestyle.

In fact, when we talk about seabirds in general, most of them actually live in the Southern Hemisphere and maybe that's because it is the ocean hemisphere. It's the hemisphere where there's not much land and lots of very large areas of open ocean. The flying seabirds, there are a number of different varieties. We can think of the gulls and the near shorebirds, the pelicans, things like that. These are transitional land marine animals. They feed at sea largely except the gulls that scavenge up a lot of food from the boardwalk when you're down at the beach and steal your French fries and things like that. But, largely they're feeding on fish and invertebrates as are the pelicans virtually exclusively.

Really the true seabirds, I think, the ones that excite us in terms of being the open ocean seabirds are the pelagic birds that are called tubenoses, not a very romantic or dramatic name, but these are incredible beautiful creatures like the albatross and sooty shearwaters that travel across open areas of the ocean and are exquisitely good fliers and fly specifically over the sea. What they have in common with each other is the tube in their nose literally, which is almost like the Pitot tube on an airplane, something that samples the airflow and tells them about their speed through the air, but also include special salt excreting glands that concentrate the salt in their bodies because they have no access to fresh water and flows it out much like if you would have a runny nose, but flows the brine out over their beaks to get rid of the excess salt.

Most of these seabirds, in fact virtually all marine birds, are organisms that live a fairly long time, have few offspring, and mate monogamously or nearly monogamously, largely on remote rocks and islands in the Southern Hemisphere, so uninhabited places where their nests are virtually undisturbed. They only return to nest and otherwise spend virtually all their time wheeling across the ocean and feeding on surface fish and surface invertebrates like squid. Let's take a look at the tubenoses, the albatrosses, sheer waters, petrels, and things like that.

The largest seabird in the ocean is the wandering albatross of seafaring lore. These are incredible birds. They have wingspans up to 3.6 meters, something like 12 feet, yet only weigh about 10 kg or 22 pounds or so. They're very light, very large wingspans, very delicate bone structure, and optimized wing shape for soaring. They barely flap their wings at all. In fact, many of them, the albatross in particular have a resting heartbeat that's lower while they're flying than while they're actually sitting on the water bobbing up and down, suggesting how comfortable they are in flight. One albatross has been tagged having traveled 500 miles over the course of a day at an average of speed of more than 35 miles an hour. They're just tremendous fliers. They actually fly off and wheel in very low over the water when they're out in the open sea.

On ships sometimes, you'll see these albatross, I have myself, and they use the actual updrafts created by the rise and fall of the waves so they'll swoop over the water, get lift from being just above the water's surface, and then use the updrafts to keep them aloft off of each individual wave. They only go ashore to breed on remote islands. Again they mate for life over time, but they will spend many, many months at sea and then bring food back to the chicks, finding these remote islands and navigating to them over thousands of mile distances across the open ocean, possibly again because they have some magnetic sensing ability in their bodies somewhat similar to what we talked about with the sharks.

Another example of this tubenose class is the sooty shearwater. It's a Southern Hemisphere bird as well. They're just the most amazing long distance fliers, perhaps in the ocean. As part of the Census of Marine Life, a number of researchers from the U.S. and New Zealand tagged a number of these birds; you can see Dr. Scott Shaffer tagging a sooty shearwater here with geolocation devices, basically GPS units. They found these sooty shearwaters could fly incredible distances, as much as 950 kilometers, more than 500 miles again in a single day. They dive also to great depths in the ocean, 68 meters depth. They're not very large birds, but can dive to such depths for fishing.

The most amazing thing about the sooty shearwaters of all is just the mapping of what these birds do over the course of a year. They live in, as Dr. Schafer describes, an endless summer, meaning they spend their summers in the Southern Hemisphere in their rookeries, the areas that they nest and mate in, in the region around New Zealand and the great southern islands of the far south Pacific. Then annually they take off and fly all the way across the equator to the far distant Northern Hemisphere to spend the Northern Hemisphere summer up there and return. They fly across the entire Pacific Ocean and these tagged birds were shown to fly across the ocean in a figure eight pattern making stops in Japan, Hawaii, and Gulf of Alaska, or the Aleutian Islands, but this is the longest electronically recorded bird migration.

These 19 individuals, only 19 birds actually represent all of the track lines that are shown on this map over the course of just two-thirds of a year. They traveled an average of something like 70,000 kilometers in that year, flying mostly alone actually. They don't fly in flocks, but they fly as individuals and you can see how the tracks show you the very different patterns they took as individuals across the ocean, all ultimately returning back to their Southern Hemisphere, southern home around New Zealand and their Northern

Hemisphere summer home up around the Pacific Northwest in the Gulf of Alaska; truly amazing birds, the longest migrations of any bird on the planet.

Related in some ways to birds through their common relationship to the dinosaurs and other even earlier organisms are the marine reptiles. Of reptiles today, each mean group of the present day reptiles has some marine species, not many; they're mostly land-dwelling organisms, but some marine species. We have the turtles. We have lizards and snakes and we have crocodiles are all representatives of different types of reptiles. As reptiles, they all breathe air. None of them are aquatic in the sense of having gills. They also have special salt glands to excrete excess salt from their bodies so they've evolved those in another example of convergent evolution.

There are 7 different species of sea turtles. Like birds, they come ashore to lay eggs, but at very infrequent intervals and they spend virtually all of their life history in the ocean. Some of the species of sea turtles come ashore either every 2, 3, or 4 years, but otherwise spend all their time at sea. They hone back to their original beach and, in fact, the original spot on the same beach that they were born in to lay eggs even several years later with the incredible sense of navigation and ultimately presumably smell and taste that allows them to find not only the same island let's say or the same general region that they were hatched, but the same location on the same beach using something about the characteristics of their particular environment to hone in on that location.

Sea turtles, like the green sea turtles that you'll see if you go on vacation in Hawaii or perhaps in Mexico or Florida, are a little bit different from land-based turtles and tortoises. They can't retract their heads and limbs into the shell. The shell is protection from predators, but their fins, which are of course evolved from forelegs and hind legs and heads are always out. They swim through the water with relatively slow gentle propulsion. They're incredibly beautiful to see if you happen to have the good fortune to see them snorkeling or diving or something like that. Amazingly the adult sea turtles essentially have no predators in the ocean so they don't have to move very fast and they're not afraid of anything.

Unfortunately, the one predator they do have is human beings who will hunt them for food or for their shells or other material and we've become the sea turtles predator. All of the major sea turtle species are threatened species and some are very much in danger. They all feed in shallow water on algae, sea grass and plants, so they hug coastline areas and low shelf regions where there is a lot of this vegetative material for them to feed on.

Let's turn our attention now to the marine mammals, the big organisms that we're so familiar with and know and love so well from all of the different marine shows and wildlife television programs and everything else. We'll talk about 3 different groups of marine mammals, each one that evolved independently from land mammals that moved into the sea and all of which have lost the ability to live totally on land, though as we'll see some of them spend a little bit of their life cycle on land the way that the birds and the reptiles do. The 3 types are the Sirenia, the Carnivora, and the cetacean that is the manatees and their relatives, the seals and sea lions, and in the whales and dolphins. Let's look at them sequentially.

Let's talk first actually about the common features that each of these organisms have. All of them are mammals so that implies they feed live young. They have live young and they feed them with milk. They breathe air so all their time spent at sea, as we know, they breathe air through their blowholes or nostrils, other organs. They all have the streamlined body shape of good high energy, high activity swimmers. They have slippery skin or hair that has developed special oils to both retain heat and retain a slippery smooth profile. All of them are internally heated, they're warm-blooded organisms. They have to maintain a high endothermic body heat and so they need a high metabolic rate. They need to consume a lot of food and burn a lot of food as well as be well-insulated with fatty tissue and actually their large size is good for retaining heat because they have a good surface to volume ratio. They don't radiate too much heat because they have a large body volume that's generating all of that heat.

They also have unusual respiratory systems that officially use oxygen. As we'll see many of the marine mammals have special biochemistry that's optimized to retain and use oxygen during deep prolonged dives. A diving whale or elephant seal can use up to 80% of the oxygen that it takes in with each breath and officially exchange it in its lungs. You or I are much less efficient. We only use 25 to 30% of the oxygen that we take in. the lungs can collapse in some of these organisms to tiny volumes to accommodate the pressure of going very deep. Gases collapse under high pressure and they accommodate that by actually allowing their lungs to collapse after they've taken oxygen into their bloodstream or while they're doing that. In fact, the pressure helps drive the dissolved oxygen into the bloodstream.

They also have very strong osmotic adaptations to living in saltwater, a recurring theme with all these organism we've been looking at. There's little to no intake of seawater. They don't drink water at all for the most part, all of these different marine mammals. Instead, they get their fresh water from food tissues so directly from the food that they're ingesting and also from the metabolism of carbohydrates. Remember the photosynthesis respiration give and take, the process of respiration that involves combining carbohydrates with oxygen has a byproduct of producing H_2O, there's free water that's generated by that process. They recycle and reuse the water, reabsorb the water from their digestion, from their metabolic process in order to retain water. Virtually none of them need any fresh water whatsoever.

Let's look at a few of these marine mammals then in more detail. First of all, I'd like to talk about the Sirenia, the ones that are like sirens of the ocean. In mythology and in historical lore, they were seen as something like the mermaids of the sea. These are the manatees. Manatees actually even strike some poses when they're feeding their young that reminded sailors of the old days or people of the old times of mermaids as they held a calf close to their bodies to nurse it. The manatees and the dugongs of Indonesia are virtually the only examples. There are 3 species of West India manatees and one of the related dugongs in Indonesia. They're the only 4 species of these organisms on the planet.

All of them are herbivorous marine mammals. They're the only herbivorous ones so they basically graze on sea grass. They're closely related to the land-based grazers like elephants and water buffalo and other ungulates. Calling them sea cows is not much of a stretch. They are pretty much organisms that have adapted to being in the water so much so they have no legs. They have fins, but they exclusively graze on sea grasses and things like that. They're all very large bodied, slow-moving, and virtually unafraid of most predators. They stay in quite shallow water where, for the most part, the large marine predators like orca whales don't come in or sharks don't come in and graze in these sea grasses. So they've been an easy target for human beings. The manatees and dugongs are both endangered species to this day or at this time.

Maybe the most amazing story is the story of the Sirenia that's no longer around, the Steller sea cow. Now these were even larger than manatees, up to 30 feet long and 20,000 pounds. Steller sea cows were discovered, at least to science in 1741, names by George Steller who named so many different organisms as a naturalist on Vitus Bering's exploration voyages. They were in the Bering Sea, named for Bering himself, and they were in the Commander Islands of the Bering Sea between Russia and Alaska, and perhaps native people knew about these, but the Europeans described them first in 1741 and gave them this name.

Seal hunters who were just beginning to move into this area from Russia, namely, found them to be pretty easy pickings. They basically don't move very fast. They're enormous and there's a lot of food on them. They're great for provisioning and unfortunately they only inhabited a relatively small number of islands up there in the far northern Pacific and Bering Sea. They were hunting for meat and only 27 years after they were first discovered they were extinct and they've been gone since 1768, a thing that we hope doesn't happen to the manatees and dugongs as well. The next group I'd like to talk about is what is called the pinnipeds and fissipeds. They're all of the order Carnivora. The Carnivora are dogs, cats, bears, and weasels, all the animals like that, but the pinnipeds are the seals and the sea lions and the walruses and the fissipeds and the sea otters that swim in the sea.

All of these are relatively recent arrivals, at least in evolutionary sense in the ocean. The pinnipeds themselves, seals and sea lions, are mostly marine living. They spend almost all their time in the water, but they come on land to mate and to fight over mating and to birth their young and then head back out into the ocean and spend most of the year at sea. The difference between seals and sea lions is something you've probably learned somewhere but forgotten multiple times; seals have no external ear parts whatsoever, a more streamlined shape. They swim with a fused set of hind limbs that's essentially turned into a single flipper and don't swim with their forelimbs at all, while sea lions have external ears. They look a little bit more dog-like in the face somehow. Their hind limbs are still partially separated and then their front flippers are used for swimming actively as well. They're a little bit more mobile on the land and sea lions are what are in all of the seal shows that you might see at an aquarium or something like that.

The walruses are the largest of the pinnipeds and the most massive and live mostly in very cold water environments where their massive size is an advantage to maintaining body heat. The largest of the seals and the most interesting is one that you can actually get a chance to see if you're on the California coast and they're very beloved by people there because there a number of locations where the elephant seals come out on land, spend lots of time on land, and are relatively easy to observe in their mating and birthing their young stages of their lifecycle. Elephant seal bulls can reach 5 meters in length, 2700 kilograms, they're called elephant seals due to the large proboscis that they have. They're the greatest divers of all of the pinnipeds and have been documented diving as deep as or deeper than most the whales, 1500 to 2500 or more meters in depth.

All the pinnipeds, including the elephant seals, mate and give birth on land. Elephant seals in large colonies with harems of females that are fought over by the alpha bulls for the opportunity to mate. Seals and sea lions can be seen on land too in many place, especially along the west coast pulled out on piers and beaches and things like that sunning themselves and pretty much ignoring the human beings that are paying attention to them. Most seals and sea lions have a pretty rough life cycle though. The pups that are born basically have to make their own way out to sea after they're born. They head down to the water and they are targets for sharks and other organisms that want to prey on these easy to catch young, still immature mammals. An elephant seal pup has only about a 1 in 5 chance of survival till they're 6–8 years old that it needs to reach in order to reach breeding age.

The sea otters are the last of this group that I want to talk about. They're the geologically most recent newcomers to the ocean. They're the only marine fissipeds. All the other fissipeds are land organisms and just one group, the sea otters, actually went to sea. We see them in the kelp forest of California, in large numbers in the Pacific Northwest, as well as many other places around the Pacific. They feed on mollusks, crustaceans, and sea urchins in great numbers. They actually have to consume something like 20% of their body weight each day in order to maintain their high metabolism and stay warm in that chilly water. The sea otters have the fur that was the most prized by people so they nearly went extinct from hunting. The entire Pacific otter population descends actually from just a few individuals that were leftover from early 20th-century hunting.

Now finally I want to discuss the cetacean, the whales, the dolphins, and the porpoises. These are the big organisms that are the most fully adapted perhaps to oceanic life among the mammals because they spend their entire lifecycle at sea and don't come out for giving birth to live young at all. They all evolved from early ungulates so they've been in the sea longer most of the others. The closest land relatives are actually sheep and horses. We can break down the cetaceans into 2 classes or 2 categories, the Odontoceti, the toothed whales and the Mysticeti, the baleen whales. Odontoceti has the word dont in it like going to the orthodontist or something like that so you can remember that they're the toothed whales in particular.

These toothed whales are the top predators in the ocean in many ways, top predators of many fish and invertebrates. They exist for the most part at a very high trophic level. They tend to consume relatively large fish that are already several trophic steps removed from the base. The dolphins, porpoises, orca and beluga, the narwhal, are all examples of the toothed whales. They all have small to moderate sizes, at least relative to their cousins the Mysticetes. The sperm whale is the largest of the toothed whales. They're all extremely skillful, fast-moving predators.

The sperm whales when you look at a depiction like this are virtually always depicted with a giant squid in their mouth and that's because, as we said, it turns out the giant squid is probably a primary source of food, a primary diet, although not the exclusive diet of sperm whales. The reason that we know this is that during all the years of whale hunting, of course whales were cut open all the time, and sperm whales stomachs, in particular, are virtually always filled up with the indigestible hard part of a squid, the so-called beak of a squid, which collects in the sperm whales stomach and is never expelled. Based on the size of the squid beaks, the species were identified as the giant and colossal squids in large parts and in vast numbers occur in sperm whale stomachs.

All the Odontocetes share echolocation. We're familiar with the idea of dolphins and their sonar and the other toothed whales use it as well. They use combinations, very sophisticated combinations of clicks that we've heard before and hearing dolphin sonar sounds and actually rising or falling tones that you hear, which is a way of sending out different frequencies that give you different kinds of depth range information from the low frequency to high with a rising tone or vice versa with a falling tone as they hone in on and echolocate their prey that they're going towards. It's been said that their sonar is sophisticated enough that they probably, in those large brains, those large convolute brains we know, and the reason why we expect that dolphins and whales are very intelligent organisms, one of those things those brains are probably for is actually building mental images using sonar. Much the way we see with our eyes and form an image of what's around us, dolphins and whales almost certainly form a direct image of things in the water in front of them using their sonar.

There's evidence too that the sonar is not just for location of prey, it's not just echolocation, but actually used offensively to stun their prey with extremely loud bursts. In fact, bursts of sound energy up to 230 decibels, many times higher than the loudest sounds we might hear on land and something that would probably actually stun or even kill another organism. It's not understood why the dolphins themselves can generate this loud burst of sound without hurting their own delicate structures in their heads and brains. We know the dolphins and whales are playful. They're great swimmers seemingly using the ocean effortlessly and can move very rapidly due to their very streamlined, optimized shapes and well-developed fins that again all evolved from limbs and examples of converging evolution.

Let's take a look at the baleen whales now, the Mysticetes. They're maybe mystic and mysterious in a way. None of them have teeth. They have the plates of baleen, which you've probably seen, but is this horn-like fibrous material which hangs down inside their mouth in such a way with overlapping plates that creates a kind of mesh or net so they can take in great mouthfuls of water as they feed in surface waters. They don't dive deeply. They basically feed just at the surface, especially in Arctic and Antarctic zones taking in great amounts of krill, strain the water back out to the baleen and then capture all that zooplankton and phytoplankton and live directly on it.

The blue whale, the largest of all animals on earth, eats 3 metric tons of Antarctic krill per day during feeding season. They're living at a very low trophic level. They are basically living in a food chain that just involves phytoplankton to krill and straight to these big whales. It's an efficient use of trophic energy. Remember the 10-fold increase in the amount of biomass that has to be consumed at each trophic level. That's perhaps what can support these very large organisms.

The baleen whales use sound as well. They are famous for their whale song and they emit low frequency, but also very loud sounds that can be heard over long distances, perhaps thousands of miles across the open ocean. Recently researchers have been learning a great deal of new things about whale song in whales like the humpback, which create very complicated song patterns that the meaning of which is unknown, but they're clearly for communication among members of particular groupings or families over short distances and long. Interestingly, the whale song has recently been shown to actually change and evolve over a course of a few seasons and whale songs were found originally in a few individuals on the eastern side of the Pacific near North America and then spread from group to group and individual to individual such that a couple of seasons later that same new song had spread to the far South Pacific in a sort of top 40 chart or something like that of humpback whales. Understanding the mysteries of baleen whales and their whale song is something that's going to occupy marine mammal researchers for a long time to come I'm sure.

These baleen whales and humpback, the gray, the blue whales, and the minke whales, which are actually the most abundant whales on the planet, these are the ones you're likely to see if you go out on a whale-watching cruise either in the Atlantic or Pacific Ocean. Certainly in Baja California, humpbacks are there in great profusion, or Maui, if you go during the wintertime. They are actually migrants similar to the sooty shearwaters and in fact most of these whales in the summertime, in the high productivity zones that we've already seen and the Bering Sea and the Antarctic waters and they migrate to places like Hawaii and Baja California and more tropical waters to overwinter and to do their mating after they've fattened up during the course of the summer.

One of the unusual features of whales is whale strandings. We've heard about these. An example in this photograph of 55 pilot whales that beached themselves on South African beaches in 2009, 20 could be rescued. It's very common when whale strandings happen, the whales beach themselves. Well-meaning people try to get them back in the water and some of the whales turnaround and come right back on shore again. The reasons for whale beaching are just entirely unclear. They mostly happen in toothed whales, not baleen whales and in whales that tend to live normally out in open ocean in deep water and they just come into shore for these beaching. One thing we do know about strandings is they've been going on for a very long time and probably are not the result of human disruption of their activities because for hundreds and even thousands of years they've been described. Here in this 1577 engraving, we see 3 beached sperm whales by a Dutch artist showing that this has certainly been something that is well-known to people for at least hundreds of years.

We've taken a very quick look at the marine birds, the reptiles, and mammals and seen how they're all derived from land organisms that successfully returned to the sea using different, but similar and converging adaptations. They all had unique ways to adapt to the life of the mariner and become part of the pelagic ocean environment. In the next lecture, we'll take a look at the human use and the human interaction with these as biological resources. We're going to talk about the topics of whaling and fishing both in history and today.

Whaling, Fisheries, and Farming the Ocean
Lecture 22

O cean fisheries are a major source of food and a highly efficient industry, but most species are being overfished to unsustainable levels, necessitating fish farming, or aquaculture. Whaling, now so controversial, was the foundation of much of the U.S. and European economy in the 19th century. In the past 15 years, there has been a more than 60% increase in the total catch from the ocean. Aquaculture is an increasingly important part of the overall fish supply—with its own impacts on the ocean environment.

The Whaling Industry

- Whaling, now controversial, was the foundation of much of the U.S. and European economy in the 19th century. People have hunted whales for thousands of years. Indigenous people of the Pacific, in particular, were adept at catching whales for food and for all of the different potential products they could derive from whales over long periods of time.

- Inuit hunters to this day in the northern regions of Canada are still engaging in traditional whaling and, by international convention, are allowed to take a certain number of even large whales that are otherwise protected.

- The whaling industry took off in the late 1700s and early 1800s and then again in 1868 with the invention of the harpoon gun. A few decades later, the beginnings of mechanized ships instead of sailing ships caused the rate at which whales were being taken to rise exponentially.

- By the 1930s, whale stocks were down to tiny percentages of their original numbers. Blue whales were down to 4% of their original stocks—almost extinct—and the same was true for many other large marine mammals.

- The International Whaling Commission (IWC) was founded in the mid-1940s to try to manage the whale population through international treaty. In the 1980s, the IWC banned all large whale hunting. Basically all the countries of the world stopped whaling—except for traditional uses and for Japanese so-called research whaling for minke whale.

- Today, most species are commercially extinct and not recovering quickly. Some are endangered and some are threatened, but species such as fin, gray, bowhead, humpback, and blue whales are at best recovering very slowly even though they're not being fished.

- There are a lot of whales in the ocean, but most of them are minke whales—a particular species that represents 700,000 or more of the probable population numbers today.

- Because the minke whales were relatively abundant and not seen as threatened or endangered, Norway and Iceland decided to resume harvest of these whales in the 1990s. Japan was already doing it and continued to raise their number of harvested minke whales. This is also being done for sperm whales and Bryde's whales.

- Today, there's a present catch of minke whales in the hundreds per year, which is believed by most marine-mammal experts to be sustainable. In other words, there are enough numbers of them out there—and they reproduce fast enough—that the rate at which they are being harvested does not really pose a threat to the minke whale populations.

© iStockphoto/Thinkstock.

In recent years, the population of bluefin tuna has been rapidly declining due to the increase in popularity of sushi.

Ocean Fisheries

- Ocean fisheries are a major source of food and a highly efficient industry. The most interesting thing about ocean fisheries is that of all the things human beings eat on this planet and commercially expend energy to produce and sell as food, it's the only significant source of wild-captured animal food.

- About 79% of all fish from the ocean is wild capture, and 21% of the fish from the ocean is **mariculture**, or fish farming of the ocean. By contrast, the land-based freshwater aquaculture—the growing of fish for food in freshwater using freshwater species—is a rapidly growing industry that has become 46% of the total supply.

- Globally, fish are being caught at phenomenal rates, and they're largely not reproducing fast enough for the wild fisheries to keep up.

- Data from around 1992 shows that the commodity fish—white fish such as cod, hake, and haddock—represented a fairly large proportion, greater than about 10–15% of the total catch of wild fish. Tuna, bonito, and billfish were about 4% of the total catch. All the various fish represented about 87 million metric tons of weight in that particular year.

- Today, the total wild-capture fisheries have largely plateaued and not grown in size much since the late 1980s and early 1990s. Less than 8 million metric tons of the commodity fish—cod, hake, haddock—are being caught today. By contrast, the catch rate of tuna and bonito are going up rapidly, as are mollusks such as squids.

Fish farming involves using the ocean as a medium to grow fish for human consumption in contained areas.

- Both scarcity and fashion shape these trends: For example, the global explosion of the popularity of sushi has changed tuna fishing greatly. This trend, however, appears to be on a collision course with a rapid decline as these populations are overfished as well.

- Quite simply, human population growth is driving all of this growth in the fishing industry. The number of people on the planet is continuing to increase at an exponential rate. There are twice as many people on Earth today as in 1965, and fish is a high-quality food that is relatively inexpensive to produce in aquaculture, so it's taking up the slack.

Worldwide Fish Production

- For a long time, the North Atlantic Ocean was the biggest fishery, with the Pacific Ocean second to it. Today, the Northwest Pacific Ocean accounts for 20% of the fishing industry, and the Pacific Ocean accounts for well over 50%.

- This is partly the historical trend of fishing having been developed in different parts of the world earlier versus later. In addition, this trend is due to the great growth of the Chinese fishing industry as well as other countries—including the United States—intensively fishing the Northwest Pacific and Bering Sea.

- The Atlantic Ocean catch is declining rapidly after peaks in the early 2000s. The Pacific Ocean trends have been growing rapidly over the years but are now leveling off, and catches are not increasing despite an increase in effort by increasingly technological fishing fleets. The Indian Ocean catch is sustaining, but patterns are changing—especially with a declining tuna catch.

Capture Fishing

- By far, the largest type of open-ocean capture fishing in tonnage is trawling for fish, which involves trawling with large nets. The mouth of the net is open, and the net mesh in size is configured to catch particular species or groups.

- There are fundamentally 2 types of trawling: mid-water trawling, which involves dragging a trawl net through the middle of the ocean, and bottom trawling, which involves a trawler with heavy weighted wheels that roll across the bottom of the ocean and scoop up everything in its path.

- **Bycatch** is a huge problem in the fishing industry because up to 25% of all the fish that are caught through trawling are non-targeted species. Basically, any type of fish that is a bycatch of what is being targeted is mixed in with the targeted fish but is dumped back into the ocean as a dead fish.

- A second major type of fishing that's used to target large open-ocean fish like tuna and swordfish is **pelagic longline fishing**, in which long filament lines are stretched out from ships that have floats along them to keep them in the near surface and individual baited hook lines that hang to catch fish. This type of fishing has relatively small amounts of bycatch, but unfortunately the bycatch tends to be organisms that are endangered.

- One type of open-ocean fishing that is essentially banned by international convention is drift-net fishing, which is similar to longline fishing by deploying very long nets that actually act like fences in the sea. Fish are caught by their gills as they try to swim through these nets, but the nets also catch anything that runs into them—including dolphins and seals. Drift-net fishing has been banned, but it is still practiced.

Fishery Management

- The **maximum sustainable y`ield** refers to how much of any fish species can be harvested each year in a given fishery region without depleting stocks for future years. There's a current estimate of all fish as food in the global ocean of between about 100 and 135 million tons per year, but that includes fish farming activities as well.

- The open-ocean fishery appears to be right at the maximum sustainable yield—or perhaps even on the high side—for the wild-capture fish that we're currently fishing economically in the ocean. Many of the specific species in the ocean are certainly overfished.

- An estimated 72% of all fisheries are being overfished today, and many of the others are right at their maximum sustainable yields. Overfishing beyond sustainable yields leads to a threat of the collapse of a fishery.

- The **tragedy of the commons** is the idea that if there's a resource like a wild fishery that's available to a large group of people in common, it benefits each individual member to maximize his or her use—even if it would be better for everyone to get together and agree to limit their own catch.

- The personal economics that fishing-boat owners face forces them, in the face of a declining fishery, to redouble their efforts. The replacement for most of this is aquaculture, which might ultimately take some of the pressure off open-ocean fish.

- The other form of fish farming that is becoming more common, but growing more slowly, is mariculture: the farming of marine seawater organisms such as shrimp and oysters. Mariculture is probably not going to replace the open-ocean fishing industry in the way that inland aquaculture is going to. What will make the most difference are environmentally responsible fish choices—both by business owners and by consumers.

Important Terms

bycatch: Non-targeted fish caught collaterally during commercial fishing; often discarded as noneconomic.

mariculture: Fish farming, or growing fish for food in ocean-water tanks or pens.

maximum sustainable yield: The amount of a given target species that can be caught each year without long-term depletion of the stock.

pelagic longline fishing: Fishing method employing baited hooks on a kilometers-long main fishing line, used for fish that have high trophic levels—such as swordfish and tuna.

tragedy of the commons: Concept articulated by Garrett Hardin that when a resource is available to a large group in common, it benefits each member to maximize his or her use—even if it would be better for everyone to limit their use. Applied to the problem of fishery management.

Suggested Reading

Greenberg, *Four Fish*.

Melville, *Moby Dick*.

Philbrick, *In the Heart of the Sea*.

Questions to Consider

1. A question to ponder, or discuss with others: Is (a) all whaling morally wrong; (b) acceptable as long as the species being hunted is harvested sustainably (i.e., not to the point of endangered or threatened status); or (c) all whaling acceptable as morally neutral economic activity? How does your answer differ for whales versus fish or versus the hunting of wild land mammals?

2. Should fish farming replace all wild-caught fish as production of commercial meat on land has become exclusively farmed, or could there be a place for wild-caught fish for the foreseeable future?

Whaling, Fisheries, and Farming the Ocean
Lecture 22—Transcript

Many of us love seafood. I do myself. Human beings interaction with the ocean for a very long has been dominated by extracting biological resources from the sea meaning fishing, whaling, and other ways of obtaining food, shellfish, and other things like that. What I'd like to do in this lecture now that we've introduced all of these different organisms that are living in the ocean is take a look at both the history and very different present day industry that is represented by both fisheries and whaling and ultimately by farming of the sea using the ocean as a medium in order to actually grow the fish and other organisms that we like to eat.

Well ocean fisheries are a major source of food in the world and a growing source actually of food to feed a hungry world with a growing population. It's become a highly efficient industry with amazing technology to efficiently extract organisms from the ocean and catch the fish. Many or most of the species are now being overfished or are very close to unsustainable levels and so that's really necessitating the growth of fish farming or aquaculture and mariculture and we'll take a look at.

What I'd like to do is start with a look at the big historical industry, the whaling industry and we only have time to really talk about a few of the main features of both the historical and present day whaling industry and whaling controversies. But, it is controversial today and yet it was the foundation of so much of the U.S. and European economy in the 18th and 19th centuries. It was, in some ways, the big industry of its time. Let's take a look at a little bit of that history that we're all a little bit familiar with, but maybe don't know some of the tenets of it, the details of.

Well first of all, people have certainly hunted whales for thousands of years, the native peoples of the Pacific, in particular, were adept at catching whales for food and for all of the different potential products they could derive from whales over long periods of time to the Aleutian Islands, Gulf of Alaska, and regions like that. We know from historical accounts that Europeans began hunting whales; the Nordic peoples began hunting whales as early as 800 to 1000 AD, so for more than 1000 years whale hunting has been going on.

Even the largest whales started to be hunted by the 1500s or so. There are accounts of Basque whalers on the coast of Labrador so Basque from Spain all the way across in the North Atlantic on the North American side processing very large numbers of whales and actually obtaining whale oil in large amounts. The Dutch, the British were involved. By the late 18th and 19th century with the U.S. involved as well a major world industry had been born. The U.S. was the leading whale nation in the world in the early 1800s. Cape Cod and Nantucket were the center of this global industry and it was the original oil industry and what I mean by that is that whale wasn't really being hunted for food certainly, and it was sort of in a secondary way being hunted for some of the whale products that could be obtained like whale bone and whale baleen. It basically is the plastic of its day, a kind of pliable material. Famously ladies corsets were made in part for a long time of either whale bone or whale baleen.

The real reason to go after the whales in this industry that developed that was so wonderfully documented by Herman Melville in his novel *Moby Dick*, but the novel that was based on a true story or inspired by an 1820 true story of a whaler that was brought down by a sperm whale. The reason for this industry was fuel. It was oil to burn in lamps, into fuel, the lighting up of America in Europe in those times. The parlors that needed to be lit by gas lamps, those gases were burning or those oil lamps were burning whale oil. It was literally the Exxon Mobil of its time and Cape Cod was the Houston of its day. This was a very large industry; hundred and hundreds of whaling ships traveled far across the world's oceans and were instrumental in the opening up and exploration especially of the South Pacific. We know that those late 1700s, early 1800s, whalers were traversing all sorts of regions in the South Pacific, *Moby Dick* in part is about a whaler who comes from one of the South Pacific Polynesian islands and ends up back there in Cape Cod.

Let's look at a little bit of a history of whaling because all of that whaling industry caught and rendered and brought back many different whales. Now we have the traditional use of whales and Inuit hunters to this day in the northern regions of Canada are still doing some traditional whaling and by international convention are allowed to take a certain number of even large whales that are otherwise protected. We can see an image of them carving up or flensing, as the word is, whales in the Inuit regions as well as the Pacific Northwestern regions of other Native American tribes.

Whaling as an industry took off in the late 1700s and early 1800s and then took off again in 1868 with the invention of the harpoon gun. That followed a few decades later by the beginnings of mechanized ships instead of sailing ships meant that the rate at which whales were being taken went up exponentially. By the 1930s whale stocks were down to just tiny percentages of the original numbers. Blue whales are down to 4% of their original stocks, almost gone extinct, same as for the sperm whales and many other organisms, many other of the large marine mammals.

The International Whaling Commission was founded in the mid 1940s to try to basically through international treaty, an agreement, manage the whale population so they wouldn't go extinct. They would actually be managed in such a way that they would recover and allow for the sustainable or responsible harvest of some large whales. The restrictions began to be in place, at first they weren't large enough, but in the 1980s the International Whaling Commission reached the point where it concluded it had to ban all large whale hunting for the big animals. Basically all countries of the world stopped whaling except for some of those traditional uses and the Japanese so-called research whaling for minke whale. I say so-called because it brought in under a loophole that we know of today as research whaling, but large numbers of individual whales were taken and they were also put onto the commercial food market so it's hard to call it simply research whaling.

By this time in the 1980s and up to the present day, most species are commercially extinct. They're not recovering quickly. Some are actually endangered, some are threatened species, but species like fin whale, gray whale, bowhead, humpbacks, and blue whales are at best recovering very slowly in the present day ocean even though they're not being fished.

Minke whales are by far the most abundant whales. Of all whales, in 1900, our estimate that there is something like 4.5 million whales present in the ocean. Actually estimating the numbers of any organism or the health of any ecosystem in the ocean before the industrial era or the large human interaction is a difficult thing to do. How do you estimate the number of whales in the ocean in 1900? Well it's based partly on a detailed examination of accounts of how many were taken and how many ships were out there trying to and estimates of their efficiency. It's based on the genetic diversity of whales and an understanding of what their DNA tells us about how many there might have been, what size of population was breeding in the period leading up to that time. It's an inexact science certainly and this carries through to lots of other organisms as well. But, an estimated 4.4 million whales at that time translates into about 1 million whales today.

There are a lot of whales in the ocean, however, most of them are minke whales. One particular species that represents 700,000 or more of the probable population numbers today. Since the minke whales were relatively abundant, not seen as threatened or endangered, Norway decided to resume harvest of those whales in 1993 and Japan was already doing it and continued to raise their number of harvested minke whales. Iceland joined Norway and now there's a present catch of minke whales in the number of hundreds per year, hundreds to 1000 per year, some whaling, some research whaling, small numbers. This is also being done for sperm whales and Bryde's whales, but the vast majority of what's going on in the present day and that creates all of the controversy that we see with groups like the sea shepherds down there trying to stop the Japanese whalers in the Antarctic waters.

All of that is based on the whaling fishery, as they call it, whaling of the minke whales. Most marine mammal experts do believe that the present catch of minke whales is sustainable. There are enough numbers of them out there and they reproduce fast enough that the rate the Japanese and others are going right now it's not really a threat to the minke whale populations. The question of whether whaling is sort of fundamentally right or wrong or one supports it or not, is really based more on valuation of the whales and whether it's right or wrong to catch them as opposed to direct threat to these particular mammals. Many marine mammal experts also believe that if the doors are open by the International Whaling Commission to much more whaling of other species, that might drive some of them back the other direction into the brink of extinction once again. It's interesting that the present catch probably is sustainable despite its deep unpopularity, at least on this side of the Pacific Ocean.

Let's look at fisheries then. Ocean fisheries are a major source of food as I said, a growing source of food in the fishing industry. The interesting thing about ocean fisheries perhaps, the most interesting thing is that of all the things human beings eat on this planet and commercially expend energy to produce and sell as food, it's the only significant source of wild captured animal food. Most of the fish that come from the ocean are still wild fish. It's as if we were rounding up buffalo and selling them in the supermarket from the open plains in very large numbers today.

Something like 79% of all fish from the ocean is wild capture so that's most of them. But, 21% of the fish from the open ocean or from the ocean; that is seafood, is mariculture. That is fish farming of the ocean. Much of this is actually in pens, but held in the sea, some of it as we see is even done in different ways. It's a growing proportion, but it's not the majority by far of the saltwater fishery or saltwater fishing industry. By contrast, the land-based fresh water aquaculture, so the growing of fish for food, but in fresh water and using fresh water species is a rapidly rising, rapidly growing industry, something like 46% of the total supply of all those fish and quickly changing, and quickly changing in different parts of the world where the protein from fish is in high demand and so is continuing to grow.

Well what's happening globally to catches of fish though is that through all this pressure and the efficiency of the industry, fish are being caught at phenomenal rates and they're largely not reproducing fast enough for the wild fisheries to keep up. There are some exceptions, but most of the wild fisheries are being fished to a point where no more can in fact be found and caught and their numbers are at very small proportions of their parent preindustrial or historical levels. If we look at data from around 1992, so a couple of decades ago, we see that they're the commodity fish, the white fish, like cod, hake, and haddock represented a pretty big proportion, something greater than 10 or 15% of the total catch of wild fish. Tuna's and things like that we're only about 4%, the tunas and bonitos. All the various fish represented about 87 million metric tons of weight in that particular year.

If we look to the present day, we see that the total wild capture fisheries have largely kind of plateaued and not grown in size much since that time. There was increasing catch, increasing catch up until the late 1980s or early

1990s and then with fluctuations it's largely flattened out. Actually most of the world has somewhat decreased its catch of open ocean capture fisheries, but China has become a major player over that time going from very little, almost insignificant proportion of the world's total capture to the largest single catcher of fish of all wild captured fish of the entire planet. That's only maintained that fairly steady level.

The interesting thing about this steady apparent continuous number or fraction of total fish that are captured, which still remains around 90 million or so metric tons per year is that it's not the same species over time. One will come in to replace another whose population is declining then as that formerly less desirable fish species also starts to decline a new one will start to be caught. We've seen over the last few decades different fish come and go literally on restaurant menus and in supermarkets as they become more available and then less available as they were overfished to the point where their populations were not sustaining themselves.

If we look at the catch trends by individual groups we can see that those I referred to as the commodity fish, the biggest grouping in the early 1990s have been in inexorable decline since the `90s and now only about something less than 8 million metric tons, a much smaller quantity of the cod, hake, and haddock, and all of those fish, are being caught today. Unless the amount of fish that are being caught declines, that decline will simply continue to go down because they're not reproducing at the rate. They're not being caught less because people don't want to catch them; they're being caught less because the fishing industry, the fishing fleets are working harder to catch as many as they can and still finding declining productivity of those fish are declining catches.

By contrast, the catch rate of things like tuna, bonito, and the other tuna-like fish are going up rapidly as are the invertebrates like squids and cuttlefish and octopus. These are growing in popularity and they're replacing he big fleshy fish, fin fish because those fin fish are getting harder to catch and so the squids and things like that are becoming more popular fish to obtain. The tuna story, in particular, is largely one of changes in taste, taste meaning fashion and popularity of those fish over time.

Well scarcity shapes these trends in the sense that the whitefish are going down, the Pollock, the cod, and haddock are just simply not available in the same kinds of numbers. The fashion though of basically the world discovering Japanese sushi and starting to eat it all over the planet and the popularity of sushi in American and Europe and in South America and everywhere else has led to an incredible increase in the rate of fishing for bluefin tuna, yellowfin tuna, bonito, and all those tunas, and one that has been growing through the early part of the 21st century, but appears to be on an absolute collision course with a rapid decline as these populations are overfished as well.

Well aquaculture and especially the inland or fresh water fish aquaculture has taken up the slack between the growth of ocean fish, worldwide capture fish, and the increasing need for fish food as the world population grows. We see a diverging trend of flat ocean capture fish, but a growing trend of generation of aquaculture and inland aquaculture is the most growing part of the fishing industry overall. We could ask the question what's driving all of this growth in the fishing industry. What is driving the pressure on the open ocean capture fisheries? And the answer is fairly simple. It's one that was talked about a lot a few decades ago, but really isn't being talked about quite so much anymore, but hasn't gone away and that's human population growth.

The number of people on the planet is continuing to increase at an exponential rate. There are twice as many people on earth today as in 1965 and the rate of doubling for the next doubling on the planet is going even faster. The population may level off at 9 billion or 10 billion or some number like that, but in the meantime there are many, many more people on earth and they need food. Fish is obviously high quality food and relatively inexpensive to produce in aquaculture so it's taking up the slack. If we look at even longer trend in world population we see that we live again in some singularity in change of the way the planet works because there were very, very few people, much less than a billion for tens of thousands of years. We look at 10,000 BC to the present, we see the rise in population with the agricultural revolution and then ultimately with the industrial revolution we see the sudden rise to the 6-1/2 billion and counting that are on the planet today.

Well we can ask the question where are the fish, where are all the big fisheries in the world? For a long time it was the North Atlantic was the biggest fishery with the Pacific second to that. But decades ago, that transition to the point where the Pacific Ocean as an aggregate is the vast majority of fishing on the planet. The Northwest Pacific, itself, the region of high productivity in the high latitudes in the northwest represent something like 25% of the total global capture fishery, global wild fishing, in other parts of the Pacific Ocean added together come up to something close to or well over a half of all the ocean fishing. Of course, this is partly the historical trend of just fishing having been developed in different parts of the world earlier and then later, and then the great growth of the Chinese fishing industry as well as other countries, including the United States, intensively fishing the Northwest Pacific and Bering Sea.

What are the trends in global fisheries? Well the Atlantic catch is declining rapidly at this point. Many of the different fisheries peaked in the early 2000s, if not much earlier than that for certain fish, like cod, but now they're declining rapidly in recent years. The most recent assessment in 2010 by the UN FAO says that 13 to 30% declines in the catches of important Atlantic fin fish, the large fish that we think of as the major players in what we buy in the supermarket or at the restaurant. The Pacific trends have been growing rapidly over all those years, but are now leveling off and catches are not increasing despite increasing effort by increasingly technological fishing fleets. The Indian Ocean catch is sustaining, but patterns are changing especially with a declining tuna catch.

Let's look at how open ocean capture fishing is actually done for a few minutes. Well by far the largest tonnage is trawling for fish, trawling with big nets that their mouths are held open, the net mesh in size is configured to catch particularly species or particular groups that one wants to catch. There are fundamentally 2 types of trawling that we can look at, midwater trawling, which is simply dragging a trawl net through the middle of the ocean as you might imagine and then bottom trawling which involves a trawler with heavy weighted wheels literally to roll across the bottom of the ocean and scoop up everything in its path with the mouth of the net hugging the bottom very closely so that it catches bottom-dwellers, but also water-dwellers for some distance up above the actual benthic environments.

It's pelagic fishing and benthic fishing as it were. This trawler netting is the majority of commercial catching and it involves nets that are very large open nets that can stand hundreds of feet in height. They catch a great number of fish, but they also catch a great number of fish that were not the fish they were intending to catch. This is called bycatch and it's a very large problem in the fishing industry because up to 25% of all the fish that are caught are non-targeted species. They're caught, they're even edible perhaps, but when they're brought on deck of the ship if the ship is set up for processing of a certain type of fish then those are the ones that are kept and everything else is literally just swept over the side. Unfortunately, dead by the time it gets there because they've been caught in this net and brought to the surface. It's a fish kill that's unfortunate because it's completely a byproduct of the actual food industry that's involved.

A second major type of fishing that's used to target the large open ocean fish like tuna and swordfish is what's called pelagic long-line fishing. Long, up to 10 kilometers or more long filament lines are stretched out from ships or deployed from ships with floats along them to keep them in the near surface and then just simply individual baited hook lines hanging down off of them to catch those predator fish that like to go after that bait. They have relatively small amounts of bycatch, but unfortunately the bycatch that they do come up with tend to be sea turtles and marine mammals and so organisms that we place a high value on often are endangered so even catching a few of them is kind of bad news.

One type of open ocean fishing, for these same organisms, that was essentially banned with the big move to come up with dolphin-safe tuna, was open ocean drift net fishing, similar to the long lines by deploying very long nets that actually act more or less like fences in the sea. Fish are caught by their gills as they try to swim through these nets, but the nets also catch anything that runs into them and unfortunately when a marine mammal runs into one of these open ocean drift nets, a dolphin or a seal or sea lion, they'll drift around before the net is reeled back into the ship to take the fish off because those are mammals, they have to breathe.

We see many, many examples of dolphins and seals caught in these open ocean drift nets. Drift netting has been banned. But, it doesn't mean the practice has completely stopped because it still is economically valuable so fishing industries from some countries will still practice open ocean drift netting despite international treaties banning that practice.

Well when we look at fisheries management then, we can talk about something called the maximum sustainable yield. How much of any fish species can be harvested each year in a given fishery region without depleting stocks for future years. There's a current estimate of all fish in the global ocean of something between 100 and 135 million tons per year, but that includes all the fish farming activities as well. The open ocean fishery appears to be right at the maximum sustainable yield or perhaps even on the high side for the wild capture fish that we're currently fishing economically in the ocean. Many of the specific species in the ocean are certainly overfished.

An estimated something like 72% of all fisheries are being overfished today and many of the others are right at their maximum sustainable yields so they're what is called fully utilized or fully exploited fisheries and very few fisheries that are economically viable are underexploited. The industry is good at getting out there and finding the fish. Perhaps you've heard about the scale in which the open ocean fishing industry operates. Out in the deep water, especially away from the exclusive economic zones of different countries, then large fishing fleets operate with individual trawlers, fishing a given region, finding the fish using satellite imagery, using specialized sonar and all sorts of things, using spotter boats trawling up large amounts of fish and actually bringing them to factory vessels that are big, industrial, essentially fish canneries that operate at sea that are processing those fish right at sea, literally down to the point of putting them in tuna cans or anchovy cans and shipping those back off to land with cargo vessels. The factory fishing ships sometimes don't leave the ocean literally for years at a time. They're resupplied and re-staffed periodically, but they stay out at sea in the productive fisheries.

Well the fisheries that are over-exploited, the numbers are starting to rapidly dwindle and the fisheries are in danger of collapsing. This isn't a new story. This has already happened to a number of fisheries over the course of the 20th century. If we look at a recent scientific estimate of the total biomass of what are called the high trophic level fish in the North Atlantic over the course of the 20th century, cod, perch, anchovies, and flat fish, the big fish that are the familiar ones that represented seafood for most of our lives, estimates of the total biomass that existed in 1900 compared to 1999 show a really disturbing trend. These are where the big Newfoundland banks fisheries were, the New England fishers, all up and down the Atlantic seaboard where cod was big and all these other fish, there were many tons of fish per square kilometer, many large areas with 10 tons or more of fish per square kilometer based on computer simulation, catch rates in those days, and all sorts of complicated analysis in 1900.

If we look at how that evolved to 1950 and then ultimately to 1999, the shrinkage of those fisheries and the collapse of those ecosystems is remarkable. There are now virtually no areas with 10 tons of fish per square kilometer in the entire North Atlantic region and even the few areas that are viable fishing grounds anymore are down to 3 to 4 or so. It's been a collapse of a major chunk of the world's ocean fishery over the span of a century and the same thing is now playing out with different organisms in the Pacific Ocean and Indian Ocean and other places around the world.

The bluefin tuna is the current example that's maybe the poster child, but the most frightening one, bluefin tuna catch as we saw was rapidly increasing. It peaked in 2007 and just in the years since then there've been rapidly declining stocks. It's not an endangered fish, but it's pretty clear it's on its way rapidly. It's because, again, of all that sushi and sashimi that are on the plates of diners all over the world with a taste for bluefin tuna. It's not surprising that they're being fished to this level. When an individual highly prized Atlantic bluefin can sell on the Tokyo fish market, as makes the world regularly, in excess of $200,000 they're individual fish, this big, $250,000 for sale if they're really high quality bluefin tuna.

This really brings us to the question of why does the fishing industry overfish. Well it's fundamentally something that's referred to often as the tragedy of the commons, the idea that if there's a resource like a wild fishery that's available to a large group of people in common, it benefits each individual member to maximize his or her use, even if it would be better for everyone to get together and agree to limit their own catch. The story comes from the commons, meaning the open grazing areas in the British Isles from the medieval period where everybody had the rights to graze ship on the common ground, so it was always to your benefit to graze more sheep than you used to or than your neighbor does because you get more of the benefit back from the resource that's held in common.

The fisheries work this way too and without government regulation, a few fishing industries, a few groups of associations of fishing boat owners have been able to voluntarily limit their catch, but largely this has not been possible in the world. It's not a surprise because the personal economics that each of those fishing boat owners face really forces them, in the face of a declining fishery, to redouble their efforts. If the catch is going down, they already have a large investment in fishing boats and nets and they have to support their crew, they have to support their families and so they'll go out and for each individual they want to get the most of whatever is out there for themselves relative to all of their competitors in the region. In the face of that declining catch, they try harder and harder. When individual fish are worth a lot of money, there's a good chance literally down to the very last one or at least the very last viable breeding population will be caught one day of many of these fish unless real intervention happens.

Well the replacement for most of this is aquaculture. Today something like 37% of all fish for human consumption is represented by fresh water or what we call inland aquaculture. A large amount of this is tilapia. Tilapia is an African fresh water fish that happens to be very well-suited to growing in fish farms and it's showing up on restaurant menus everywhere. It's a large part of the growth of that Chinese aquaculture industry. Maybe this will ultimately take some of the pressure off open ocean fish. The other form of fish farming that is becoming more common, but growing more slowly is mariculture. That's the farming of marine seawater organisms. Shrimp are cultured and Atlantic salmon are cultured in large numbers. Oysters are another example.

Still only about 20% of saltwater fish, and most fish species are just not amenable to culture in closed pens. With salmon there's been some success with what people have referred to as ranching like a ranch in the wild west, spawning salmon in pens, but then sending them out to sea and then relying on then relying on their natural homing instinct to come back when they're fully grown so they can be harvested once again. All this mariculture is probably not going to replace the open ocean fishing industry in the way that inland aquaculture is going to.

Well in closing of this overview of fishing I want to say that maybe there are some things that we should all think about doing and that in particular is make the environmentally responsible fish choices. Overfishing is a stark reminder of the limited nature of resources in what used to seem like a limitless ocean. We can make choices of fish that are being sustainably harvested or being cultured in a sustainable way. It's very confusing often there are so many different kinds of fish that show up on the menu at the restaurants, but there are some resources. The Monterrey Bay Aquarium, in particular, publishes an excellent pocket seafood selector you can print out and actually take with you or look at, as an app on a mobile device or something like that, and see immediately which fish to avoid and which fish are given the green light to enjoy as seafood from the ocean.

We've seen that the global wild fish populations are under some intense pressure driven by economics and demand for food. Inland and marine aquaculture will have to carry more of the burden if these wild stocks are to recover. In the next lecture, we're going to follow those fish perhaps inland in some sense and head up to the shoreline and look at the processes that govern its development ultimately to lead us back into the benthic realm and starting in shallow water and going deeper and deeper and looking at all the habitats at the bottom of the ocean.

Where Sea Meets the Land and Why Coasts Vary
Lecture 23

T he characteristics of coasts are governed by the interplay of erosional and depositional processes resulting from sea-level changes, plate tectonics, glacial cycles, and other factors. Erosion-dominated coasts exhibit rock cliffs and fjords—resulting from land uplift due to plate tectonics or glacial retreat—or drowned river valleys that result from rising sea level. Mechanical breakdown of rock to sediment by wave action is the major erosional process. Net accumulation and movement of sediment dominates on depositional coasts, producing long beaches, barrier islands, coastal plains, and wetlands.

Coastal Processes

- The characteristics of coasts are governed by a dynamic balance between 2 fundamental sets of processes: erosional processes and depositional processes resulting from sea-level changes, plate tectonics, sediment transport, and other factors.

- The shore, or the shoreline, is the physical place where the ocean meets the land—the location of interaction of the waves and the tides with the landscape. The coast, or coastal zone, more typically refers to the whole region of interaction of the 2—from some distance above high tide (perhaps marshes, sand dunes, and cliffs) to the immediate offshore sandbars and channels.

- The coast is an active place, subject to geological processes of both the land and the geological and oceanographic processes of the sea. It's a battleground between all of these forces and a dynamic balance, in fact, among all of them, which causes a place where basically nothing is static.

- The position of the shoreline is determined by factors that constantly change through time. The first one is tectonic activity (or the lack thereof), which can include motions due to plate tectonics and changes in the land level due to a process called glacial rebound—involving areas that have large glaciers on the surface, weighing down the land.

- An additional factor governing sea level is the movement and trapping of sediments, which involves the way sediments move around and build up in piles, dunes, sandbars, and reefs that potentially change the shoreline position.

- Perhaps most importantly, or most rapidly changing, is global sea level—also called eustatic sea level—which is defined as the variations in sea level that can be equally measured all over the world.

- Sea level has fluctuated on the geologic timeframe quite rapidly. The recent level is near the highest it has ever been—or at least over the past 250,000 years. Shorelines change in response to the rising and falling sea level, so shorelines change over time as a result.

- The long-term eustatic sea level is complicated because not only does the sea level rise relative to land, but the land doesn't stay in one place. Even the volume of the ocean can change; for example, more productive mid-ocean ridges raise the sea floor.

Erosional Coasts

- Erosional coasts are dominated by the breakdown of rock and the creation of sediment—the active modification of the rocky landscape of the planet. The mechanical force of the surf pounding on the coastal rocks, the hydraulic pressure driving water into the cracks in those rocks, the abrasion by the sand and gravel, and even boulders that water carries are the main agents of change for erosional coastlines.

- Since sea level goes up and down, the waves make **wave-cut platforms**—flat regions of bare rock that have been chopped out by the waves—in different regions, cutting the cliffs back and adding sediment to the sea, which ultimately moves around and forms beaches.

- A typical erosional coast has some basic features. The sea cliffs have active wave-cut platforms at the base, and the sediment that's produced on those will start to fill in some areas with what are called exposed beaches, or pocket beaches. There are headlands of rock areas that are out beyond the beach that are sometimes eroded offshore as **sea stacks**, which are large rock promontories that jut out of the ocean but are no longer connected to the land—at least not at high-tide levels.

In coastline areas of Norway, Alaska, and New Zealand, narrow inlets known as fjords often exist between cliffs.

© Hemera/Thinkstock.

- In areas around the world's strongly erosional coasts, there are very active promontories of headlands of rock with cuspate pockets that will develop beaches in between them. When tectonic activity is strong and the land is actively being uplifted by the motion of faults, abandoned wave-cut platforms are developed.

- These cuspate bays are areas where waves are less strong, so sediment tends to fall out of the water. It deposits sediment in the bay—producing pocket beaches—while it focuses its energy and keeps the sediment in suspension, abrading and breaking down the rocks of the headlands. Given enough time, coasts that are craggy will slowly develop long, extended beaches from pocket beaches.

- Erosional coasts can also be shaped by land erosion. When the sea level was lower and the shoreline was out near the edge of the present-day continental shelf, rivers would cut river valleys down through the landscape. Ultimately, if sea level rises again, these regions become flooded by the influx of the sea, producing flooded river valleys.

- Perhaps the most dramatic example of that kind of erosional process is the development of **fjords** in places such as Norway, Alaska, and New Zealand, where there are dramatic glacially cut valleys from large glaciers that were present during the ice ages when the sea level was lower.

Depositional Coasts

- Depositional coasts are regions where the net accumulation and movement of sediment (sand and mud) shapes the fundamental morphology of the coastal area. The deposition of beaches, barrier islands, sandbars, and spits is associated with sand transport along a depositional coast.

- In the absence of ongoing tectonic activity and major sea-level changes, erosional coasts will gradually turn into depositional coasts. Long, sandy beaches are the result of the deposition of sand.

- In the near-shore region, where the waves break on the beach, the part of the beach that is actively washed back and forth by waves in typical weather and tides is called the foreshore. The foreshore is backed by what is called the backshore. The boundary between the foreshore and the backshore is the upper limit of the highest high-tide wave action—an area called the beach **berm**.

- There can be several beach berms on a given beach. Sometimes there's a higher beach berm that is the break and slope between the steeply sloping foreshore and the more gently sloping backshore. The highest beach berm might be produced by the largest recent major winter storm, and there can be a second beach berm that might be associated with the most recent tidal cycles or wave action.

- In the backshore region, instead of wave-dominated or water-dominated processes, sediment transport is taken over by wind-dominated and land-dominated processes to form such elements as sand dunes. There is often a very prominent break in the slope of the beach that defines that beach berm.

- Equally offshore, there is a region where sand and sometimes mud—finer-grained materials—are being actively transported back and forth by turbulent wave action right in the foreshore region, which builds a foreshore terrace on a flat spot.

- This flat spot often drops off into a longshore trough, which is a trough that runs along the length of the shoreline. The turbulent action of the water flowing back to the ocean digs out the sand a little bit and piles it up into a **longshore bar**.

© Thinkstock/Getty Images/Comstock/Thinkstock.

The Outer Banks region of North Carolina is dominated by extensive barrier islands created by longshore drift.

Longshore Drift and Current

- Sand moves up and down the beaches in very specific directions. **Longshore drift** is a very important process that continuously transports sand and sediment along the beach so that a dynamic balance of sand moves through that system.

- An offshore current called the longshore current is similar to the longshore drift—both involve the oblique approach of waves. For longshore current, the way waves break along the beach produces water moving in the near-shore offshore region laterally along the beach in the same direction as longshore drift, carving out the longshore trough and moving sediment laterally along the beach.

- Sediment transport by longshore drift and the presence of storms produce some very distinctive features that exist along the coastlines of the world such as barrier islands, lagoons, and sand spits.

- In some cases, the longshore bar can gradually turn into barrier islands—the long, extended islands that lie just off the main coastline that dominate many regions of depositional coast.

- As sand is drifting along the coast with the longshore drift, if it reaches an embayment—the mouth of a bay or river—then it reaches a point where the water gets a little deeper and the wave action is a little less strong, so a lot of the sediment will be dropped out of suspension and deposited as sand spits and sandbars that partially or completely cover those river mouths and harbor areas.

- Barrier islands are incredibly well developed around the eastern and Gulf coasts of the U.S. The North Carolina barrier islands (the Outer Banks region) and all the regions from the eastern shores of Maryland and Virginia down the coast are dominated by extensive barrier-island systems that are all offshore bars created by the longshore drift.

- Some of the features of typical east-coast barrier islands of the United States include the beach; the dune fields; and behind those, a broad and extremely low-elevation salt-marsh and tidal-flat region. Often these extend over many square miles into a saltwater lagoon or even brackish-water lagoon before reaching the mainland.

- One interesting feature of beaches with coarse sediments is that the beach tends to have a steeper slope to the ocean. On these slopes, water percolates into the coarse sand, so the beach develops a steeper face that has a very regularly spaced pattern of what are called beach cusps. The formation of beach cusps and their regular spacing is enigmatic; there are a number of theories about how they might've formed, but none offer a clear explanation.

U.S. Coastal Areas

- The Pacific coast of the continental United States and of Alaska is dominated by the fact that it's an active tectonic margin. It's a region where plates are converging, or moving past each other. The effects of recent tectonic activity render it dominated by erosion.

- By contrast, the Atlantic coast is a passive continental margin. Remember that the plate boundary is far out in the Mid-Atlantic Ridge, and there's no boundary between the ocean plate and the land plate. It's a depositional-dominated coastline—except for the flooded valleys that exist there.

- The Gulf coast, similarly, is a region that has smaller wave sizes; it's an enclosed basin. It's a passive continental margin, so it's also a depositional-dominated coastline.

Important Terms

berm: The prominent break in slope on many beaches that marks the highest elevation of wave washing.

fjord: Glacially formed deep and steep-walled valley flooded by the sea.

longshore bar: Sandbar parallel to the coast and just offshore in the tidal range.

longshore drift: Net transport of sediment parallel to the coast due to prevailing wave directions and variable swash and backwash on the beach.

sea stack: Rocky outcropping near the shore but isolated from the mainland created by erosional retreat of sea cliffs over time.

wave-cut platform: A near-flat bedrock plane cut by wave action eroding the coast between high- and low-tide levels.

Suggested Reading

Carson, *The Edge of the Sea.*

Pilkey, Neal, Kelley, and Cooper, *The World's Beaches.*

Sverdrup and Armbrust, *Introduction to the World's Oceans*, chap. 18.

Questions to Consider

1. Can a coastal area be both erosional and depositional at the same time?

2. Is a sandy beach on a deposition-dominated shoreline the same from season to season and year to year? What are some ways in which it is not the same?

Where Sea Meets the Land and Why Coasts Vary
Lecture 23—Transcript

For the past few lectures now, we've focused on the biota that dwell in the open ocean, the pelagic zone, but of course many, many marine organisms are tightly connected to the bottom and even to the coasts and the land. What we're going to do now is start to examine the benthic or bottom-dwelling habitats and ecosystems over the course of a series of lectures. But, first what we need to do is understand the physical environment that those organisms dwell in. let's turn to the coastlines, shorelines, estuaries, and the processes that govern the existence of all these features where the sea really meets the land.

Have you ever walked along a sandy beach, maybe in Cape Cod or the outer banks of North Carolina or conversely stood on a sea cliff or a promontory in say Oregon or Northern California and watched the waves crash below and wondered how it all got that way. Why does one landscape, one coastal landscape, look so dramatically different from another? What is the governing process that makes it such that we have areas with long extended sandy beaches versus regions with rocky shorelines and very craggy nature to them? Why is the shoreline so dramatically different in all these different locations?

In this lecture, I'm going to examine the processes that govern the range and variety of these coastal environments. I'll discuss how the characteristics of coasts are governed by a dynamic balance between 2 fundamental sets of processes and we'll break them down as erosional processes and depositional processes. In fact, we'll define coasts as either erosion dominated coasts or deposition dominated coasts. All of these processes basically result from the interplay of a few different key things. One is sea level changes, the level of the sea at a given time in its motion up and down as well as the short-term sea level changes like tidal range and things like that, and then plate tectonics, the movements of the land up and down, and sediment transport, or the motion of sand and mud through the coastal environment. All of these things are going to govern the nature and shape of many of the coastlines of the world.

If we want to talk about coastal processes, first we have to define some really basic terms and maybe these are common everyday terms, but let's get specific about them. First of all the shore or the shoreline is the physical place where the ocean meets the land, the location of interaction of the waves and the tides with the landscape. On a sort of broader scale, the coast or even the coastal zone to an ocean scientist more typically would refer to the whole region of interaction between the 2 from some distance above the high tide line, perhaps including salt marshes, sand dunes, sea cliffs, and the region around the sea cliffs off to the immediate offshore region including things like sandbars and channels of just below the low tide line.

The coast is an active place. It's subject to geological processes of both the land on the one hand and geological and oceanographic processes of the sea. It's a battleground between all of these forces and a dynamic balance, in fact, among all of them, a place where basically nothing is static. The coast is constantly shifting and moving, the material and sand is constantly shifting and yet maintains some level of equilibrium that defines a particular characteristic coastline for a given region.

First of all, let's think about sea level because the coast or the shoreline itself is an arbitrary point right. It's just where the waterline happens to meet the landscape. You might not think of it as very arbitrary; we can certainly think of it being different when you're out of the water versus when you're in the water. The position of the shoreline is determined by factors that change through the time, constantly in fact. One is tectonic activity or the lack thereof, there's the landscape itself, does the crust of Earth move up and down usually over relatively slow geologic time periods. That can include motions due to actual tectonics, the movement of faults in Earth. It can also include changes in the land level due to a process we call glacial rebound, areas that have large glaciers on top, weighing down the land literally to press the land surface.

Since the glaciers melted off tens of thousands of years ago the land has been slowly springing back up just like a couch cushion you just sat down on and got up and then it springs back into place slowly. An additional factor then governing sea level is the movement and trapping of sediments, so how are sediments moving around, building up piles, dunes, and sandbars, and things like that, perhaps coral sediments then help build up reefs that change the shoreline position potentially. Then most importantly perhaps or most rapidly changing in some ways is global sea level and that is what we also call eustatic sea level and that's defined as the variation in sea level that you can measure all over the world equally. It turns out, because of those things like tectonic changes; we will also have to consider local sea level change.

For the moment let's just consider how global sea level, eustatic sea level has changed over time and is changing today in fact. If we look at a reconstruction of what sea level has been over the period throughout the last few ice ages, the periods where the glaciers have grown and receded and taken up lots of water into fresh water on the planet and cooled the planet off and then melted out and the planet warmed up again. Over the past 250,000 years, sea level has ranged from the present day level to as much as 125 meters lower, about 18,000 years ago for example at the height of the last glaciation to as much as 6 meters higher than the present day when things were melted a little bit more than they are today, and there's was a little bit warmer.

Sea level has fluctuated up and down on the geologic timeframe quite rapidly over this span of about 130 meters or so. The recent level is near the highest it ever is actually, or it ever has been during at least the 250,000 years. We're in a relatively warm period and the ocean as we'll see not only gets more water in it from the melting of the ice caps, but also expands due to the extra heat in the ocean. We'll examine that in a later lecture.

So sea level changes over time, and that means that the position of the shoreline changes over time. I discussed the continental shelves earlier on and this continental shelf is essentially the region that is where the shoreline passes back and forth as the glaciers come and go. We look at the position of the likely continental shelf 18,000 years ago at the peak of the last Ice age, for example the Florida Peninsula would've been a much broader region and the shoreline would've been much further off shore relative to today. The shoreline has moved over that period since about 10,000 years ago when the glaciers receded to reach the present-day shoreline and they've been rapidly changing over millennia, over periods of thousands of years.

Shorelines change in response to rising and falling sea level. If we look even further back in geological time, before there were any glaciers on the planet or even icecaps in the Arctic and Antarctic regions then sea level was actually much higher. There would be something like a 60 meter rise of sea level if we melted the entire Arctic polar icecaps off the planet. That's not likely to happen very quickly, but it's possible at current rates a few centuries in the future we would see 60 meters of sea level rise. That would make the coastlines look very different still. In fact, large parts of the Florida peninsula would be missing completely with 60 meters of sea level rise.

The long-term eustatic sea level actually gets complicated because not only does the sea level rise relative to land, but the land doesn't stay in one place. Even the volume of the ocean can change, if the mid-ocean ranges are more productive that raises the sea floor for example. We won't get into that level of complications. The point is that sea level goes up and down over a variety of different timescales, some quite short. All of these features then govern the erosional and depositional coasts of the planet and so I'd like to walk through the differences in the forces that shape these 2 kinds of coastlines.

First the erosional coast, erosional coasts are any coasts that're dominated by the breakdown of rock and the creation of sediment, the active modification of the rocky landscape of the planet. The mechanical force of the surf pounding on the coastal rocks, the hydraulic pressure driving water into the cracks in those rocks, the abrasion by the sand and gravel, and even boulders that water carries is the main agent of change for erosional coastlines. Even beyond that actually biological activity is part of the story too. Roots of trees get down into the cracks in the rocks and break them down, make them more susceptible to erosion. Boring organisms, not boring as in dull, but organisms that bore into the rock like clams and things like that can breakdown he rock as well.

All of this has an effect on erosional coasts and we see the power of the sea breaking down the coastline in this photograph that I took myself actually standing on the cliffs 40 or 50 feet above the shoreline, above the surf level, near Bandon, Oregon and just watch these enormous Pacific swells coming down from the Gulf of Alaska pounding into the rocks and you really can literally feel up through your feet the vibrations of the strength of that hydraulic force of the ocean. The erosion by the surf then undercuts those sea cliffs, undercuts the rocks, and erodes them back irregularly at first, building these very regular shorelines, very craggy and complicated shaped shorelines.

That erosion process typically happens in a specific way, maybe when the waves aren't quite so enormous as the pounding waves in that last photograph, but the waves come in and at the mid to high tide level, they keep cutting in and eroding notches in even sea caves at the base of the cliffs. Those undercut the cliffs, the cliffs keep collapsing into the water, and so the erosion takes place right at the level of the strongest wave action in that intertidal zone and cuts back and forth. It typically makes something called a wave-cut platform within the tidal range, a flat region of bare rock that has been chopped out by the waves and we can see this wave-cut platform or sometimes called marine terrace exposed at the low tide, especially at very low tides as shown in this image, but then at high tide that's actively being down cut by the present day sea level.

Since sea level goes up and down it will make these specific wave-cut platforms in different regions cutting the cliffs back and adding sediment to the sea which will ultimately then move around and form beaches and things like that. If we look at a typical erosional coast, we see some basic features of it. We see the sea cliffs themselves with their active wave-cut platform at the base and then the sediment that's produced on those will start to fill in some of those areas with what are called exposed beaches or sometimes pocket beaches if they fill in little pocket areas. There are headlands of the rock areas that are out beyond the beach where it's just rock and sea and sometimes those headlands are eroded around and behind and actually left behind out offshore as what are called sea stacks, these big rocks, rock promontories jutting out of the ocean, but now no longer connected to the land, at least not at high tide levels.

This image actually comes from a region near Melbourne, Australia, a region called the Twelve Apostles for the 12 large sea stacks that were there although now there are apparently only 11, as one of the large apostles collapsed just in recent years, a multistory building level rock. That's just an indication of the rapidity and the strength of these processes of erosion going on on erosional coasts.

If we look at areas around the world's strongly erosional coasts, we see these very active promontories of headlands of rock with cuspate pockets that will develop beaches in between them. Sometimes when tectonic activity is strong and the land is actively being uplifted by the motion of faults we actually see what are called abandoned wave-cut platforms. In this photography, you can see the flat terraced area on top of the sea cliff region before the mountains that is the old wave-cut platform from the last time sea level was at a high stand and the sea receded and abandoned that platform. The land continued to come out so when the sea came back in then it started cutting a new one and that one's left behind as a legacy of a previous geological era.

We talked in another lecture about wave refraction and so let's remember how wave refraction actually bends the waves in to focus their energy to attack the headlands and then actually focuses their energy away from the gentle dissipated waves in the bay. These cuspate bays are areas where waves are less strong and so sediment tends to fall out of the water. It deposits sediment in the bay producing the pocket beaches while it focuses its energy, keeps the sediment in suspension abrading and breaking down he rocks of the headlands. In this way, we get the pocket beaches forming and then given enough time coasts that are craggy in erosional coasts will slowly develop more and more sediment, straighten out, the headlands will broken down, the beaches will get bigger and bigger and we developed towards the long extended beaches we see on more depositional coastlines or more mature, in some sense, coastlines.

We can also have erosional coasts that are built up a little bit differently and it's less obvious maybe that this is from erosion, but there are coasts that are shaped by land erosion. What I mean by that is that when the sea level stand was lower, so during the glacial periods, and the shoreline was out near the edge of the present day continental shelf then rivers would cut down through the landscape and cut river valleys. Ultimately if sea level rises again, these regions that were produced by terrestrial or on land erosion get flooded by the influx of the sea again. So, we see these flooded or drowned river valley that make up many areas, especially of the east coast of North America, and other parts of the world, like the Chesapeake and Delaware Bays or the Hudson River Valley are all examples of flooded river valleys. These are really erosion dominated processes on that particular part of the coastline, but it's really the land erosion that we see as the dominant process and then the sea is just reflooding that.

The most dramatic example, perhaps of that kind of erosional process, is the development of fjords, places like Norway and Alaska and New Zealand, where we see dramatic glacially cut valleys from the large glaciers that were present during the ice ages. They carve out these deep channeled valleys with the glaciers and then glaciers receded, sea level rose and inundates the valleys often putting deepwater seawater into these very steeply sided, essentially land erosion dominated valleys. The land is actually moving vertically upward even as the sea flows in because of that post-glacial rebound that I described a few minutes ago. We see coastlines that are incredibly convoluted and craggy, like the southern part of the south island of New Zealand where a famous place called Milford Sound is that many people have seen perhaps on tourist trips, but where many, many tens of miles inland you can see these large ocean fjords going into the coastline carving it out.

From our erosional coast then let's turn to depositional coasts. These are regions where the net accumulation and movement of this sediment shapes the fundamental morphology of the coastal area. This is really about the transport of sand and mud and the coastal environment is defined by and dominated by the distribution of those kinds of sediments. We have the deposition of beaches and barrier islands and all of the different sandbars and spits and things like that, that are associated with sand transport along a depositional coast. In the absence of ongoing tectonic activity or big scale glacial rebound, major sea level changes, erosional coasts will tend to evolved into depositional coasts and that's essentially what we've seen with large parts of the coasts of the eastern coast of North America. The long sandy beaches are the process fundamentally of deposition of sand.

Let's take a look at the beach itself. You go out to the beach and you look around and maybe just lie on the sand and stare at the waves and don't want to think about too much, but next time you go to the beach let's look for some of the fundamental features of what the beach morphology is. Basically we break the beach down into a series of regions that are dependent on the general sea level or where the wave action occurs and then where the high tide and low tide lines mark it. We have the near shore region, which is offshore where the breakers are, where the waves are actively breaking on the beach. Further out, we'll just collateral ligaments the offshore beyond essentially the low tide where the water depth gets significantly greater than the low tide level.

We go through the near shore region and the waves break on the beach. The part of the beach that is actively washed back and forth by waves in any typical kinds of weather and tides is called the foreshore region, so the foreshore. The foreshore is then backed by what we call the backshore region. The boundary between the foreshore and the backshore is the upper limit of basically the highest high tide wave action, perhaps associated with the strongest winter storms that are still common. That will produce an area called the beach berm.

There can be several beach berms. Sometimes there's a higher beach berm that is the break and slope between the steeply sloping foreshore where the waves are washing back and forth and the more gently sloping backshore. The highest beach berm might be produced by the largest recent major winter storm or something like that. Then there can be a second beach berm, which might be the one associated with the most recent few tidal cycles or wave action that's been going on in recent days on a given beach.

We break the beach down then into these different regions and then in the backshore region, instead of wave dominated or water dominated processes, sediment transport is taken over by wind dominated and land dominated processes. The sand may reach the beach berm. It dries out; it's not getting wet anymore because it's at the high winter berm or the high storm berm. Then it will get blown off of there and form sand dunes and things like that. We often see a very prominent break in the slope of the beach that defines that beach berm.

Equally offshore, we see a region where sand is being actively transported back and forth and sometimes mud as well, so finer grained material. The waves are washing back and forth and you have a turbulent action right on the foreshore region and as the water swashes back down into the near shore it will often build a little bit of a foreshore terrace on a flat spot. You often find this if you walk out into the water and it's flat and then it drops off into a longshore trough. That's just a trough that runs along the length of the shoreline with the turbulent action of the water flowing back to the ocean digs out the sand a little bit and piles it up into a longshore bar. You'll walk out into the water it gets deeper and then all the sudden you find yourself standing in only ankle deep water on top of that longshore bar.

Not every beach has every one of these elements, but this is sort of the composite of typical sandy beaches in various regions around the world. That region where we see the longshore troughs and bars really is from mean sea level down to the low tide region. If you walk on the beach, look for the beach berm, or look for the beach berms. See if you can see a higher winter berm and a lower summer berm. Notice that slope difference between the foreshore and the backshore. Look at how the dunes are dominated by wind processes and perhaps have started to have some vegetation growing on them.

If you look at examples from aerial photography of various beaches around we see beautiful examples of this from all over the place, the barrier islands on the east coast of the U.S. or this beach in Kenya where you can see the berm line in the middle of the sand just as an absolutely, extremely well-defined line, defining the difference between the foreshore where the waves are swashing and then the backshore. The berm line can actually be the highest point on the beach with the beach dropping off behind it. The dune field here is well-developed and begun to be stabilized by vegetation growing on that dune field as well. Behind the dunes then, we'll often see a lagoonal area, a lower area where the sand now is not piled up anymore, lower elevation, and if the ocean is breaking through in different channels that are cutting across the entire beach region, they'll fill water in behind the beach into a lagoon.

Sand moves up and down the beaches in very specific directions and there's a very important process that is actually continuously transporting sand and sediment along the beach so the sand on a given beach in one year is not the same sand literally as it was in the past year or as it will be in the next year, even if the beach looks virtually the same. There's a dynamic balance of sand moving through that system. That's due to a process called longshore drift. The process is very simple. Waves generally don't approach the beach head-on. They usually approach from some angle and in most parts of the world there's a prevailing wind and wave direction. In North America, both east coast and west coast we see waves approaching from northerly directions. In the northeast, the waves come from the northeast from the North Atlantic.

What they do then is the waves approach from this oblique direction. When they wash sand up the beach the sand goes along with the waves right up the beach at a diagonal angle. The water that rushes down the beach doesn't rush down the same direction it came up. It rushes down the beach because of gravity. Gravity pulls it straight down the beach face and so the backwash, the swash in is diagonally up the beach. The backwash is directly down slope and so you get a zigzag pattern that gradually transports sand along the beach from north to south in North America really on both coasts typically.

There's also a current offshore we call the longshore current that is somewhat the same thing, the oblique approach of waves and the way they break along the beach produces water moving in the near shore offshore region laterally along the beach in the same direction as the longshore drift and carving out in part that longshore trough and moving sediment laterally along the beach. When you feel those strong currents when you're playing in the waves that are pulling you along the beach, you're feeling the longshore current and the longshore drift.

Sediment transport by this longshore drift and the presence of storms especially that move a lot of sediment produce some very distinctive features that we see along the coastlines of the world. As the sediment transport comes along and beaches have a little bit of embayments and headlands and things like that we will see the longshore drift moving sediment along. In some cases that longshore bar, the sand that has moved offshore being deposited just outside the region where a wave base is or where waves are breaking builds up so high that it becomes what we would call subaerially exposed meaning exposed as new land or as a sandbar that's above at least low tide if not all tidal levels. Those sandbars can gradually turn into actual barrier islands, the long extended islands that lie just off the main coastline that dominate many regions of depositional coast.

Even less well-developed than barrier islands, but very important is that the sand is drifting along the coast with the longshore drift, if it reaches an embayment or something like that, a bay or a river mouth, than it reaches a point where the water gets a little deeper, the wave action is a little less strong, and so a lot of that sediment will be dropped out of suspension and deposited as things like sand spits and sand bars that partially cover those or even completely cover those river mouths and harbor areas. We can see lots of examples if you look around in satellite photography. Here's one from Wilmington, North Carolina where you see the river entering the ocean and the sand hook or sand spit extending range of motion the north part of the way across a river mouth and often these have to actually be dredged out. You could even see the sediments from the river being pushed out into the ocean.

The sand spits are a very well-developed feature due to that deposition at the mouth of the river. Barrier islands are incredibly well-developed around the east and Gulf coasts of the U.S. Galveston Island, Texas is a classic example of a barrier island system with a well-developed sandy island that the island has no rocky underpinnings whatsoever. It's simply a sandbar with a slack water lagoon in behind it and some inlet channels that allow the high tide and storm waters to flow back and forth. As we'll see later with hurricanes and extreme storms this becomes a real problem when the whole barrier island can be potentially over washed by the sea.

One more example, North Carolina barrier islands, the Outer Banks region and all of the regions actually from the eastern shores of Maryland, Virginia, on down are just dominated by these extensive barrier island systems that are all offshore bars total hip arthroplasty are created by the longshore drift. The fact that they're created by longshore drift means that they're not static in place at all. The sand first of all is moving into them on a literally annual basis and out of them on an annual basis. They're moving back and forth with changes in sea level so over geological times since the last 10,000 years as sea level has come up since the last Ice age, the barrier islands have been moving steadily towards the shoreline.

In a later lecture, we'll look at the present day effects of some of those changes and we'll look at the present day effects of human interactions in the form of trying to stabilize these barrier islands that really want to be in motion. Some of the features of barrier islands then are really clear if you look at them from the air, but also if you're looking at them on the ground. If we look at any of the typical east coast barrier islands of the U.S. we see the beach, the dune fields, and then behind then we usually see a broad and extremely low elevation salt marsh and tidal flat region. Often these extend over many square miles of region eventually grading out into an actual saltwater lagoon or perhaps even brackish water lagoon before you reach the mainland itself.

One interesting feature of beaches in general, if you go to many places around the world especially beaches with coarse sediments on them so very large sand grains, maybe small pebbles and rocks as opposed to fine light sand, you see that the beach tends to have a steeper slope to the ocean on those coarse sandy beaches. The water can infiltrate the beach and drain right into the beach more easily on these beaches so the swash then sediment up, but instead of running back down the beach it tends to just percolate into this coarse sand and so the beach develops a steeper face. On many of those steep face beaches we see a very regular pattern of what are called beach cusps, these cuspate almost rhythmic looking in terms of how regularly spaced they are patterns on the beach of very small, a foot high or inches high, promontories and depressions.

It turns out that the formation of these beach cusps and their regular spacing is enigmatic. There are a number of theories about how they might've formed, but it's not clear that any of them really answer the question. Once they get formed you can see how they continued to develop because the cusps themselves actually divide the waves through the wave refraction process, but the initiation of these beach cusps is a mystery to science even today. On the other hand, they're there and so we have to find some way to account for them.

U.S. coastal areas then are fundamentally controlled by large-scale processes and so we can really place this erosional and depositional coastline into a framework of tectonics. The Pacific coast of the continental U.S. and of Alaska is dominated by the fact that it's an active tectonic margin. It's a region where plates are converging or moving past each other. The effects of that recent tectonic activity render it erosion-dominated. By contrast, the Atlantic coast is a passive continental margin. Remember that the plate boundary is way out in the Mid-Atlantic Ridge and there's no boundary between the ocean plate and the land plate. It's depositional dominated except for those flooded valleys which are a special case. The Gulf coast similarly is a region that is smaller wave sizes; it's an enclosed basin. It's a passive continental margin and so it's also a depositional dominated coastline.

To sum up then, erosional, depositional, and sediment transport processes work together to produce all of the characteristic coastlines of the world. There are a few types of coastlines that we haven't really examined yet including ones that are dominated by biology in some ways, coral reefs, mangrove forests, and things like that. We're going to take a look at those a little later on. In the next lecture, what we're going to do is really take this one step further and we've come all the way to the coastline. We've seen how the sea interacts with the land right at the beach and right at the cliffs, but we'll examine the locations where actually the fresh water, the water from the rivers comes in and meets the sea. The next lecture is really where the rivers meet the sea.

Where Rivers Meet the Sea—Estuaries and Deltas
Lecture 24

Human activity is now extensively modifying the natural deposition and erosion processes on coastlines and, combined with gradual sea-level rise, is causing loss of beaches and natural barriers in many areas. Construction of breakwaters and jetties interferes with natural longshore drift and has caused wholesale changes in Atlantic coast shorelines. Seawalls and other structures designed to protect buildings ironically can make beach erosion worse. Loss of sediment supply and protective vegetation leaves many coastal areas more susceptible to storm damage. Private property rights, insurance, and public interest often collide over these issues.

Estuaries

- River mouths, deltas, tidal inlets, fjords, and enclosed bays are all regions where freshwater and seawater mix in a complex and dynamic environment of very high biological diversity and productivity. Many marine organisms have parts of their life cycle in these settings or even up freshwater rivers, including larval stages of **anadromous fish** like salmon as well as many crustaceans.

- **Estuaries** are bodies of shallow water that are partially surrounded by the land but with an open though limited connection to the ocean. Water in these areas is diluted to less than seawater salinity, but it is not as fresh as river water is.

- Estuaries are typically affected by the tidal range and are marked by exceptionally high biological productivity. Shallow, sunlit waters that have nutrients from both the land and the ocean mixing together produce a very fertile region on the planet.

- One example of an estuary region is the Chesapeake Bay and the flooded river mouths that enter it—such as the Susquehanna River. Another example is the San Francisco Bay, which is on the opposite coast but is also a shallow-water estuary.

Types of Estuaries

- The 4 types of estuaries are defined by their origin. Some are drowned river mouths, such as the Chesapeake Bay. In the continental United States, the Puget Sound region is a drowned fjord. Others are tectonic estuaries, which are formed by the action of faults and the upwarping and downwarping of the crust—San Francisco Bay is an example. The fourth type is the bar-built estuary that exists behind the barrier islands and sandbars where there are **lagoons** and salt-marsh regions—such as Pamlico Sound in North Carolina.

- Instead of the container—the estuarine basin—estuaries can be defined in terms of salt water and freshwater mixing.

- A salt wedge estuary is a region where there is very strong river flow into a confined basin that leads out to the ocean. This type of estuary is dominated by freshwater flow.

- Salt water is denser than freshwater, so the dense salt water is trying to move up the estuary with tidal cycles and wedges underneath the freshwater that's flowing over the top of it. There's a sharp boundary between the 2 water masses, and there's relatively little mixing. There's such a density difference between the cold, dense seawater and the river water that the river water flows on top of the seawater.

- One process that takes place in salt wedge estuaries is one-way mixing, an entrainment of salt water with some turbulence at the edge of the boundary up into the freshwater, which becomes more brackish as it heads toward the ocean. The salt wedge itself doesn't get much freshwater mixed into it.

- A second type of estuary is a well-mixed estuary, which has relatively low river flow and strong tidal mixing. The water coming in from the sea and the water coming in from the river are balanced. The waters mix actively and quickly, so there's a salinity gradient that doesn't have the depth stratification as in a salt wedge estuary but instead has nearly uniform depth.

- In between these end-member categories are partially mixed estuaries, regions where there is a strong flow of river water and also a relatively strong influx of seawater that produces even more turbulence and 2-way mixing—entrainment of some seawater up into the river water but transfer of some of the river water down into the seawater by turbulent vortex mixing at the boundary between the 2.

- The fourth type of estuary is a fjord-type estuary. Fjords commonly have deep water in them; they have what is almost a shallow-water barrier at the front end of the estuary, and the fjord is filled with a deep pool of fairly dense seawater. The river water enters the deep pool of salt water but remains at the surface and mixes very little. Many fjords have a very strong inversion in which the surface water is almost purely fresh but is completely saline water below a certain depth.

Well-Mixed Estuaries

- The Chesapeake Bay is an example of a well-mixed estuary. The salinity is measured in per mil—one part per thousand—and the peak salinity near the entrance of the estuary is in the 24–25 per mil range, and then it goes up to mostly freshwater at the upper reaches of the Chesapeake Bay. (The salinity of seawater is about 35 per mil.)

- The pattern of salinity is not particularly symmetrical in the Chesapeake Bay. As the salt water enters with the tides and, conversely, as the freshwater comes down from the rivers, the Coriolis effect causes the salt water to bend to the right (east) as it enters the Chesapeake Bay and the freshwater coming down toward the ocean to also bend to the right (west).

- The mixing of freshwater and sea-water nutrients in this shallow, well-lit, protected environment provides a fertile habitat for animal life that's specific to the estuarine waters. In particular, crabs, oysters, and many different types of fish dwell in estuarine environments and provide great fisheries and food sources for the ecosystem and for human beings.

- In addition, estuaries serve as nurseries for the juvenile stages of many major oceanic species. Examples include perch, anchovy, and Pacific herring.

- The Chesapeake Bay is home to the famous blue crabs, which have a fascinating life cycle. They mainly live in the low-salinity areas, relatively high up the estuary. A female mates only once in its life and carries the male sperm, but she needs to create and fertilize eggs—spawning the larval stage—which depends on getting to a high-salinity region and having lots of tidal water cycling.

The famous blue crabs of the Chesapeake Bay region are a very tasty product of this estuarine environment.

- In high-estuarine environments that are well up into the upper reaches of the intertidal zone, where water reaches and creates brackish but also very slack water conditions, there are regions that are coastal salt marshes. In coastal salt marshes, there are salt-tolerant species—those that have evolved the ability to excrete salt—of many vascular plants and many aquatic organisms that thrive in that same environment.

Types of Deltas

- River deltas form where rivers with heavy sediment load reach the sea, especially in a region where the continental shelf is relatively broad and there's relatively low-energy wave action to carry that sediment away once it's been brought down to the sea.

- The combined effects of waves, tides, river flow, and sediment determine the 2 fundamental delta shapes: river-dominated deltas and tide-dominated deltas.

- **River-dominated deltas** are fed by a strong flow of sediment from the land with large distributary channels—regions where the river dumps its sediment load in one area for awhile and, as that builds up, moves off to a different region and dumps its sediment there.

- **Tide-dominated deltas** are molded by tidal currents that rework or move around the sediments that are being dumped by the rivers on the land.

- Both river-dominated deltas and tide-dominated deltas can be sites of major wetlands and salt-marsh regions, estuarine systems that can be extensively developed along the coastline.

- The Mississippi River delta, a river-dominated delta, builds out into the Gulf of Mexico at the coast of Louisiana and dumps sediment out over a large area. There, huge coastal wetlands—mud flats essentially—are interacting with the tides on a daily basis and are flooded by seawater, but they are also affected by the freshwater coming from the land.

- A river-dominated delta has the characteristics found at the Mississippi delta where the distribution of salt marshes and the channels are well defined by the fact that the river is putting sediment in the water out toward the sea.

The Mississippi River delta, off the coast of Louisiana, produces hundreds of thousands of acres of coastal wetlands.

- By contrast, the Ganges River delta is a tide-dominated region, so the river is still coming down to the ocean and is still delivering a lot of sediment to the ocean, but it's delivering a little less sediment—spreading it over a broader and flatter region—and the tidal cycling is strong enough that it's taking all that sediment and redistributing it.

Biologically Dominated Coastlines

- Mangrove trees are rooted down into the salt water of a saltwater-dominated estuarine system but have leaves that are up in the air; they are partly marine and partly subaerial. Mangrove regions trap sediment, hold it in place, and build the land in tide-dominated regions.

- Coastlines can be dominated not just by erosion and sediment transport, but also by the biology that lives on them. Mangrove trees represent a whole type of coastline.

- At the fundamental geological level, coastlines start out as deposition dominated or erosion dominated, but the shore region and environments of the shoreline can often be substantially modified by the existence of ecosystems of various kinds of organisms.

- Mangrove trees can build huge areas of biologically dominated coastline by trapping large amounts of sediment and providing habitat for various organisms that then colonize the estuarine environment and use it productively.

- Mangrove forests essentially armor the coastline, making it less susceptible to storm surges and extremely high tides because they provide a buffer zone between the coastline and the main part of the land.

- Unfortunately, mangrove as wood is a potential commodity, and the mangrove regions are being taken over for various kinds of development. Globally, there's been about a 20% reduction in the total area of mangrove forests since 1980, but that rate is rapidly diminishing.

- Another type of biologically dominated coastline is carbonated banks and platforms. Coral reefs build large structures of carbonate; the reef itself is the living carbonate. The reef is constantly broken down, producing huge volumes of carbonate sediment—essentially limestone—over geological time. This process builds up a rocky substructure that's incredibly strong and becomes the main coastline feature.

- Many of the coral islands around the world were corals that grew up to close to sea level when the sea level was substantially higher than it is today. As the sea level drained back down, these corals dried out and died but left behind islands. The Florida Keys and the Bahamas are examples of such islands.

- Estuaries, deltas, and marine wetlands are among the most biologically productive regions on Earth and have in fact supported the flourishing of major world civilizations throughout human history.

Important Terms

anadromous fish: Fish that spend part of their life cycle in freshwater and part in the ocean, such as salmon.

estuary: Coastal body of water where seawater and stream- or river-supplied freshwater mix.

lagoon: Shallow saltwater region trapped between the beach dune zone and the mainland area.

river-dominated delta: A river mouth in which the strong flow from land determines the pattern of sediment deposition and channel geometry.

tide-dominated delta: A river mouth in which the waves and tides determine the pattern of sediment deposition and channel geometry.

Suggested Reading

Davis and FitzGerald, *Beaches and Coasts*.

Questions to Consider

1. What are some of the ways that pollution in estuarine waters are especially harmful to ecological communities relative to in the open ocean? See how many different aspects you can think of.

2. What might you expect to happen to present-day river deltas if sea level continues to rise?

Where Rivers Meet the Sea—Estuaries and Deltas
Lecture 24—Transcript

Another aspect of the coastal region is the place where the rivers meet the sea. River mouths, deltas, tidal inlets, fjords and enclosed bays, these are all regions where fresh water and seawater are mixing and they form a complex and dynamic environment, a very high biological diversity and productivity. They're important because they're the place where the seawater and the fresh water actually mix so the place where the interaction takes place and the chemistries exchange, but maybe even more importantly they're the locations where many marine organisms carry out parts of their lifecycle. There are a number of larval stages of crustaceans and fish and different species that are lived out in the brackish waters of estuaries. There are even anadromous fish like salmon that go from the sea all the way up to completely fresh water environments up rivers and streams in order to spawn.

We're going to take a look in this lecture at estuaries and we're also going to look at river deltas and other areas where the rivers meet the sea. Estuaries, first of all, are bodies of shallow water that are partially surrounded by the land, but with some sort of open connection although limited connection to the ocean. You end up with water that's diluted to less than seawater salinity, but is not fresh as river water is. Estuaries are typically effected by the tidal range and they're certainly marked by exceptionally high biological productivity, shallow sunlit waters, nutrients from both the land and the ocean mixing together, produce sort of a very fertile region on the planet.

One example of an estuary region is the Chesapeake Bay and the flooded river mouths that enter it like the Susquehanna River. Another example is San Francisco Bay, opposite coast, very different setting in a way, but also a shallow water estuary, rivers that drain most of the area of California feeding into San Francisco Bay and producing a very fertile ground for the growth of all sorts of different organisms, including many formerly important fisheries. The types of estuaries, as is exemplified by Chesapeake Bay and San Francisco Bay and some of what we learned in the previous lectures, are defined by their origin. Some are drowned river mouths, the Chesapeake Bay, Delaware Bay kind of origin. Some are fjords. In the continental U.S.

the Strait of Juan de Fuca or the Puget Sound region are basically drowned fjords. Alaska is certainly filled with them as well.

Some are what we call tectonic estuaries that are formed by the action of faults and the upwarping and downwarping of the crust. San Francisco Bay is an example of a tectonic estuary defined by the San Andreas faults on one side and the Hayward-Calaveras faults on the other side. The fourth type is actually the bar-built estuary meaning behind the barrier islands and sandbars where you have lagoons and salt marsh regions like Pamlico Sound in North Carolina, for example, you develop an estuarine system where waters mix. These geomorphic features determine how the waters mix and they define the overall shape and depth of the water in estuaries, but in a sense they don't serve to define their characteristics as habitat and in terms of the water and nutrient exchange.

We're going to think of 4 types of estuaries in a little bit different terms. Instead of the container, the estuarine basin, we'll think of it in terms of water mixing. These 4 types are basically divided into categories based on how the salt water and the fresh water mix with each other. All of them are essentially artificial divisions of a continuous spectrum of different types of water mixing. We're talking about literally a fluid environment with fresh water and salt water coming together, but we can break them down into at least some end members or typical cases.

The first one is the salt wedge estuary. This is a region where there is very strong river flow so a large volume and strong flow of river water into a confined basin that leads out to the ocean. What you see then is that it's dominated by this fresh water flow. Salt water is denser than fresh water, so this dense salt water is trying to move up the estuary with tidal cycles and things like that and so the dense saltwater wedges in literally in a shape of a wedge underneath the fresh water that's flowing out over the top of it.

There's a sharp boundary between the 2 water masses actually in a salt wedge estuary and there's relatively little mixing. There's so much density difference between the cold dense seawater and the river water that the river water just flows out on top of the seawater. One process that takes place in salt wedge estuaries is something called one-way mixing and that is that there's an entrainment of the salt water with some turbulence at the edge of this boundary up into the fresh water so the fresh water becomes more brackish as it heads towards the ocean. The salt wedge itself doesn't get much fresh water mixed into it.

Some typical examples of this sort of end member or extreme case estuary of the salt wedge is the mouth of the Columbia River or also the mouth of the Hudson River on the east coast. The Columbia River has incredibly large amount of flow, a relatively deep river basin heading out to the sea. The salt wedge actually comes many, many miles, as much as 20 miles in shore up the Columbia River valley or up the Columbia River bed beneath the fresh water that's flowing over the top of it in a real salt wedge estuary style. A second type that we can describe in the second end member or main case for estuaries is what we call a well-mixed estuary. This is really a complete contrast in the sense to the salt wedge because it has relatively low river flow so you have a less active strong river system and strong tidal mixing going on.

Up the estuary you see that the water is coming in from the sea and the water coming in from the river are kind of balanced with each other in some way. What happens is that the waters mix actively and mix quickly and so there's a salinity gradient that doesn't have that depth stratification we saw in the salt wedge, but is nearly uniform over depth. Instead it just makes a gradient for more saline out at the ocean outlet to fresher as you get up towards the rivers that are input to the estuary themselves. Many of the shallow water, but large-scale relatively open to the estuaries along the east coast, the drowned river valleys like the Delaware Bay, the Chesapeake Bay, certainly at least seasonally and other days like that are really well-mixed estuaries.

In between these different end member categories, we have partially mixed estuaries, regions where there's a strong flow of river water and also a relatively strong influx of the sea that produces even more turbulence and what's called 2-way mixing then, so entrainment of some seawater up into the river water, but transfer of some of the river water down into the seawater by turbulent vortex mixing at the boundary between the two. Areas where there is cold dense seawater on the one hand, but also strong river flow, so it's some of the characteristics of both of our salt wedge and well-mixed estuaries typically have this kind of characteristic of being partially mixed.

Some of the deeper estuaries with more water depth and in more active colder ocean, like the San Francisco Bay region or like the Puget Sound in Washington are of this partially mixed type.

An even more extreme case of something a little bit like the partially mixed morphology, but a very different kind of mixing in the estuary is what we call a fjord type estuary. We've described the fjords already as these deeply incised glacial valleys that come out and meet the ocean. Fjords very commonly have deep water in them. The glaciers at low stems of the sea level in the past carved out deep basins even hundreds of feet deep. They often when they reach the sea, the glaciers themselves, they would stop there and then eventually receded so they left behind a marine, a deposit that was pushed in front of the glacier that is close to the edge of the land to sea transition. Those marines may be covered by water, but they sort of form a doorsill on the estuary itself, around the fjord itself. They have a shallow water, almost barrier at the front end of the estuary and then deep water back up the fjord.

What happens in that case then is that the deep water is filled with a pool, fairly dense seawater, salty water, the river water comes in, but it remains at the surface and it mixes very, very little with that deeper pool of salt water. That deep water often stagnates often becomes anoxic, and you get very cold, deep, salty water conditions that just sits there while river water runs over the top of it. Many fjords actually have this very strong inversion where the surface water is almost purely fresh, but if you just go down to some depth you get completely saline water.

Let's look at a little bit at one of these well-mixed examples. I'll use the Chesapeake Bay as an example of this. The salinity as we look up the estuary varies a lot from the ocean outlet in the Atlantic byte all the way up to the inlets of the many, many streams and Susquehanna River and other things that feed into the Chesapeake Bay. If we look at the salinity mapped out over the surface waters or over the waters through the work of lots and lots of measurements made by scientists around the region, you see that the entire Chesapeake Bay is brackish to different levels. The salinity measured per mil, remember seawater is about 35 per mil, so the peak salinity down near the entrance is in the 24-25 per mil range and then it goes up to almost completely fresh water at the upper reaches of the Chesapeake Bay.

If you look at this map you'll notice that the pattern of salinity is not particularly symmetrical in the Bay and that's an interesting feature. It actually turns out that as the salt water enters with the tides and conversely as the fresh water comes down from the rivers the Coriolis effect affects the motion of that water on the planet. It literally causes the salt water to bend to the right as it enters the Chesapeake Bay and conversely it causes the fresh water coming down towards the ocean in the Bay to also bend to the right. The fresh water hugs the essentially west coast line of the Bay and the salt water hugs the right or east coast line of the Bay as we look at it. That's a pattern that's governed by global scale forces, but affecting the salinity directly of this relatively small feature called the Chesapeake Bay.

The mixing of fresh water and seawater nutrients in this shallow and well-lit and protected environment provides this fertile habitat for animal life that's specific to the estuarine waters. We have many, many different forms of animals that are evolved to take advantage of this environment in particular, crabs, oysters, many different fish that dwell in the estuarine environments and provide an incredibly good fisheries and food sources for not only an ecosystem in general, but for human beings over a lot of time. Also, they serve as nurseries for the juvenile stages of many major oceanic species. Example of this include perch, anchovy, and Pacific herring.

The larvae stages or the young stages, fundamentally while they're very small, live in the estuaries in part for protection from the open ocean waves and currents that would carry them along when they're too small a size until they grow to a reasonable size to spend time out in the open waters of the ocean along the continental shelf or even off. The estuaries are fundamentally important for their sort of protective nature to these major oceanic species. An interesting organism to look at in the estuary in the Chesapeake Bay is the famous blue crabs, a very tasty product of the Chesapeake Bay region. Blue crabs have a life cycle that's absolutely fascinating. They mainly live in the low salinity areas, relatively high up the estuary. They mate actually only once in life, a female mates only once in its life with male blue crab and then carries that males sperm, but needs to create eggs and the fertilize those eggs. It turns out that creating those eggs, fertilizing them, and spawning the larval stage of the blue crabs depends on getting to a high salinity region and having lots of tidal water cycling.

The females move long distances to the mouth of the estuary to spawn the eggs. They will move literally tens and tens of miles down over the course of a season, over the course of several months, from the high estuary portions to very close to the Atlantic Ocean entry to the estuary. They spawn their eggs by the millions at a time and then the larvae are actually planktonic. These are forms that take the appearance of at first something that looks very much like small krill or something like that and then eventually mutates or changes into a form that looks more crablike and then goes through a whole series of molting to become an adult crab, initially are completely planktonic. They float in the water and what they do is ride the tidal currents back up into the upper reaches of the Bay. The blue crabs follow this salinity gradient on a spawning cycle to take advantage of their appropriate chemistry and also water movements to support the life cycle that has evolved in the Chesapeake Bay region.

If we look at the high estuarine environment then well up into the upper reaches of the intertidal zone where water reaches and creates brackish water conditions, but also very slack water conditions then we see regions that are coastal salt marshes. These don't have to be that far from the ocean, lagoons, and as we'll see deltas can be dominated by coastal salt marshes as well, but the upper reaches of many of these estuarine basins is dominated by these ecosystems. In coastal salt marshes we have salt tolerant species of many vascular plants so ordinarily what we'd think of as land-based plants, but that have evolved the ability to excrete salt and many aquatic organisms that thrive in that same environment, the mussels and the things that go along with living around the protected waters in the root zones of all these plants. Salt marshes are an important part of the estuary environment for dominating the uppermost reaches, the highest tide reaches of the system.

So far I've been talking about estuaries, so regions that we think of as encroachments of the sea onto the land, rivers that come down, but flow into flooded valleys or down-dropped valleys, if we're talking about tectonic action that produced an involution of the coastline or an influx of the sea onto the land. Many rivers that come into the sea under the appropriate conditions actually do the opposite. They form a river delta. They form a region where products of the land essentially build out into the ocean and dominate the coastline in an inversion of the estuarine concept. River deltas are formed specifically where rivers with heavy sediment load reach the sea, especially in a region where the continental shelf is relatively broad and there's relatively low wave energy action to carry that sediment away once it's been brought down to the sea.

It requires rivers that are very different from something like the rivers of the east coast that produce the Hudson Valley or the Chesapeake Bay or the Delaware coming into the Delaware Bay estuarine system. It requires rivers that are carrying very large amounts of sediment. In the continental U.S. that could include the Mississippi River where draining a third of the continent and putting all of that sediment into the water that's coming out the Mississippi delta and building out off the coast of Louisiana the whole Mississippi River fan or delta system.

In the Mediterranean, we see the Nile River draining North Africa or draining the dry regions of North Africa carrying a heavy sediment load to the sea every year and actually building out the Nile delta into the Mediterranean. The fertile grounds of the Nile delta are green in a satellite image. We can actually see where the delta got its name. It's literally the shape of the Greek letter Delta, this triangular shaped region where the river comes down from the land and as it meets what was formerly the coastline builds out a whole network of distributary channels, as they're called, regions where the river dumps its sediment load in one area for awhile and then as that builds up it moves off to a different region to the side, dumps its sediment there, moves off to another region and over tens of thousands of years fans back and forth putting the sediment out just like a fire hose spraying sediment onto the coastline and building this delta out into what was formerly coastal waters on the continental shelf.

If it's dumping all that sediment, but there's really heavy oceanic wave action and a narrow continental shelf like where the Columbia River, which also carries a lot of sediment, meets the sea, you don't really build a major river delta. You might build a deep water or deep sea fan and submarine canyon system, but not a delta. The combined effects of waves and tides and river flow and sediment load then determine the delta shape. We can think of 2 different fundamental shapes of deltas that we can categorize them into on the planet. One is the river dominated deltas that are fed by a strong flow from the land, a strong flow of sediment from the land with large distributary channels.

Then we can think of tide dominated deltas that are molded more by the ocean tidal currents and so those tidal currents are reworking or moving about the sediments that are being dumped by the rivers on the land. Again it's an interplay between the rivers on the one hand and the sea on the other and how they interact with each other that determines the shapes of these deltas. Both of them though can be the sites of major wetlands and salt marsh regions, estuarine systems that can be extensively developed along the coastline.

If we look at the example of the Mississippi River delta building out into the Gulf of Mexico off the coast of Louisiana or at the coast of Louisiana it's dumped sediment out over this large area and so we have huge, hundreds of thousands of acres of coastal wetlands, mud flats essentially that are interacting with the tides on a daily basis and are flooded by seawater, but also affected by the fresh water coming from the land. You see the actual channels that form that feed the water from the Mississippi River out over what's called the Bird's Foot Delta for its remarkable shape and satellite imagery and then the salt marshes that surround the channels and the flood bank levees that are around those channels. Levees are a natural feature of rivers that are dumping sediments on their side and they're also an artificial feature of human activity when we build levees to try to keep rivers in those channels.

A river dominated delta has these characteristics that look like the Mississippi delta where the distribution of salt marshes and the channels are well-defined by the fact that the river is putting that sediment in that water out towards the sea. By contrast, a delta like the Ganges river delta is a tide dominated region and so yes the river is still coming down to the ocean. It's still delivering a lot of sediment to the ocean in the case of the Bay of Bengal and the build out of the Ganges and Brahmaputra River deltas that are the region of Bangladesh, for example, but they're delivering a little less sediment spreading it over a broader and flatter region and the tidal cycling is strong enough that it's actually taking all that sediment and redistributing it. You still see in satellite photographs of the Ganges River delta the channel waves that are from the rivers meeting the sea, but they've been modified by all this tidal flow.

We see tide dominated deltas with different kinds of wetlands and especially well-developed in tide dominated deltas are regions dominated by mangrove trees, so large areas that have mangroves growing in them. Mangrove trees are rooted down into the salt water and the mud flats and marshes of a saltwater dominated estuarine system, but of course their leaves are up in the air. They're a plant that's partly marine and partly subaerial, but the mangrove regions trap the sediment, hold it in place, and build the land out in this tidewater dominated delta region like the Ganges.

If we take a look at mangrove trees, those actually represent a whole type of coastline. We haven't talked about much so far in the course and that is coastlines that are dominated not just simply by erosion and sediment transport, but also by the actual biology that lives on them. At the fundamental geological level, all these coastlines start out as depositionally dominated or erosion-dominated, but the actual shore region and environments of the shore and in particular the estuarine environments around the shoreline can often be substantially modified by the existence of ecosystems of various kinds of organisms. The main distinguishing feature, in this case, is they're organisms that hold the sediment in place through one type of structure or another or physically create a strong and almost armored coastline.

Mangrove trees are one of the best examples of that. Because of their extensive network of almost impenetrably complicated roots and roots that grow down in and the mud filters into that region and doesn't wash out as easily as it would in open water regions. Mangrove trees trap that sediment that's coming from the river areas and they start to actually build up areas over time. You can see the mangrove branches grow out and then drop down hanging roots that eventually meet the water, meet the mud and start to create their own root structures and so the mangroves can spread laterally by this kind of growth. They will build new land literally in many places around the Gulf of Mexico and the gulf side of Florida, but also all over subtropical regions of the world, the Indian Ocean regions for example; many other places around the Caribbean, mangrove trees really dominate the coastline.

They can build huge areas of biologically dominated coastline by trapping so much sediment and providing habitat for all kinds of different organisms that then colonize this estuarine environment and use it productively. Mangrove forests also then essentially armor the coastline, make it less susceptible to things like storm surges and over washing by very high tides and by tsunami, hurricanes, and things like that because they provide a buffer zone between that and the main part of the land where perhaps construction is done where human beings are living. Unfortunately globally speaking mangrove itself as wood is potentially a commodity, a product, and also the mangrove regions, like many wetlands around the world, are being taken over for various kinds of development, perhaps for mariculture and aquaculture in many regions or simply to create channels or new land to live on.

According to the UN FAO, once again, globally there's been about a 20% reduction in the total area of mangrove forests since 1980, 20%, one-fifth of all the mangrove forests around the planet have been lost since 1980. There is a little bit of good news though in that the rate of that change or loss of mangrove forests is rapidly diminishing. Many countries around the world have recognized that mangroves are an important buffer zone and resource for their coastlines and so have banned the practice of replacing them with other constructed features. Bangladesh, for example, has essentially protected all of its mangrove forests or most of its mangrove forests and slowed down this rate of mangrove loss. It's really a wonderful success story for maintaining coastal structure.

One more type of biologically dominated coastline is what we call carbonated banks and platforms. Now coral reefs build large structures of carbonate and the reef itself is the living carbonate as we'll see in a lecture to come. The reef also is broken down all the time and it produces huge volumes over geological time of just carbonate sediment, essentially limestone. It builds up this rocky substructure that's incredibly strong and becomes the actual main coastline feature over a lot of time. If you look at the Florida Keys or the Bahamas, those are islands; those are now on land exposures of coral reefs that built up over the past few hundred thousand and few million years in fact.

Why would they be islands? We know that corals live under the water so why are the Florida Keys exposed as islands. If you remember back to the sea level curve, you'll remember that there was a time in the last period between the glaciations, a hundred thousand years ago, where sea level was 6 meters higher than it is today. Many of the coral islands around the world were corals that grew up to close to sea level when it was substantially higher than today. Then as the sea level drained back down they were left high and dry, the corals died, but left behind islands. Sea level has come back up, but left them just enough exposed to still be inhabitable islands and wonderful places to visit like the Florida Keys. These are regions where the coastline is rocky and it becomes dominated by erosion as opposed to deposition even though they're along coasts that ultimately were originally depositional coasts.

We've looked at a whole bunch of different regions around the world now and we've seen that these estuaries, deltas, and biologically dominated coasts are among the most biologically productive regions on earth. They have supported a huge amount of the organisms that live on the planet and their productivity rivals the tropical rain forest. Maybe even more than that, these kinds of regions in the world have supported the flourishing of the major world civilizations throughout human history. You could make the argument that estuaries have been critical to the development of our modern civilization. I can give you lots of different examples, the lower regions of the Tigress and Euphrates Rivers, the Nile delta itself, the mouth of the Ganges River, the mouths of the rivers that flood into the South China Sea, where the Chinese cities have developed over time.

Modern examples were also built around estuaries over the course of the past few hundred years in the U.S.A. New York City at the mouth of the Hudson River is one great example. San Francisco Bay is another example. These were places where people lived and actually Native Americans lived in large numbers in relatively high population concentrations because of the availability of all the resources, all the food that was available in those estuaries. They became concentrations of people, they became cities over time, and grew into the very modern cities that perhaps ironically take on as a major activity of filling in of the wetlands and salt marshes and things like that and basically eliminate much of the health of the estuary itself that was once the underpinning and the reason that that city actually exists in that location.

Coastal Erosion—Beaches and Sea Cliffs
Lecture 25

Human activity is extensively modifying the natural deposition and erosion processes on coastlines, and combined with gradual sea-level rise, is causing loss of beaches and natural barriers. Construction of breakwaters and jetties interferes with natural longshore drift and has caused wholesale changes in shorelines along the Atlantic Coast. Seawalls and other structures designed to protect buildings ironically can make beach erosion worse. Loss of sediment supply and protective vegetation leaves many coastal areas more susceptible to storm damage. Private property rights, insurance, and public interest often collide over these issues.

Coastal Erosion

- Sea level has been rising slowly for many decades as a consequence of long-term natural climate change and is accelerating in recent decades due to global warming—affecting estuarine habitat, beaches, barrier islands, and wetlands alike.

- Sea level rose rapidly as Earth came out of its last ice age about 18,000 years ago; over several thousand years, it rose at a rate of about 2 millimeters per year. Several thousand years ago—between 2500 and 4000 years ago—sea level stabilized, slowing down to a few tenths of a millimeter per year.

- The present-day rate of sea-level change is about 3 millimeters per year, which is significantly faster than the rate at which sea level changed as Earth came out of that glacial period. This current rate is also accelerating.

- As sea level rises, communities want to protect coastal real estate and preserve beaches, which are a main source of recreation and income for coastal communities. Coastal communities use various methodologies and engineering to achieve these goals. Engineered structures vary in their efficacies: Some work well, but others do not.

- Many of these engineered structures are extensively modifying the natural deposition and erosion processes on the coastlines, causing the loss of beaches and natural barriers in many areas.

Sea Level

- **Eustatic sea level** is the global change of sea level, which is averaged over the whole planet. There's an interplay of eustatic change with local changes in land elevation due to tectonic activity and land subsidence.

- Tectonic activity refers to the uplift of the land through fault action or glacial rebound in many areas on the west coast. Especially in the Gulf Coast and Mississippi delta region, subsidence can occur due to the compaction of the soft sediments that lay beneath the ground, resulting in the extraction of water from trapped pore spaces.

Changing Sea Level around the U.S. Coastline

Sandy Hook, New Jersey: 3.90 mm/yr since 1933, about 1 foot total.

Galveston, Texas: 6.39 mm/yr since 1908, or about 2 feet total—due to the process of land compaction.

Seward, Alaska: –1.74 mm/yr—due to tectonic activity (huge jump in sea level in 1964 due to earthquake).

- In most places, sea level is rising at a rate of several millimeters per year—and from 3 to 6 millimeters or more per year around most of the North American coastline. If present trends continue, sea level will rise even more over the course of the next century.

- One of the effects of local sea-level rise is that it causes problems at the coast; storm surges, large waves, and the highest of the tides cause flooding at increasingly higher levels in many coastal communities, especially along the U.S. east coast.

- Storm surges and the erosion of beaches result when large waves invade coastal areas. The erosion-deposition balance is upended or modified by the higher sea level and stronger wave action. Barrier islands migrate toward the mainland, causing more beach loss.

- In addition, local sea-level rise causes the balance in estuaries and wetlands to change. If sea level is higher, estuaries and wetlands are flooded by seawater to an increasingly greater extent. The salinity zones also tend to migrate inland, changing the habitats for various organisms. Habitats change and can't always migrate along with the changing salinity zones and changing mixing zones in the estuaries.

Jetties are built in coastal areas to protect the harbor entrance and to stop longshore drift.

Responses to an Eroding Shoreline

- We human beings like to respond to an eroding shoreline in different ways, but mostly what we tend to want to do is stabilize the shoreline.

- One response is referred to as **hard stabilization**: the construction of seawalls, breakwaters, groins, and jetties—engineered structures whose purpose is to stop the sand from moving around too much.

- Another response is called soft stabilization, which involves beach replenishment or nourishment.

- A third response is to move, relocate, or retreat from the shoreline as shorelines erode and sea level rises.

Hard Stabilization

- In terms of hard stabilization, there are a number of different protective structures that can be helpful. First, jetties are rock structures—essentially walls—that are built perpendicular to the shoreline to protect harbor inlets by temporarily blocking or deflecting longshore drift.

- Building jetties, however, prevents the longshore drift from continuing to deliver sand to the down-shore side, which needs that sand to replace the longshore drift that it in turn is handing off to the next part of the beach.

- A groin is like a jetty. It's a smaller type of seawall that is built perpendicularly and in periodic distances along beaches to prevent the loss of sand from longshore drift that is occurring along the beach.

- Groins and jetties interfere with longshore drift and have caused major changes in some shorelines on the Atlantic coast over the course of recent decades. Preventing the sand to move is actually preventing the natural process that replenishes the beaches over the course of the entire Eastern Seaboard.

- **Breakwaters** are structures that are built parallel to the shore and in shallow water off shore to provide an area protected from the waves. The process involved with blocking wave input causes wholesale changes in the ocean—or in the coastline—given enough time.

- Another type of structure that's designed on the coastline to protect buildings and keep the beach or sea cliffs from eroding are called seawalls. Seawalls are any kind of hard structure that's meant to armor the coastline and make it more resistant to the eroding power of the waves. Ironically, seawalls can actually make beach erosion worse at times.

© Andy Coburn, Western Carolina University
Program for the Study of Developed Shorelines.

Beach replenishment is necessary when communities lose their beaches to beach erosion.

- Southern and Northern California are places where expensive beachfront real estate is being protected by very large-scale, massive engineering projects—called hard-barrier construction. In these areas, concrete and very large boulders are piled up at the base of a cliff to try to prevent the waves from breaking on the bottom of the cliff. If waves continuously undercut the cliff, the cliff eventually slumps down and becomes sediment.

- Typically, hard-barrier constructions are eventually battered against by the waves enough that they become undercut. When the wave energy hits a seawall instead of dissipating on an open sandy beach, it undercuts the seawall region, causes greater offshore erosion, and eventually undercuts it so much that the seawall collapses.

- Seawalls can also be built right on a beach, as opposed to in a sea-cliff region, to provide a hard barrier so that manmade objects like houses and hotels can be built very close to the shore. If this is done in the right part of the beach—well into the backshore region above the highest of the potential berms—then it can be a reasonable structure.

- Unfortunately, because people want to maximize their beachfront real estate, they build seawalls a little too far out. If the seawall is built out into the active berm region or into the foreshore region, then the waves will wash up to it at high water and in storm surges and will reflect off the seawall and undercut it, exacerbating beach erosion as opposed to preventing it.

Soft Stabilization

- **Soft stabilization**, beach nourishment or replenishment, is another process that's become much more popular in recent decades. Soft stabilization involves importing sand to the beach to replace sand that has disappeared through the active erosional processes associated with either sea-level rise or longshore drift.

- Beach nourishment can take the form of dredging up sand from longshore bars off shore and placing it back onto the beach or mining sand from somewhere else. Both practices involve building up the amount of material on the beach.

- Beach replenishment has been done in many places, especially along the Eastern Seaboard in the United States. It's a popular activity with local beachfront communities because as they lose their beaches to beach erosion, they lose their livelihood.

- Many tens of millions of dollars have gone into beachfront replenishment of limited areas of the shoreline in well-developed communities. It works very well for a time but depends on the local region and significant storm events. Beach replenishment is not going to stop sea-level rise; it's just a way of adding more material for the sea to move along in longshore drift.

- In the estuarine regions of the planet, such as marshlands and mangrove forests, the loss of sediment supply or the loss of the mangroves is leaving many coastal areas more susceptible to storm damage and to loss of land area because of rising sea level.

Sea Level and Society

- Private property rights, insurance, government, and public interest often collide over issues of coastal erosion. The fundamental problem is not so much that the sea level is rising as the fact that the coastline is, in its natural state, a dynamic environment where the landscape is shifting at all times.

- Beaches will continue to exist whether the barrier islands migrate landward or whether sea level drops and barrier islands migrate seaward. What causes the problems is the act of trying to fix them in place and denying the fact that they are dynamic structures on a geological basis.

- Sand beaches and barrier islands are all naturally in dynamic equilibrium with longshore drift. As sea level rises, they're going to inexorably change and migrate landward. Eventually, engineering will not be able to stop it because sea level will continue to rise.

- The government funds beach-nourishment projects for recreational beaches at expenses of up to hundreds of millions of dollars, and it's only a short-term solution. Society can direct that the money be spent for the public good of having recreational beaches in place.

- In addition, there are long-term solutions that do not involve moving people back from the beach or reconstructing the same areas after storms but that instead involve making provisions for retreat from what is surely a retreating shoreline.

Important Terms

breakwater: A rocky barrier constructed parallel to shore and just off shore to protect from wave action.

eustatic sea level: The globally averaged elevation of the sea surface.

hard stabilization: Construction of a solid barrier such as a seawall to lessen or delay the effects of beach or sea-cliff erosion.

soft stabilization: Addition of sand to a beach through beach replenishment or nourishment to mitigate beach erosion.

Suggested Reading

Garrison, *Essentials of Oceanography*, chap. 11.

Pilkey, Neal, Kelley, and Cooper, *The World's Beaches*, chaps. 4–8 and 12–13.

Pilkey and Young, *The Rising Sea*.

Pugh, *Changing Sea Levels*.

1. We've seen that sea level has always risen and fallen in cycles over time immemorial. What's the problem with sea-level rise now?

2. What is likely to happen to most barrier islands as sea level rises? What about coral reefs?

Coastal Erosion—Beaches and Sea Cliffs
Lecture 25—Transcript

We've looked at beaches, rocky shorelines, estuaries, tidal marshes, and tidal flats and what all of these have in common is that they're tremendously dynamic environments. Their natural state is one of change; things are changing all the time. But, they're also the locations very often where people want to live or build structures. We have this desire to stabilize those regions for very good reasons. We want to have real estate and things like that and we want to have stable locations. We expect Earth to stay the same.

But, multiple factors are really modifying our coastlines all the time. We're going to take a look in this lecture at what some of those factors are. The most basic one is that sea level has been rising slowly for many decades now as a consequence of really two different things; one is simply long-term climate change, but the second is an acceleration of that process in recent decades due to global warming. That affects the estuarine habitat. That effects the locations of beaches and barrier islands. That affects the erosional processes on cliffy and rocky shorelines as well. If we look at sea level, we've seen already the sea level curve in general. At the high point of the last Ice age, sea level was much, much lower, 125 meters lower than today.

Since 18,000 years ago, it's risen rapidly until it came up to the present day level. It hasn't done it absolutely continuously. What happened was sea level rose very rapidly as Earth came out of that Ice age period and over several thousand years it rose at a rate of about 2 millimeters per year. It doesn't sound like a lot, but every decade that gets you a couple of centimeters, close to an inch per decade, something like that. Over thousands of years that's a substantial change in sea level.

Several thousand years ago, between 2500 and 4000 years ago or so it really stabilized, all that process slowed down, the glaciers had essentially retreated their present positions more or less, and so it slowed down to what looks like a few tenths of a millimeter per year, just a very small amount. Now just over the span of basically the amount of time that we've been accurately measuring these properties though, it's pretty clear that sea level's been rising faster than that. That may be in part just due to natural cyclicity of climate change initially and certainly it appears to be accelerating in recent years as we'll see in a later lecture to a much more rapid pace. The present day rate of sea level change is about 3 millimeters per year, actually even a little bit faster, significantly faster than the rate that sea level changed as we came out of the glacial period. Something's going on and something's really changing things on the planet.

As sea level rises, communities want to protect coastal real estate. They want to preserve beaches that are their main source of recreation and often for coastal communities, also their main source of income. They use a lot of different methodologies and coastal engineering in order to try to achieve these goals. These engineered structures vary in the efficacies. Some work well, others do not. Sometimes it's because of the location, sometimes it's because of the types of engineering. We'll take a look at all of that in the course of this lecture.

Many of these things are extensively modifying the natural deposition and erosion processes that I've already defined for you on the coastlines. They cause loss of beaches or cause loss of sea cliff areas in the very places where they're actually intended to protect those things. The natural processes are being modified by engineering processes, sometimes to very good effect and sometimes to not so good effect.

Let's talk a little bit more about sea level because it's a little more complicated than I've let on so far. I've defined the term eustatic sea level for you before, so that's global change of sea level, something averaged out over the whole planet. We actually know that there's even variations in what global sea level means because of oceanographic effects and things like that. We've seen the maps of surface water height around the world's ocean already.

Let's say we have something defined as eustatic sea level or global sea level. How does that play into local sea level? There's an interplay as I described or mentioned before between the eustatic changes with local changes in the land elevation due to a variety of processes. One of these processes I mentioned before was tectonic activity, the uplift of the land through fault action, perhaps the uplift of the land through glacial rebound. There's also the converse, land subsidence. Regions that are underlaid by soft sediments can be subsiding due to the actual compaction of all of that mud and sand and sediment, the squeezing out of the water that's trapped in its pore spaces along especially the Gulf coast and Mississippi delta region, this causing land subsidence.

Sea level at the local scale, right in a particular area, is a balance between these different things, what the land is doing and what the sea is doing. Let's take a look at some examples of changing sea level around the U.S. coastline. First of all we'll take a look at Sandy Hook, New Jersey in the New York and New Jersey region. If we look at the mapping of the actual level of sea level, this comes from the tide gauges present on that shoreline and look at it going back with data to 1933 or so, we see that it fluctuates on sort of annual and storm and tidal and all sorts of different cycles making it a spiky signal, but there's an overall trend that's very much a linear increase in sea level. It averages out to about 3.9 millimeters per year since 1933; actually it's slightly in excess of that apparent global average. There's a very small amount of uplift of the landscape in that region. That's about a foot of total sea level change since 1933. It's already been substantial over this time. There's no question that in this region local sea level is rising.

Let's compare that to Galveston, Texas. The Galveston, Texas goes back even further. We have about a century of data since about 1908 or so, right after the big storm in Galveston. What we see is again a variable and spiky signal, but a much higher rate, a much higher slope to the curve. In fact, since 1908, the average has been 6.4 millimeters per year or so, almost double the rate we just saw at Sandy Hook, New Jersey. What's the difference, why do we get about 2 feet of sea level change over this hundred year period?

In Galveston, we have a region where the coastline is actually actively subsiding due to the land compaction that I just talked about a minute ago. The region is basically the sediments of the edge of the Gulf of Mexico and those sediments in the absence of introduction of lots of new sediment will just gradually subside as the sediments compact over time. We have a larger apparent sea level rise in Texas than we do in New Jersey. It's not because the sea is doing something different, but the land is doing something different. It doesn't matter because it's still local sea level rise. It still affects the coastline and the coastal processes in that particular region.

Here's another example. This is from Seward, Alaska. We're up in the Gulf of Alaska, right along the coastline, and we see a very strange looking sea level curve. If we look at it going back from the present day to 1964, we actually see that sea level has been dropping a small amount over all of that time, about 1.75 millimeters per year decline in sea level since then. Something very strange happened in 1964, there was a huge jump in the sea level. What is that? That in fact is the 1964 earthquake; one of the largest earthquakes that has ever occurred that took place in that region and actually shifted the land in the same way I described when I was talking about tsunami in Japan or in Indonesia.

Before that sea level was more or less constant in Seward, so we see a region that the tectonic activity of the land moving upward is actually dominating sea level. Even though the sea is coming up, the land is going up faster and so the relative sea level is actually going down very slightly in this region. A tectonic reactive coastline can have very different signature and sea level change than a more passive margin coastline like the Gulf coast or New Jersey.

If we look at all of these then we have various effects of local sea level rise. The eustatic sea level doesn't matter anymore. We really just want to think about what's happening locally in a given region if we're worried about coastal structures and coastal engineering. Most places around the world are not benefitting from rapid tectonic activity. In most places, sea level is going up. It's going up quickly; it's going up at that rate of several millimeters per year from 3 to 6 or more around most of the North American coastline.

What that means then is that the sea comes up just a little, it doesn't sound like much. It does add up over time to a foot, another foot, maybe another and we'll see more sea level rise over the course of the next century if present trends continue. It causes problems at the coast because first of all coastal flooding is just higher during the highest water events. That means the storm surges, the big waves, and the highest of the tides all cause coastal flooding to higher and higher levels and many coastal communities, especially along the east coast, are seeing that the highest tides places even roads along the coast that were once high and dry at all times are now flooded at the highest tides.

We also see storm surges and the erosion of beaches when big waves come up and erode the beaches back, drive the beach berm further up, erode the sand and take it off shore and move the sand out into longshore bars and deeper water because of the stronger action of the waves acting on the beach. The erosion deposition balance is upended or modified by the higher sea level and stronger wave action. Barrier island migrate towards the mainland because you erode the beach on one side, but on the other hand the waves overwash the barrier islands and drive that sand up right over the berm and into the back dune region or into the back berm region moving the sand landward.

Higher sea level pushes the sand over the barrier island into the marshes; the marshes migrate towards the mainland. The front side or the ocean side of the barrier island migrates toward the mainland as well and the whole thing will slowly march towards that side. Now this is a natural process, but if we want to fix real estate in place, fix houses in place then it causes more beach loss because you're eroding from one side.

Additionally, local sea level rise causes the balance in estuaries and wetlands to change. They're flooded by seawater to a greater and greater extent if sea level is higher naturally. The salinity zones tend to migrate inland. That changes the habitats for different organisms, a place that was a nice place for a blue crab to mate at one time might turn into a place where they have to move upstream and upstream might already be inhabited or might already be blocked off by development or other things. Habitats change and can't always migrate along with the changing salinity zones and the changing mixing zones in the estuarines themselves.

Human beings then, we as a society, like to respond to an eroding shoreline in different ways. Mostly what we tend to want to do is stabilize that shoreline. Nature would be perfectly happy to allow the barrier island to migrate. In fact, a barrier island will have a healthy beach on its seaward side even as it over the decades migrates towards the mainland even by several miles, eventually closing up those lagoons. If we have a lot of expensive real estate along the barrier islands coastline then we prefer to try to keep it in place. We practice a number of different responses to this eroding shoreline.

The first response is one that we'll call hard stabilization, the construction of seawalls, breakwaters, groins, and jetties, and things like that, engineered structures to try to stop the sand from moving around too much. The second is one we'll call soft stabilization and that's what we describe as beach replenishment or beach nourishment. Then finally the other response is simply to move, relocate, or retreat from the shoreline as the shorelines erode and sea level rises. Let's take a look at all those in a little more detail.

First hard stabilization, if we look at it there are a number of different protective structures. I just named them quickly and let's define them a little bit more. First of all jetties are rock structures, walls essentially that are built out perpendicular to the shoreline specifically to protect harbor inlets, so jetties are fairly large constructions, and their purpose is fundamentally to block or deflect the longshore drift that's naturally occurring. If you remember what we talked about with the longshore drift and what happens at a harbor entrance or a bay is that the sand that's moving along the coast in the longshore drift reaches that region where the bay mouth exists. The water motion, the wave energy is a little less because the mouth of the harbor is typically a little bit deeper water and so the sand that's suspended and turbulently carried by the water is dropped down to the bottom. You build out a sandbar or a sand spit that will ultimately close off the harbor entrance. People will build a jetty out to protect the harbor entrance, to stop the longshore drift.

The problem is that that prevents the longshore drift from continuing to deliver sand to the downshore side, the distance on the other side of the harbor further along, which needs that sand to replace the longshore drift that it in turn is handing off to the next part of the beach. Jetties are one structure to protect harbors and groins. A groin is the name of a structure that is like a jetty, just some kind of seawall that's built usually periodically along beaches or in periodic distances along beaches, to prevent the loss of sand from the longshore drift happening along the beach. This is actually not really even dependent on sea level rising or falling at all. It's just simply trying to stop the fundamental process of longshore drift going on.

If we look at the construction of these jetties we'll see that they interfere though with the longshore drift and it's caused really major changes in some

Atlantic coast shorelines even over the course of recent decades or the past century or so. Here's an example from Cape May, New Jersey where you see a series of individual groins that were built to keep the beach in place where the beach was eroding. You can see that the longshore drift is going from the bottom of the photo towards the top, you're looking towards the south, and you can see that on the updrift side of each groin there's a thick beach, a wide beach where the sand has been trapped in place and then a deficit of sand on the downdrift side of each one of those individual groins.

That works okay as long as the groins keep getting constructed all along the coastline. But, you can see the effect of the last groin at the edge of the city region at the top left of the photograph where then beyond that there's a sediment or a sand-starved region and the coastline has eroded back a long distance inland. Preventing the sand to move is actually preventing the natural process that replenishes the beaches over the course of the entire Atlantic seaboard in this case.

Another structure that are constructed very often are called breakwaters. These are actually parallel to the beach and in shallow water off shore to provide an area protected from the waves as small boat harbor and things like that. Here's an example in these historical photographs, the region around Santa Monica Pier in 1931 as it appeared and then a breakwater was constructed some time after that. By 1949, when the second photograph was taken you can see that that breakwater has caused slack water behind it and therefore the buildup of a large amount of sand adjacent to the pier and a congruent deficit of sand again down the drift direction. In this case, the drift is coming towards us along the west coast there.

We see this very large buildup of beach and interruption of sand transport in this region. The breakwater there was allowed to deteriorate over time and in this 2007 image overhead shot you can see that the coastline has now with the waves washing right over the old breakwater has now basically returned to something very similar to its original shape. This kind of process then causes wholesale changes in the ocean or in the coastline given enough time.

One fantastic example of that is the difference between the developed shoreline of Ocean City, Maryland with the relatively undeveloped shoreline of Assateague Island, the adjacent natural island that's been left undeveloped and is part of the national park system. If you look at Ocean City which is protected by a whole series of groins and then ultimately a very large jetty structure protecting the inlet to the lagoon behind it, it's in the same position essentially that it was many decades ago. Meanwhile the starving sediment supplied to the Assateague Island region has caused that barrier island to migrate many hundreds of meters, actually the whole width of Ocean City, as you can see, towards the mainland closing up the lagoon and allowing the barrier island to do what it will do when it's sediment starved which is essentially migrate landward.

This process here is due in part to the artificial disruption of the sediment supply. But, that's essentially a view of exactly the process that will be taking place and that is already beginning to take place with rising sea level. As it washes sand over these very, very low relief barrier islands it will move that sand, especially in big storm events, on shore and build up the inner side and breakdown the outer side and migrate the whole barrier island.

Another type of structure that's designed on the coastline to protect buildings and basically keep the beach from eroding away or keep the sea cliffs from eroding away are called seawalls. It's just any kind of hard structure that's meant to armor the coastline and make it more resistant to the eroding power of the waves. As we're going to see ironically these can actually make beach erosion worse at times. If we look at a hard barrier construction, and you can see so many examples all over Southern and Northern California of places where expensive beachfront real estate is being protected by very large-scale, massive engineering projects, concrete and what's called rip-rap, which essentially just means very large boulders or other heavy objects piled up at the base of the cliff to try to prevent the undercutting of the waves that I described in erosional coasts from breaking on the bottom of the cliff such that the cliff eventually slumps down and becomes sediment essentially to turn into part of the sediment deposition process on the coastline.

These hard barrier constructions have a few different problems. One is that they are typically eventually battered against by the waves enough that they become undercut. When the wave energy comes in instead of dissipating on an open sandy beach, instead bangs into a seawall and will undercut that seawall and cause turbulent water energy to actually erode away at the base of the seawall. What this does is actually undercut the seawall region, cause greater offshore erosion, and eventually undercut it so much that the seawall will collapse. If waves overtop the seawall then they erode in behind it as well.

A second type of seawall construction is when they're constructed right on a beach proper as opposed to in a sea cliff region where you're trying to prevent erosion, just to be the margin or to provide a hard barrier so that manmade objects like houses and hotels and things like that can be built very close to the shore. Resort hotels like to be right on the beach so they'll place a seawall on the beach. If this is done in the right part of the beach, well into the backshore region above the highest of the potential berms then that can actually be a reasonable structure. You sort of fix the ground in that region and until eventually sea level rise takes over then that will provide a kind of a good foundation and a good superstructure or substructure for the construction project.

Unfortunately, because people want to maximize their real estate and beachfront real estate is tremendously expensive, they're build the seawalls just a little too far out. They want to get a little bit more in terms square footage out there on the waterfront. If the seawall is built out into the active berm region or into the foreshore region then the waves will wash up to it at high water and in storm surges and again will reflect off the seawall, will undercut it, and will actually exacerbate beach erosion as opposed to prevent it. Now sometimes these were built in places that were not the foreshore decades ago, but as sea level is rising are rapidly becoming part of the foreshore region so that the sea level change is affecting where those seawalls are effective versus not effective. The only real answer to that ultimately is more construction to try to keep hardening it and then eventual retreat as sea level rise overwhelms whatever structures we want to build on these kinds of coastlines.

What we called soft stabilization is another process that's actually become much more popular in recent decades and that's beach nourishment or replenishment, essentially importing sand to the beach to replace sand that has disappeared through the active erosional processes associated with either sea level rise or longshore drift. Beach nourishment can take the form of simply dredging up sand from the longshore bars off shore and placing them back onto the beach or mining if from somewhere else, bringing it in literally in trucks and dumping it on the beach in order to build up the amount of material; simply build up the amount of material on the beach. Beach replenishment has been done in many, many places all along, especially the Atlantic seaboard in the U.S. It's a popular activity with local communities because as they lose their beaches to beach erosion and the sand moving off shore with greater wave action or with the cutoff of longshore delivery of sand then they lose their livelihood. If it's a beachfront community that's typically what the community is dependent on.

Many tens and even hundreds of millions of dollars have gone into beachfront replenishment of limited areas of the shoreline in well-developed communities. It works very well for a time, but depending on the local region and basically just depending on luck in terms of when the next hurricane is or the next really significant storm event, a beach replenishment project can last 10 or 20 or more years or it can last literally a season or two before that sand tends to be taken back off shore because the same process that was eroding the sand in the first place continues after the replenishment project is carried out. It's not going to stop sea level rise, it's just a way of basically putting more material for the sea to take away or for the sea to move along in the longshore drift.

In some places, there've been real success stories. In other places, it's been not so successful and a lot of money has been sent to either assist a very small community or to assist a community for a very limited period of time. Ultimately, all of these are going to have to succumb to rising sea level if the present trend continues of sea level going up at the pace that it's going today.

There are also all the estuarine regions of the planet and so when we look at marshlands and mangrove forests and things like that in many cases the loss of sediment supply or the loss of the mangroves themselves is leaving many coastal areas also more susceptible to storm damage and to loss of land area basically because of rising sea level once again, but interacting with the input of material from the land. What I mean by that is exemplified best perhaps in coastal Louisiana. Coastal Louisiana is this very large tidal marshland area fed by the sediment of the Mississippi River delta, Mississippi and

Atchafalaya River deltas contribute huge amounts of sediment to the coastline and have over lots of geological time.

The rivers come down; as they spread out over their deltas the water slows down. It dumps its sediment load and eventually the water makes it to the sea. The sediment is left behind and so replenishes all of those marshland areas. Development has led to channelization of those rivers such that the rivers are now directed with their sediment load at a higher velocity all the way out to the edge of the delta so that people could stabilize the land behind the artificial levees and build structures and a nice coastal environment. The unfortunate side effect is that now those distributary channels are not delivering sediment and spreading it out in periodic floods over the marshland anymore.

The mud flats of all those regions are gradually subsiding, as I described before due to the compaction of those sediments, and then that upshot is areas that were initially completely high and dry and areas that were tidal regions that were periodically flooded, but partly dry regions, are subsiding and are becoming completely inundated with seawater at all times. They are going from tidal or high end of the tidal region to below low water, below low tide. That is essentially a loss of coastal land area and it's also the loss of the buffer against the storm surges that come periodically with hurricanes into that region.

Private property rights, insurance companies, government agencies, public interest, of course these things all often collide over these issues. I would not make light of those issues because if you own a piece of beachfront property, you've invested a lot of money in it, of course you're very interested in understanding how you can stabilize it. We have an expectation as human beings I think that Earth stays where it is. If you plot out a plot of land it's not going to go away.

The fundamental problem is not so much exactly sea level rise as the fact that the coastline itself is just in its natural state, a dynamic environment where the landscape is shifting at all times. Beaches will continue to exist whether the barrier islands migrate landward or whether sea level drops and they migrated seaward. They would continue to exist in all of those cases, but it's the trying to fix them in place and keep them in one spot and deny the fact that they are dynamic structures on a geological basis that causes virtually all the problems. These sand beaches and these barrier islands and the estuaries themselves are all in natural dynamic equilibrium, mean stuff flows in, stuff flows out, and the material that's present today is not the material that' present tomorrow even if the beach looks the same.

The beaches are in dynamic equilibrium with longshore drift. The estuarines are in dynamic equilibrium with the river water, the sediments, and the seawater. The deltas in the same way build out and build back depending on sea level, but all of these things are going to be affected by the present condition which is rising sea levels. As sea level rises, they're going to inexorably change and in the case of the barrier islands they're going to migrate landward. Eventually engineering will not be able to stop it because sea level will continue to rise. We're going to see in a later lecture exactly why that is.

The government funds beach nourishment projects for these recreational beaches at expenses of up to hundreds of millions of dollars and as I've said that's essentially a short-term solution. This society can certainly make that choice by directing that that money be spent for the public good of having these recreational beaches in place. We can also look at solutions that look a little bit more long-term, perhaps not literally moving people back from the beach, but as things are destroyed in large storms not going in and reconstructing in the same areas, but making provisions for retreat from what is surely a retreating shoreline.

We've looked at the coastal environment now in a fair amount of detail in a few lectures. In the next lecture, we're going to take that physical environment and we're going to populate it again. We're going to start at the shoreline and go back off shore from our estuaries and our beaches and we're going to consider the benthic communities, the bottom dwellers that inhabit the near-shore environment from beaches to coral reefs and to the kelp forests.

Tidal Life, Sea Forests, and Coral Reefs
Lecture 26

The ocean floor hosts the most complex and varied ecosystems in the sea, which vary based on such factors as the type of substrate, access to light, and wave energy. The intertidal zone includes seaweeds and mangroves and the many organisms that live around them. Sandy and rocky beaches are relative deserts, dominated by burrowing organisms. Coral reefs and atolls are built up in the photic zone by colonies of coral polyps. The reef structure hosts a teeming community of organisms in complex predator-prey relationships.

Benthic Communities

- The ocean floor, from the rocky intertidal zone of the beaches out to the edges of the continental shelves, hosts the most complex and varied ecosystems to go along with all the locations that life can inhabit in the sea.

- These ecosystems vary—from coral reefs to kelp forests to open mudflats—based on the kind of substrate, the access to light, and the wave energy in the ocean. These regions are the benthic, tidal, and subtidal zones within the sea.

The reef structure itself is composed of limestone that is secreted by the coral polyps.

- Benthic communities are ecosystems of organisms that are located on or near the bottom of the sea. The habitat for these benthic communities range from rocky tide pools to coral reefs, sandy beaches, abyssal deep vents, and open sea floor.

Marine Ecosystems

- A community is a group of different types of organisms that inhabit a particular location or environment. By contrast, a population is a group of organisms of the same species occupying a specific area. Communities are made up of a variety of populations.

- A habitat is the specific environment in which any given organism or any given population lives. The ecological term niche refers to the specific role a particular organism plays in the community. An organism has an ecological niche, which is distinct from its physical habitat.

- Sandy and rocky beaches are relative biological deserts. There aren't vast numbers of organisms, and they aren't very productive in terms of overall biomass productivity. In fact, they're dominated by burrowing organisms.

- The reason that sandy beaches are relative deserts is because a sandy beach is an inhospitable environment. Sand is a loose, sharp, and abrasive substrate. High wave energy and shifting sand make it difficult for an organism to stay in one place. It's also difficult for an organism to keep from getting eaten if it is constantly being washed out of its habitat and into another zone.

- On the other hand, beaches are constantly washed over by waves, so even though they're relatively poor substrate regions, there is a lot of organic matter that infiltrates into the pore spaces in the sand. Every wave carries with it some organic material and plankton, providing food for burrowing organisms that can take advantage of it—such as crabs, clams, polychaete worms, and sand fleas.

- The intertidal environment includes mangrove forests as well as rocky tide-pool habitats. The major challenges for organisms living in a rocky coastline environment are coping with constant wave action and tides.

- The organisms that live in rocky tide pools have developed several strategies for coping with the high-energy, rapidly changing environment. The payoff for these organisms is that waves continuously bring in nutrients from the sea and from the land.

- A typical tide pool involves numerous different individual organisms and populations of organisms in a complex community in which they're all dependent on the different parts of the ecological process that the other ones are carrying out. A typical tide pool includes fish, mussels, crawlers (snails, chitons, and limpets), algae (seaweed), starfish, hermit crabs, gulls, and sea urchins.

- Change is a very important aspect of tide pools. As a result, many of the organisms that live in a tide pool—even the ones that are sessile like a sea anemone—have developed the ability to handle periodic drying. Organisms that can handle this kind of environment are the ones that are good at remaining in place, which is important.

- Sea anemones are cnidarians, so they are filter feeders: They open up their polyps and waft water or filter feed detritus and plankton into their mouths. When the tide pool dries out, as it periodically does, the anemones are efficient at having a harder exterior that allows them to close up to maintain the water content and protect it from damage from the sunlight.

- In rocky tide pools, there's an incredible vertical zonation: Parts of this tidal ecosystem have very specific zones relative to low-tide and high-tide lines.

Seaweed and Kelp Forests

- For many areas, especially in rocky environments and the temperate zones of the world, below the intertidal region in the euphotic zone is dominated by seaweed and kelp forests of various kinds.

- Seaweed and kelp forests are enormously productive ecosystems that rival rainforests on land for the biomass production per square meter.

- The most famous are the California kelp forest or the kelp forests of the Pacific Northwest and Alaska. These zones are where the kelp fixes itself down to the bottom—which is why they are benthic organisms—and then grows up into the sunlight for vast distances.

- Kelp are seaweeds, not plants, in terms of biological kingdoms. Kelp are protistans, a form of multicellular algae. Seaweed can range from microscopic to hundreds of feet in size. Seaweeds are autotrophs, and they photosynthesize within the euphotic zone.

- There are 3 types of seaweed: green (Chlorophyta), brown (Phaeophyta), and red (Rhodophyta) algae. All types of seaweeds have different adaptations to different environments within the ocean.

Ecosystems that are dominated by kelp forests and seaweed rival rainforests for biomass production per square meter.

- Giant kelp are the type of seaweed known as brown algae and can grow 50 centimeters per day to over 40 meters long. They dominate the kelp forests found on the west coast of North America. Giant kelp act as **holdfast** anchors to rocks on the ocean floor and grow up to the surface of the water. They also exude carbohydrates into the water.

- Kelp communities dominate especially rocky coastlines all over the world. Mangrove communities dominate many of the regions that kelp don't. Many of the tropical to subtropical regions that aren't sandy beaches or depositional coastlines are dominated by mangroves. The temperate regions and the high latitudes are dominated by kelp forests—a significant proportion of the total coastline of the world.

Coral Reefs

- Besides the mangrove and kelp forests that are so productive, the other offshore environment is the coral reefs and atolls, which are built up in the photic zone by colonies of coral **polyps**—animals that host photosynthesizing single-celled algae within their bodies. Corals are another incredibly complex environment where there are interactions among a number of different organisms to keep the entire reef healthy.

- A coral is an animal—not some kind of plant. A coral is a cnidarians related to the anemones and jellyfish. Coral polyps wave in water to entice fish and zooplankton and then sting them with their nematocysts and pull them in for digestion.

- Most corals are colonies of individual polyps. Each polyp is actually a separate animal. A coral head is a colony of many thousands of those individual animals. Most corals build up reefs, and this type of coral is called **hermatypic coral**.

- The success of corals depends critically on a symbiotic relationship. Coral polyps trap floating plankton and even small fish. At the same time, they host specialized microscopic dinoflagellates called **zooxanthellae**, which are the photosynthesizers. This is a very efficient exchange between primary producer and consumer.

- The coral creates the habitat to maximize the benefit for the zooxanthellae, which creates very strict habitat needs for the corals. First, corals need bright light; they have an optimal zone between about 5 and 10 meters deep in the water. They also need normal to slightly high salinity to keep the coral polyps in a good osmotic situation, and they need temperatures above 21°C.

- The reef structure, the limestone that's secreted by the coral polyps, is strong to withstand high-energy wave action. The coral reef is always breaking down and getting busted up by waves—almost as fast as it builds.

- The reef has nooks and crannies everywhere. It hosts many different coral varieties that are competing constantly with each other and a teeming community of other organisms in all sorts of complex predator-prey relationships.

- Corals are under increasing environmental pressure. One of the things that is an incredible challenge but is unclear why it happens is a phenomenon called coral bleaching, in which healthy corals suddenly turn into essentially completely white corals and ultimately become covered by algae.

- Coral bleaching results from a small rise in temperature in the water—for reasons that are unclear. Even a 1°C or 1.5°C change in water temperature can cause the corals to spontaneously expel all the zooxanthellae that are in their polyps. The coral turns white because of the loss of the pigmented photosynthetic algae. The polyps can continue to live for awhile based on their normal consumption of food, but if this continues for too long, the coral dies.

- Coral bleaching is a big problem all over the world. In areas such as the U.S. Virgin Islands, about 60% of the corals that were formerly healthy have now succumbed to coral bleaching. With the changing global water temperature and, more importantly, the changing acidity of the water, corals may not be able to continue to build reefs in the future.

- Other than zooxanthellae, there are other types of corals on the planet, including many that are called **ahermatypic corals**—corals that are soft and don't build reefs. Many of these don't have to live where the light is filtering down through the water. There are deepwater soft corals in regions that are much colder—off the coast of northern Europe, for example. These are much less common and much less abundant than the hermatypic corals of the classic coral reefs.

Important Terms

ahermatypic coral: Soft coral that makes no hard reef structures.

hermatypic coral: Coral that secretes carbonate and builds up reefs.

holdfast: The anchor of a kelp seaweed that fixes it to the substrate, as roots do for vascular plants.

polyps: The individual coral animals, similar to sea anemones, that collectively make up the colony in a coral head.

zooxanthellae: Microscopic dinoflagellate photosynthesizers that live symbiotically and are hosted by coral polyps.

Suggested Reading

Cousteau, *The Silent World*.

1. Benthic communities have much more diverse populations of species than open-water pelagic communities, but benthic communities are also more geographically limited in area. Why might this be so?

2. Corals themselves are only a small number of the diverse species that make up a coral-reef ecosystem. What factors might contribute to making reefs so diverse?

Tidal Life, Sea Forests, and Coral Reefs
Lecture 26—Transcript

So far we've built up an understanding of the containers of the ocean, the shape of the ocean basins and what the sea floor is like. We've looked at the life that populates the pelagic zone, all the water above that. Then we took a trip up to the coastline where the sea meets the land and the estuaries and the beach environments and everything that goes with them. Now it's time to essentially wade back into the water and take a look at the organisms and the ecosystems that inhabit the most complex and varied part of the ocean of all, which is the benthic zone, the bottom dwelling creatures that live on the bottom of the sea and inhabit these physical environments that we've developed such a nice understanding of.

In this lecture, we're going to take a look at all of the regions that are in the shallow water benthic zone, or the subtidal benthic region. The ocean floor from the rocky intertidal zone of the beaches out to the edges of the continental shelves host the most complex and varied ecosystems to go along with the complex and varied substrate or bottom features, all the locations that life can inhabit on the sea floor. These ecosystems vary greatly, tremendously from coral reefs to kelp forests, to just open mudflats based on the kind of substrate, the access to light, and the wave energy, and all sorts of other factors in the ocean. These regions are the benthic, tidal, and subtidal zones of our definition of different habitats that we've set up early on within the sea.

Let's do some defining of terms once again. Benthic remember is on or near the bottom and that means benthic communities are ecosystems of whole organisms. We consider organisms largely in terms of where they were in the trophic pyramid before when we were looking at the open ocean, but now we're only going to look at interlocking and internetworking ecosystems of communities that interact in very complex ways. The habitat for these benthic communities range from rocky tide pools, to coral reefs, sandy beaches, and then ultimately to the abyssal deep vents, and the vast areas of the open sea floor of the abyssal plains. We'll leave the deep zones for the next lecture and in this one I'll concentrate on the euphotic zone, the well-lit region in the shallow water areas.

Let's just remind ourselves of a few terms that relate to ecosystems in general because I've already talked a little bit about some of these, but they're going to become important when we really look at the benthic communities as a whole. First of all, I just used the term community, but a community is basically a whole bunch of different types of organisms that inhabit a particular location or environment. By contrast, a population is a group of organisms of the same species that occupy a significant area. Communities are made up of a variety of populations. Habitat, we defined before, is the specific environment in which any given organism or any given population lives. Then we use the ecological term niche, the niche is the specific role that organism plays in the community. It has an ecological niche, which is distinct from its physical habitat.

Let's look at some of the different environments then starting right essentially just off shore or even at the shoreline. First of all the beaches themselves and the near shore environment of the beaches, including the sand transport just off shore. Sandy and rocky beaches are actually relative biological deserts. There aren't vast numbers of organisms. They aren't very productive in terms of diversity or in terms of overall biomass productivity. In fact they're dominated as we'll see by burrowing organisms. Why is that? Why would that be?

The answer is probably pretty straightforward. If you think about what it would take to actually live in a sandy beach environment, you'd have to admit to yourself that it's pretty inhospitable. First of all, there's waves sloshing back and forth, always knocking you off your foundations perhaps, making it difficult to get a purchase and get a foothold in that particular region and stay in one place. Secondly, there's a loose and sharp substrate. We might not think of sand as sharp, but of course it is. We use it for sandpaper. It's abrasive. If you're very small, the size of a microorganism or the size of a small arthropod or worm or something like that then sand is actually a very sharp-edged terrible material to be around. It's hard to stay in place. You get abraded by the sand that's being moved around by the waves and it's hard to keep from getting eaten if you're constantly being washed out of your particular habitat and into some other zone.

On the other hand, beaches are washed over by the waves constantly so even though they're relatively poor substrate regions there is a lot of organic matter that washes down into the pore spaces in the sand. With every wave it carries some organic material and it carries some plankton. It carries bits of seaweed and everything else and all of those tend to infiltrate into this pore space down in the sand. That provides food for organisms that can take advantage of it. That means the burrowing organisms like crabs and clams, ones you may not know about like polychaete worms and so-called sand fleas, arthropods that live in this environment. All of them share the characteristic of basically actively burrowing, including clams of course. They dig their way into the sediment and they can burrow to get at some of the food resources that are down in the sand, but they can also burrow for protection.

If you're in a region where the substrate is soft like the sandy beach, but the waves wash periodically over it and the tide rises up over it and then goes back down then you may emerge either on land or under water whether you're at the high tide line or the low tide line and then when the waves are washing back and forth burrow in for protection in order to maintain your position and not get washed around and also not get eaten by an opportunistic seagull or something like that. The organisms that dominate this environment, that do well in this environment are either very well armored and mobile like the horseshoe crabs that are good at swimming around and have this carapace that protects them virtually anything that can come over the top.

They tend to stay in the shallow water offshore regions. We see them up on the beach area in the tide flats only when they're in mating season actually. Things like clams, like this example of razor clams, very large clams that burrow down into the substrate, into the mud or the sand and extend their siphon, which is just the body part that they then use to filter feed plankton out of the water, plankton and bits of detritus and things like that and then they can move around and burrow their way deeper during low tide and shallower during high tide and things like that. Each environment really is inhabited by a relativity small number of organisms. But for many other environments at the coastline and off shore, we see great diversity and profusion of individual types of organisms and populations that make up a given community.

If we continue to look at the intertidal environment for a second longer, we can look at mangrove forests. We've already examined them in some detail already and then the rocky tide pool habitats which are so much fun to go and take a look at and go tide pooling and look for all the variety of organisms that you might find in these areas. The big challenges for living in a rocky coastline environment or rocky tide pool is coping with the fact that you're periodically dried out and then submerged in water by the tides and constantly washed over by waves that are very energetic and moving all the material around in this environment. The organisms that live there have developed a great deal of heartiness and strategies for coping with all this high energy and rapidly changing environment.

The payoff for those organisms is that in the rocky tide pool you have waves continuously bringing in nutrients from the sea and you also have streams and other ways that material from the land is coming down and so nutrients from the land and nutrients from the sea are mixing in the tide pool setting. A typical tide pool, a Pacific coast tide pool that you can see all over the northwest and in California, involves numerous different individual organisms and populations of organisms in a very complex community where they're all dependent on the different parts of the ecological process that the other ones are carrying out. They're fueled by these nutrients and food from both the sea and the land.

It includes fish; it includes the sessile organisms like mussels. It includes the crawlers like snails and chitons and limpets. It includes algae like seaweeds, the starfish, hermit crabs, even the gulls, and the sea urchins of course. All interacting in such a way to take advantage of every little bit of detrital food that comes in, also photosynthesized whenever that's possible to generate food from sunlight and then a community of organisms at different trophic levels that are eating those primary producers or detritus consumers.

If you look in a tide pool the big thing is change. Many of the tide pool organisms, even the ones that are sessile, that stay in place like a sea anemone have developed the ability to handle periodic drying so the sea anemones in the water. Remember that sea anemones are related to the jellyfish and they're related to corals as well as we'll see. They're cnidarians. They open up their polyps and they waft water or filter feed detritus, plankton, et cetera out of the water into their mouths. Barnacles do the same thing. Mussels largely do the same thing. They're all various kinds of filter feeders.

When the water dries out and the tide pool periodically dries the anemones are efficient at closing in, having a harder, exterior, thicker skin that allows them to close up, maintain the water content inside the anemone until it gets wetted again and protects it from damage from the Sunlight and everything else while it's dried out, the barnacles close up and so on. Organisms that can handle this kind of environment are the ones that are good at remaining in place. If you've ever tried to pry up a Pacific starfish off of the rocks during low tide you know that they're extremely firmly attached through all of their suckers that hold them onto the rock surface and really difficult to get off of the rocks. The same goes for the chitons and limpets and other organisms like that. Remaining in place is important.

If we look at the tidal community, you see that in these rocky tide pools there's an incredible vertical zonation. Parts of the ecosystem have very specific zones relative to low tide and high tide lines. This actual famous image that comes from one of Dr. Ed Ricketts books *Between Pacific Tides*, this is the same guy I mentioned before who was the inspiration for Steinbeck's Doc in *Cannery Row*, actually published zonation that's down to the level of just tens of centimeters from going from low, low water, basically the place that's always wet during all low tides right up over the span of just 2 meters, 6 or 7 feet to the area that's only wetted at the most extreme high tides. You see the curve that shows the amount of time, the percentage of the time that a given zone is wetted and it's zoned in terms of the organisms that populate it.

The highest Zone I had lichens and cyanobacteria living in it. Zone II is dominated by the red algae, seaweed, the rhodophytes that I'll describe in just a minute. Zone III contains the mussels and barnacles, the ones that periodically are wetted, but like to be in the water more of the time. And then finally, the lowest zone IV, sea stars and anemones that I showed you in images just a moment ago. Only the vertical span of just the height of a person has all of these different biological zones within the rocky tide pool.

As we go a little bit deeper off shore we get into the zone that's well below actual low tide and we want to look at the euphotic zone. For many areas, especially in rocky environments and the temperate zones of the world, below the intertidal region is dominated by seaweed and kelp forests of various kinds. These enormously productive ecosystems, the kelp forests and seaweed dominated ecosystems rival rainforests on land for the biomass production per square meter.

Let's take a look at how they work. The most famous perhaps are the California Kelp Forest or the kelp forests of the Pacific Northwest or Alaska for us. These zones where the kelp that fixes itself down to the bottom, that's why it's a benthic organism is because it's attached to the bottom, requires that bottom attachment, then grows up into the Sunlight for vast distances. These are examples of a particular kind of kelp called brown kelp or brown algae and the scientific name is phaeophytes. Let's look at what they are because kelp are seaweeds.

The first thing to say is that they're not plants. They're not plants at least in the sense of being part of the kingdom of plants in terms of biological kingdoms. They're protistans. They are a form of multicellular algae. Some of the phytoplankton we talked about were single-celled algae. These are multicellular algae. Seaweed can range from microscopic to hundreds of feet in size. Those California giant kelp can grow to as much as 50 meters, 150, 180 feet in length given enough time to grow in the right conditions. They're all autotrophs. They are photosynthetic of course and they photosynthesize within the euphotic zone and their construction or their body plan is largely to put as much photosynthetic material into the upper parts of the water as possible.

There's 3 types of seaweeds. The green seaweeds, the brown seaweeds, and the red, the green are the chlorophyta, the brown are the phreatophytes, and the red are the rhodophytes. Rhodo being a Greek root, but it means red of course. All of them have different adaptations to different environments of the ocean region and the amount of sunlight available and the ultraviolet damage and all of that. If we look at the giant kelp as an example of all of these different seaweeds; we can look at its basic structure.

I said they weren't plants and the reason is that they don't have the complex vascular system that land plants need to move water from their roots up to their outer regions. They have much simpler internal structures. Basically there is a hold fast at the bottom, which is a set of features or small tendrils that anchor down to a rock or into the rocks themselves and then a series of stipes which are a series of stipes, which are essentially tubes, almost like straws for water. They're often completely hollow in the interior and water can percolate through them without actually having to be actively transported the way a real true plant does.

They have blades which are the big wide things that are akin to leaves on a plant that hold a lot of the photosynthetic material and then they have gas bladders. These air pockets that you can see if you find kelp lying on the beach, which float them up so that they can keep the blades in the shallowest part of the water. The kelp have the amazing ability to photosynthesize at quite prodigious rates and so because they're in the water and they're infused with water in the algae they literally exude carbohydrates, simple sugars into the water. The entire kelp in the California Kelp Forest when it's actively photosynthesizing is essentially bleeding food into the water all around it. That's why it's supporting this very rich community of plankton and then the fish that feed on the plankton and all of the other organisms that go along with that to feed on the fish and also to feed on the kelp itself are part of this kelp community.

Sea urchins, bivalves, and fish all live in this food rich environment. Sea otters live in the region and actually benefit from both the kelp and the stuff that lives on the kelp. The sea urchins themselves are actually the bane of the kelp because they crawl around the sea bottom and chew away at the hold fast and the stipes and so they separate the kelp. When the kelp forest becomes unhealthy it's usually due to an overabundance of sea urchins in that region. On the other hand, they're helped along by the sea otters who use the kelp as a kind of protective zone. They'll literally wrap themselves up in a kelp frond to stay in place as a kind of anchor and they dive down and scoop up sea urchins as well as abalone and other shellfish and eat those organisms. The interaction of the ecosystem is that all of them are keeping each other in check in such a way with their food fundamentally being provided by the anchor, which is the kelp itself.

If you live on a sandy beach region on the east coast, you might not think of kelp as a big deal. But, actually kelp communities dominate especially rocky coastlines all over the world. Mangrove communities dominate many of the regions that kelp don't. If we look at a global map, many of the tropical to subtropical regions that aren't sandy beach areas and very depositional coastlines are dominated by mangrove. The temperate regions and the high latitudes, the west coast of the U.S. across to Japan or down in Australia and New Zealand, Southern Africa are dominated by kelp forests and these kelp communities actually are a very significant proportion of the total coastline of the world.

I talked about there being many different types of seaweeds. In fact, the rhodophytes are another type that are even hardier actually than the brown seaweeds. They're not as effective photosynthesizers, but they're better at utilizing dim light. The coloring that they have, the pigment, aids them in using the dim blue light that filters to deeper in the water and also protects their cellular structure from ultraviolet radiation so that the red seaweeds can live where the brown ones and the green ones don't, which means deep and also shallow in the tide pools. They live in the more marginal zones and photosynthesize in those places. Most seaweeds are red seaweeds and they're the majority of all of them on the planet.

There are also marine vascular plants, true plants that live in the water, we've already talked about the sea grasses and those are flowering plants. They actually have a flowering structure that flowers underwater off shore. They're descended from land plants so much like the marine mammals they moved back into the water from the land. We've already discussed the mangrove as marine because they root in the tidewater zones even though they put their leaves and flowering structures out in the open air. All of these are essentially land plants that have colonized the coastal shore region so I wanted to mention them as well.

The other offshore environment, besides the mangrove forests and the kelp forests that are so productive, are the coral reefs, the coral reefs and atolls built up in the photic zone by colonies of coral polyps. These are animals that actually, as we'll see, farm or host photosynthesizing single-celled algae within their bodies. The corals are another incredibly complex environment where there are interactions between a number of different organisms to keep the entire reef healthy.

Let's look at the fundamental basics though of the coral reef that so many of us might enjoy snorkeling or diving over. If you look at the coral itself, you may not realize that the coral is an animal. Coral is not some kind of plant. It's not some kind of algae and the coral likes to be in the light, not because it photosynthesizes itself. A coral is a cnidarians related to the anemones and related to the jellyfish. It has the stinging cells. The coral polyps open up and they wave in the water to waft zooplankton or to entice fish and zooplankton in and sting them with their nematocysts and pull them in for digestion.

Most corals are colonies of individual polyps. Each polyp is actually a separate animal. A coral head is a colony of many thousands of those individual animals. Ultimately those corals, if they build up reefs, we call them a particular type of coral which is hermatypic. They build up a herm or a big massive structure so they're hermatypic reef building coral animals. The success of corals actually depends critically on a symbiotic relationship that's very, very close because these coral polyps can be carnivorous. They eat things that come along that they trap in terms of floating plankton and even small fish. They also at the same time host specialized microscopic dinoflagellates that are called zooxanthellae. That's just the name of that particular dinoflagellate. These are the photosynthesizers, the photosynthetic algae I mentioned already.

They essentially farm them. The dinoflagellates live in the coral. They're protected by the polyp and the internal structures of the polyp from the surrounding wave motion and things like that. They very effectively can photosynthesize and then their food is basically diffused into the coral polyp itself and feeds it or the corals actually digest some of the zooxanthellae they're hosting, but not enough to destroy the colony. Corals have to be in the light because the zooxanthellae need to photosynthesize and the corals open up during the daytime. They microscopic dinoflagellates photosynthesize away, the corals close down, and then digest what they've gotten during the day at night.

This is a very efficient exchange between primary producer and consumer. They're basically living together. The coral creates the habitat to maximize the benefit for the zooxanthellae. It creates a very strict habitat need for the corals. First of all they need bright light. They have to be within a couple of meters of the surface down to several tens of meters deep with the optimal zone between about 5 and 10 meters deep in the water. Coral reefs keep growing up, for example if sea level changes, to meet that depth zone. They need normal to actually slightly high salinity just to keep the coral polyps themselves in a good osmotic situation. They're not osmoregulators. Even a little bit of fresh water will kill them. In fact, that's why they can't come right to the surface because literally rainfall will freshen the water so much as to kill them.

They need temperatures above 21° C, but for some reason temperatures that don't rise too much above that as well. Corals have a very delicate life zone that they live in and that's causing corals problems today. The reef structure itself is literally this limestone that's secreted by the coral polyps. It's strong specifically to withstand a high energy wave action because corals build out on the shoulders of sea mounts and on the outer continental shelf in regions where fresh clear water is always abundant and available and brings nutrients, but also where the zooxanthellae can best live.

The coral reef is always breaking down. It's getting busted up by the waves. All that material piles up and accumulates and ultimately builds up this very large reef structure. The reef has nooks and crannies everywhere. It hosts many different coral varieties typically in a reef that are competing constantly with each other and a teeming community of other organisms in all sorts of complex predator and prey relationships, but again ultimately fed by the zooxanthellae and the coral polyps that host them. All the fish you see on the reef and the eels and all of the various kinds of urchins and everything else are in every square inch kind of matters competition for habitat and good ecological niches for themselves.

As we know, corals are under increasing environmental pressure. One of the things going on with corals that is really an incredible challenge, but is a little bit unclear even in our understanding of why it happens is this phenomenon called coral bleaching. You've heard of it or seen pictures perhaps, healthy corals suddenly turning into essentially completely white corals and they may be ultimately getting covered by algae. That's a real sign that the coral is truly dead. What's going on with coral bleaching?

It results from a small temperature rise in the water for reasons that are unclear. Even a 1° C or 1-1/2° C change in water temperature can cause the corals to spontaneously expel all the zooxanthellae that are in their polyps. The polyps are there and they basically spit out all of these photosynthesizers that they're partly dependent on for food and for living. The coral turns white because all of a sudden the pigmented photosynthetic algae is gone from the coral. When it does that the polyps are still there and the polyps can continue to live for awhile just based on their normal consuming of food, but if the zooxanthellae are out in the water then they're not in the coral and they're not feeding the coral anymore.

If this goes on for a little while, a couple of weeks, and then the temperature comes down they seem to be able to repopulate with zooxanthellae. But, if it goes on for a month or more the coral may permanently die. That particular portion of the coral reef and coral heads will not come back and those polyps will not be able to return to their former healthy state.

Coral bleaching is a big problem all over the world and in areas like the U.S. Virgin Islands something like 60% of the corals that were formerly healthy have not succumbed to coral bleaching. There's even larger impacts potentially coming on corals that we'll look at a little later in the course. With the changing global water temperature, and even more importantly with the change in global water dissolved carbon dioxide, the acidity of the water, corals may not be able to continue to build reefs into the future. For now, we have many different types of corals and we see that the coral reef distribution is in very specific areas of the planet. It's a tropical to subtropical region that most of the coral reefs are in and that's because they require this 21° C or about 70 degree water in order to live.

It turns out there are other types of corals on the planet. That includes many that are called ahermatypic corals. They're actually corals that are soft corals that don't build reefs. Many of these also don't include the zooxanthellae so they don't have to live where the light is filtering down through the water.

There are actually deepwater corals and especially deepwater soft corals in regions that are much colder off the coast of Northern Europe for example or way down off the coast of Antarctica, New Zealand, and Australia. These are much less common and much less abundant than the hermatypic corals of the classic coral reefs.

I mentioned very early in the course a long time ago that Charles Darwin is known to science in part for his discovery or his identification of the ways in which coral atolls built up. Many of the South Pacific islands today are just rings of corals. We call them coral atolls and thanks to Darwin we understand pretty well how they formed. I introduced this once before, but I just want to remind us that there are 3 types of reefs in the world, the fringing reef, the barrier reef, and then the atoll. These are based on how the corals start to form around a sea island or even along the continental shoreline like the barrier reef around Australia.

The corals grow up along the coastline initially and so they'll grow up along the sea mount or the coast of the continent as a fringing reef. As time goes by, if the land is eroded, but the corals continue to grow to stay in the light and if the land subsides in particular as a scene on the ocean does then the reef will become fringing reef and separate from the land with a lagoon in between. Take that far enough, the land or the sea mount subsides all the way beneath the waves and all that's left is the fringing reef and that's the coral atoll. We see many of these beautiful blue lagoon Pacific environments are the final stages of atoll formation as described by Charles Darwin way back in the 1830s.

We've taken a look then very briefly, hardly doing it justice for such a complex and interesting environment at the shallow benthic zone. We've seen that it's the most productive environment overall in the ocean; great complexities in the ecosystems in the numbers of different organisms that live in tide pools, that live in kelp and mangrove forests, and that live in the coral reef environment. The ones that have to deal with tide pools and beaches and adapt to these very challenging conditions of being periodically dried or wetted. The coral reefs have to adapt to a different set of environmental conditions where the symbiotic relationship requires that they stay in a very narrow environmental temperature and light zone in order to remain healthy, which also makes them ecologically delicate.

That's the shallow water benthic environment. In the next lecture, we're going to dive right down into the deep ocean and travel right off the continental shelf again down the continental slopes and into the abyssal plains and ultimately even the mid ocean ridges to look at the deep benthic zone.

Deep Bottom Life and Hydrothermal Vents
Lecture 27

The deep-sea floor is vast and populated by scavenger communities. The most fascinating of all deep benthic communities are those of the deep-sea vents, where key symbiotic relationships feed ecosystems that may be the key to the origin of life on Earth. Hydrothermal vents at the mid-ocean ridges fuel an entire ecosystem based not on sunlight but on chemosynthesis. Unique symbiotic relationships between bacteria that chemosynthesize and larger fauna such as tubeworms, crabs, and clams are the basis of these strange vent communities.

The Deepest Zones of the Sea

- In the mid 1800s, Edward Forbes began dredging up samples from along the continental shelf and into the beginnings of deep water. He found life in these samples, but they were dwindling in number with depth.

- He extrapolated to a depth of about 500 or 600 meters and said that this was the **azoic zone**—a region in the bottom of the sea that would have absolutely no life because it was deep and dark.

- However, nothing could be further from the truth. Today, we know that the deep sea is populated to the greatest depths of the ocean.

- In the late 19th century, the *Challenger* expedition found that there was a jellylike mass—some sort of protoplasm—that covered the entire ocean floor and that it was one single living organism, which was given the name *Bathybius haeckilii*.

- *Bathybius haeckilii* was simply a mistake. It was an interesting sidetrack on the way to understanding that the deep-sea bottom has a whole variety of many different species and is a zone of oases and differences.

Down the Continental Slopes

- The abundance of life, the biomass, does diminish rapidly as you move off the lit continental shelves and into the deep water. Even down the continental slopes, a number of **sessile** organisms—those rooted into the sea bottom—live on the ocean floor.

- The mud that blankets the continental slopes from terrigenous sedimentation is processed and digested by a range of both **epifauna** (live on the ocean floor) and **infauna** (live burrowing within the ocean floor). Macrofauna—fish, skates, and cephalopods in the form of octopuses and squids—live near and adjacent to the ocean floor and graze on these organisms as well.

- For example, some of the epifauna and the sessile organisms that root into the sea floor include sea fans, or gorgonians, that are common in the coral reefs, but they're also present all the way down the continental slope and into even deep water. Sea pens are another example.

© NURC/UNCW and NOAA/FGBNMS.

Gorgonians are common in the coral reefs, but they're also present down the continental slope and into deep water.

- Both sea fans and sea pens are cnidarians. They're essentially polyps, and they're filter feeders. They're related to corals and sea anemones.

- Deepwater anemones are also present in these depth zones, and they all share the trait of sticking up into the water so they can filter the slow-moving water currents.

- Deepwater corals form masses that are called bioherms, or accumulations of biological material that build up on the ocean floor. These corals do not have zooxanthellae; they don't photosynthesize. Instead, they live as polyps and as primary consumers.

- All deepwater corals are living on detrital material. In fact, at the bottom of the ocean, it's continuously snowing—called **marine snow**, which is the constant raining of dead parts of organisms that live far above in the shallow waters.

- There are many macrofauna associated with the continental slopes as well. For example, a giant isopod is truly daunting in size and can move remarkably quickly. It's basically a scavenger that is a carnivore of fish and even squid.

- On continental slopes, there is a great profusion of crabs. Skates and rays are also present. Octopus are tremendously common on the continental slopes and out on the deep-sea floor as well as rattail fish, which hover just above the sea floor and feed on the epifauna and infauna they can find there.

- There are entire sets of habitats associated with small rocky outcroppings on the continental slope and on the abyssal plains, including out on the seamounts that stick up from the deep-sea floor into shallower but still deep water.

- In many places, seamounts are rocky outcroppings that stick up from the 4000-meter ocean floor up to 2000 meters or 1000 meters in depth. Ocean currents sweep over the tops of seamounts.

- Filter feeders are especially abundant on top of seamounts. In the waters of the lower continental slope and out on the broad abyssal plains, one of the most common kinds of organisms is ophiuroids, which are commonly known as brittle stars. They are echinoderms (meaning having spiny skin) and are similar to starfish, but they're especially well adapted to life in the deep sea. They can move quite quickly and can remain sessile without eating anything for weeks.

Researchers use current meters that are placed on the ocean floor to determine how currents affect various ecosystems.

- All over the world, brittle stars are virtually ubiquitous in waters below 500 meters of depth on the slopes and out onto the abyssal plains.

Abyssal Benthic Communities

- Broad abyssal plains represent the whole sea bottom. Through the first half of the 20th century, the abyssal plains were seen as monotonous zones where the same few life-forms probably dominated.

- Starting from the 1960s, when scientists became more sophisticated about how they sampled benthic fauna, it was discovered that there are surprisingly diverse life forms and robust ecosystems—even if the total biomass is relatively small on the deep-sea floor.

- Scientists from Woods Hole Oceanographic Institution devised a special sampling trawl called the epibenthic sled. They found hundreds of species and tens of thousands of individual organisms in each area of the epibenthic sled in an average place on the abyssal plain.

- Later, another study found 4500 organisms representing 798 different species in a single square meter of a typical abyssal plain. Overall, abyssal plains have a vast diversity of life existing in very specific niches that have evolved to work together and exploit every available resource in this relatively scarce zone of the deep-sea floor.

- Most of the surface of Earth is composed of abyssal plains, zones that are dominated by worms and echinoderms. Worms called polychaete, or bristle worms, are some of the best-adapted organisms on the entire planet.

- An acorn worm forms a U-shaped tube in the ocean floor and basically eats its way through the sediment.

- The kings of the deep-sea floor are the **holothurians**, which are echinoderms called sea cucumbers.

- A sea urchin tends to be circular with a pentagonal symmetry (a 5-pointed body plan), a central mouth, and an anus to expel food waste.

- All of these species that are similar to starfish and sea urchins are echinoderms, which are the dominant species in terms of processing the ocean floor.

- The real kings of the ocean floor, at least in terms of photograph ability, are the holothurians, the sea cucumbers. They're the real waste processors of the deep. They are completely soft and are inflated by water. When they want to move, they pump water into a particular pseudopod, or leg, and inflate it to move it—kind of like a hydraulic system.

- Sea cucumbers sometimes turn up in great profusion—by the thousands—in herds of sea pigs, or herds of holothurians, and are one of the most abundant organisms on the ocean floor.

- Every part of the ocean floor has moved through the gut of some organism multiple times over. Tiny differences in the available resources on the ocean floor have led to the evolution of different species in a patchwork all over the planet.

- Whale carcasses and presumably other large organisms that die in the water column somewhere and fall to the bottom are a great source of food.

- Hagfish, specialized worms, sea cucumbers, and crabs all come in great numbers somehow smelling or sensing dead whales and digest all the available flesh right down to and including the bones—which is why we don't find as many fossils as expected in deep-sea sediments.

Deep-Sea Vent Communities

- There are vast profusions of organisms living around black smokers and hot hydrothermal vents in deep-sea vent communities. All the marine ecosystems we've discussed so far, including the detrital ones, are ultimately based on photosynthesis fueled by the Sun.

- Until the late 1970s, it was believed by all biologists that all life on Earth was based on photosynthesis. In 1977, the accidental discovery of a thriving benthic community—the deep-sea tubeworms and clams that were living at the hydrothermal vents of the East Pacific Rise—showed that an entirely different way of life exists.

- Chemosynthesis is a different pathway than photosynthesis that uses chemical energy, not sunlight, to make the carbohydrates and sugars that life depends on for food.

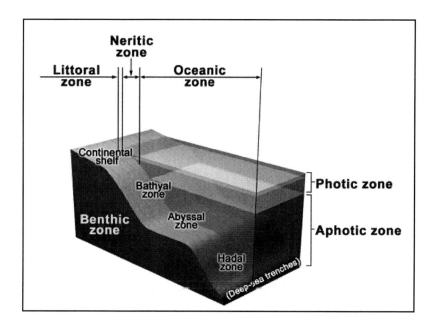

- If there is carbon dioxide, oxygen, and hydrogen sulfide in an environment, then an organism that can exploit this can use the energy in the hydrogen sulfide to make glucose. These organisms have had to develop an ability to resist the toxicity of sulfur to manage it and get it out of their bodies.

- Hydrogen sulfide comes out of the hot vent water of black smokers. There are bacteria that can oxidize the sulfide to make carbohydrates. These bacteria live freely in the water within some of the mid-ocean ridge vent rocks adjacent to the hottest water but also within the guts of the larger organisms that are around them in great profusions. There's a symbiotic relationship going on between them.

- In the gut of a very large tubeworm called rift tubeworms are great masses of these bacteria, which chemosynthesize. The bacteria make the food, and the worm lives on the food—the only food it receives.

- Very large clams, mussels, and crabs live in deep-sea vent communities and feed off the food generated by the clams, mussels, and tubeworms—the **chemoautotrophs**—which all share one really interesting trait: Their flesh is red. They have this red flesh because they bear hemoglobin, which they need to bind the sulfur and get it out of their systems. Their red flesh stinks of hydrogen sulfide.

- Shrimp living in this environment have special organs on the backs of their heads and can sense the heat from the hot vents coming out of the water. They orient themselves around these hot vents. Based on a totally symbiotic relationship with the chemosynthetic bacteria, these communities evolved early and have been present at the bottom of the ocean for at least hundreds of millions of years.

- More than 900 species associated with hot vents have been catalogued. Organisms that can live in these hot-vent areas are sometimes called hyperthermophiles because they love heat. The hyperthermophiles can live in water in excess of 100°C.

- Chemosynthetic communities of other types have been located in environments that do not have hydrothermal vents. Some of the best-known ones are the communities of cold seeps, in which methane or hydrogen sulfide seeps out of the ocean floor. No special heat is involved, but the chemical energy is present.

- These cold-seep communities are comprised also of clams and tubeworms and some similar organisms. As oil and gas seep on the ocean floor, there are profusions of life because there's more energy coming out in places where those hydrocarbons are leaking out of the ocean floor.

Important Terms

azoic zone: Edward Forbes's briefly popular theory of the mid-1800s that no life existed below depths of about 900 meters; the theory was soon disproven by trawls and dredges.

chemoautotroph: Organism that manufactures food (carbohydrates) from the energy of chemical bonds.

epifauna: Benthic organisms that dwell on or above the sea floor.

holothurian: The sea cucumber or sea pig, a soft benthic echinoderm that scavenges the mud of the sea floor.

infauna: Benthic organisms that dwell within the sea floor.

marine snow: Clumps of whitish organic detritus that form a constant "snowfall" to the sea floor in deepwater environments; fuels scavenger ecosystems.

sessile: Animals unable to move about that are usually permanently fixed to their substrate, such as barnacles or corals.

Suggested Reading

Gage and Tyler, *Deep-Sea Biology*.

Van Dover, *The Ecology of Deep-Sea Hydrothermal Vents*.

Questions to Consider

1. One might think of the deep-sea floor as an unchanging habitat—a place with no seasons, cycles, or even events. In what senses is this true? Conversely, can you think of anything that could be seasonal or eventful there?

2. Why might chemosynthetic communities exist only in places like the deep-ocean floor rather than across a wide range of land and sea habitats, the way photosynthesis-based communities are?

Deep Bottom Life and Hydrothermal Vents
Lecture 27—Transcript

In this lecture, we're going to take a look at the denizens of the deepest zones of all, the bottom dwellers or benthic communities of the bathyal, abyssal, and even hadal zones of the deep-sea floor. If we think about the deep-sea floor, it's a hard place to access. No human eyes had ever seen any scene from the bottom of the deep ocean until the 1940s when Bruce Heezen, he of the mapping the Mid-Atlantic Ridge fame, rigged up an automatic camera to lower down on a cable and photograph the sea bottom and that was the first illumination to human eyes of what the sea floor looked like. What it looked like was muddy and vast and yet apparently with a great deal of life living in it.

In the mid 1800s, people began dredging up sea bottom samples before the *Challenger* expedition even after a man named Edward Forbes, in particular, began dredging up samples from along the continental shelf and into the beginnings of deep water. He noted that he found life in these samples and we'll talk about some of the different life forms that are found on the deep-sea floor once we get out of the photic zone, but they were dwindling in number with depth in his samples. He took a straight line and basically extrapolated to a depth of about 300 fathoms, 500 or 600 meters or so and said that his line extrapolated to zero, no life forms whatsoever. He made the leap of logic that this was the azoic zone, a region in the bottom of the sea that would have absolutely no life because it was deep and dark. It was cold and at high pressure and perhaps this was a place where biology simply couldn't exist.

It turns out that nothing could be further from the truth. The deep sea is populated to the greatest depths of the ocean as we know today. This was already beginning to be disproven even as Forbes formed this azoic zone hypothesis, although the azoic zone persisted in the scientific literature and understanding for a number of decades even as people were dredging up materials and finding there was life in the deep sea. One early theory at the same period in the late 19th century, because the *Challenger* expedition and other expeditions that were pulling plankton nets through the water were finding that there was this jelly-like mass that I described already once, that jelly-like mass was actually a sample of some sort of protoplasm that covered the entire seabed everywhere in the ocean and that it was one single living organism, which actually was given the name Bathybius, Bathybius haeckilii. It even got a specific scientific name after one of the Huxley's, the founders of this idea.

Bathybius haeckilii was simply a mistake. There is not one single living organism covering the entire ocean floor. In fact, it was partially identified on the basis of some mistakes of understanding how the preservative that was used to preserve all the jellyish samples were interacting with the chemistry of the seawater and the seabed mud. Bathybius was an interesting sidetrack on the way to understanding that the deep sea bottom has a whole variety of many different species and is a zone of oases and differences even as it seems monotonous when we take our first look at it and when he even took his first looks at it.

Let's take a ride down the continental slopes then and look at what the benthic fauna and benthic ecosystems are as we go down through the disphotic zone into the twilight waters and into the deep, dark waters and eventually merge out onto the abyssal plains. As we drop down, one thing is certainly true about what Forbes said. The abundance of life, the biomass does diminish rapidly as we move off the lit continental shelves and into the deep water. There's certainly not as much productivity out there and different organisms take hold.

However, even down the continental slopes a number of both sessile, meaning rooted in organisms into the sea bottom, live on the sea floor. The mud itself that's blanketing the continental slopes from all this terrigenous sedimentation is processed and digested by a whole range of different kinds of both epifauna and infauna. Remember fauna that live on the seabed and fauna that live burrowing within the seabed and then macrofauna, fish, skates, and cephalopods in the form of octopus and squid live near and adjacent to this sea floor and graze on all of these organisms as well.

There's a pretty diverse ecosystem down the continental slopes even. For example, some of the epifauna and the sessile organisms that root into the sea floor include things like sea fans or gorgonians that are common in the coral reefs, but they're also present all the way down the continental slope and into even deep water. Images of some of these sea fans from the Gulf of Mexico show these fanning forms that are rooted into the sediment or rock and then stick up into the water. Sea pens are another example in this image from the Pacific Northwest, a continental slope off the coast of Vancouver Island.

Both of them are cnidarians. They're essentially polyps and they're filter feeders. They're related to corals and sea anemones and things like that. Deepwater anemones are also present in all these depth zones and all of them share the trait of basically sticking up into the water so they can filter the slow-moving water currents that glide up and down along the bottom and bring various detrital materials, stuff that's raining down, organic matter raining down from above them and landing on the sea floor and swirling about in the waters of depth. They take advantage of that and digest whatever material they can find as well as whatever living organism, microorganisms, plankton happen to be in this particular zone at depth.

Deepwater corals as I described in a previous lecture also exist. There are a whole number of both soft and even semi-reef forming corals that live in the deep water. This example is called bubblegum corral for its particular kind of configuration. It has little bits of bubblegum stuck all over it, but those are just the coral polyps themselves and there are even these deep water, they're not really reefs, but they form masses that are called bioherms or accumulations of biological material that build up on the sea floor. These corals are not, they don't have zooxanthellae. They don't do any photosynthesis. They live simply as polyps and live as primary consumers.

All of them are living on detrital material. In fact, at the bottom of the ocean you may be surprised to find out that it's continuously snowing. It's not snowing snow; it's snowing something called marine snow. Any camera tow through the bottom of the sea, especially on the productive continental margins we'll find what looks like a constant rain of little white particles that look a lot like snow swirling in the water. What they actually are is little bits of organic detritus. They're dead parts of organisms that live far above in the shallow waters. They're bits of the mucus nets that I talked about being cast by pteropods and other marine organisms that then have cut loose with little bits of organic detritus stuck to them. Marine snow is ubiquitous. It's snowing all the time at the bottom of let's say the slope off the coast of either eastern or western North America. That material is what the detritus feeders are feeding on.

There are lots of macrofauna as well associated with the continental slopes and as we go down through the sea floor in areas that are productive then we have organisms crawling around on the bottom that are not really exactly like anything we've seen on land or maybe are something from our worst nightmares on land. This example of what's called a giant isopod, an organism that's related to the pillbug or woodlouse on land is truly daunting in size and kind of frightening looking the way it's been sampled here. It's basically a scavenger. It crawl around the seabed as epifauna and scoops up and eats whatever it can find along the way, but it's actually a carnivore of fish and even squid and these isopods can move remarkably quickly as video surveys have shown. They're very common on the Gulf of Mexico sea floor in particular as well as out in the Atlantic Ocean.

The continental slope has numerous macrofauna that are crawling around and living there. All of the various studies and *Alvin* dives and things like that to the deep continental margins have found a great profusion of crabs including the large crabs that are actually the target of some of the deep sea trawling. Skates and rays are present. Octopus are tremendously common on the continental slopes and out on the deep-sea floor as well as these ubiquitous fish that are known as rat-tail fish because of their elongate shape, no really strongly developed tailfin. They don't have to move very often and very quickly, but they hover just above the sea floor and feed on the epifauna and infauna that they can find in that location.

Much of the continental slope is just a muddy, gentle slope leading down to the deep seabed. Like the deep seabed, it has relatively small concentrations of fauna in any given location, although they are ubiquitous at the same time. any particular place where there's something to hang on to, something to stick to and for sessile organisms to root into, produces essentially an oasis of life, so a rocky outcropping on the sea floor, or even just a ball of clay mud that has rolled down from above and landed in a particular place, but is a little firmer than the surrounding soft goody ooze will create an oasis of life. It will have innumerable numbers of sea pens and fans, deep sea sponges, and various kinds of species of anemones living all over those rocky regions and then those fuel a larger ecosystem that includes a lot of macrofauna. There are entire sets of habitats associated with just small rock outcroppings on the continental slope and on the abyssal plains as well including out on the sea mounts that stick up from the deep-sea floor into shallower, but still deep water.

In many places, those sea mounts are rocky outcroppings that stick up maybe from the 4000 meter sea floor up to 2000 meters or 1000 meters in depth and ocean currents as we'll see later sweep over the tops of those kind of concentrated. The filter feeders are especially abundant on tops of these sea mounts. In the water's of the lower continental slope and then out on to the broad abyssal plains, one of the most common kinds of organisms that you'll see moving around on the surface of the sea floor are these ophiurans or ophiuroids, which are commonly known as brittle stars. They're another form of the echinoderm and they are similar to starfish that we see in the shallow water, but they're especially well-adapted to life in the deep sea. They can move quite quickly when they want to. They can remain sessile and not eat anything at all for weeks and apparently even months at a time, but they're opportunistic and whenever there's a source of a small amount of food they'll move over to it and start consuming it.

They consume in the same way that a regular starfish does by passing from their arms using the suction grip that they have passing food in towards the central mouth at the center of the organism. Brittle stars are virtually ubiquitous in waters below 500 meters depth, or so, on the slopes and out onto the abyssal plains and all over the world. A whole variety of species that all have the same basic brittle star; the long and skinny 5-pointed arms are found on the organisms and we see them all over the sea floor. They're the first thing that I saw when I looked out the view at the sea floor the first time that I visited the bottom of the ocean in *Alvin* myself.

If we go and take a look at the broad abyssal plains that represent the whole sea bottom. Even after the discovery that yes there was life out there in the late 1800s with the *Challenger* expedition and on through the first half of the 20th century, it was seen as a place where life forms existed, but it was seen as a monotonous zone where the same few life forms probably dominated the brittle stars as I said, a few types of worms, and a few types of fish, maybe an octopus or two lived all over the sea bottom all over the world. The conditions were about the same everywhere. Temperatures were similar, currents were slow, the only food available was essentially marine snow, detritus raining down from above and so perhaps this was a zone that was populated, but pretty boring. It turns out again that that was upended once people were able to do a little bit more sophisticated job actually sampling the deep abyssal forms.

Certainly there's no sunlight and there's little energy down there and it's cold so these are scavenger-based food webs just as they were on the continental slope. The organisms that exist down there mostly do move and grow slowly. Starting from the 1960s when scientists got a little bit more sophisticated about how they sampled that benthic fauna, it was discovered really that there are surprisingly diverse life forms and robust ecosystems even if the actual total biomass is relatively small on the deep sea bed. It's far from a desert in the sense of having diverse life.

A couple of scientists from Woods Hole actually devised a special sampling trawl that would sample the deep-sea floor a little bit better than it had been done before. They called it the epibenthic sled and it was just a rig that would basically sample, scoop into the mud so it would sample the upper few centimeters or so, a few tens of centimeters of mud, but sample at the same time the water for a meter or so just above the bottom. What they found when they dragged this sled through the mud and after just trawling along for an hour or so and pulled up what they got, it was incredibly diverse and an incredible large surprise to them how many different species they found. They found literally hundreds of species and thousands or even tens of thousands of individual organisms in each toe of the epibenthic sled out there in just an average place on the abyssal plain in the Atlantic Ocean or in the Gulf of Mexico.

One study later on found that when they really looked at a specific zone in the ocean, employing cameras every square meter of the sea floor in the Atlantic Ocean, on the garden variety abyssal plain, found 4500 organisms in a single square meter representing 798 different species. This zone may be relatively unpopulated, but it's certainly not depopulate. It has a vast diversity of life existing in very, very specific niches that have evolved to work together and exploit every available resource in this relatively scarce zone of the deep-sea floor.

Let's take a look at a typical scene then from about 50% of planet Earth. Most of surface of Earth is the abyssal plains. This is a zone that's dominated by worms and echinoderms. Worm burrows and small mounds that are the places where the worms have expelled mud from the seabed are ubiquitous. These worms called polychaete, bristle worms, are one of the best adapted organisms on the entire planet. They exist from the shallow coral reefs all the way to having been discovered at the bottom of the *Challenger* deep now; the deepest place in the entire ocean is populated, at least in part, with what are called bristle worms. They're also adapted to the mid-ocean ridges as we'll see.

Another type of worm that lives down there, a little bit more complicated organism, is called an acorn worm that forms a U-shaped tube in the seabed and basically just eats its way through the sediment, taking in all the mud and sand, digesting every bit of organic material that's in it and then expelling what's left out behind into these convoluted looking worm castings that cover large parts of the sea floor. They're a little bit like the earthworms of the sea bottom. In addition to the worms, we can really say that the kings of the deep-sea floor are the echinoderms, holothurians, which are called sea cucumbers. Brittle stars I've already described.

Another organism called a crinoid, all of these are like starfish or like sea urchins that we see in the shallow water are really the dominant species in terms of processing the seabed and being what you find present on the seabed all over the world. There are many thousands of different species of echinoderms. Echinoderm literally means spiny skin so when we think of a sea urchin we think of an echinoderm. If you remember what a sea urchin looks like, they tend to be circular with a pentagonal symmetry, a 5-pointed body plan and a central mouth and an anus to expel food waste.

All of these different organisms in very many different shapes and profusions are all echinoderms and we'll take a look at a few of them. One thing about the echinoderms that's interesting is they're the largest phylum, remember a phylum is the most basic class within the kingdom of animals,

Animalia; they're the largest phylum that has no fresh water or terrestrial representatives. They're exclusively marine, exclusively oceanic.

The real king of the sea floor, at least in terms of photograph ability, are the holothurians, the so-called sea cucumbers. This example is actually called a sea pig and they're crawling around the abyssal plains and even the deep sea trenches in the hadal zone in great numbers. They're the real waste processor of the deep. They're essentially little machines for eating mud once again. They have a body that is unlike most of the other echinoderms, not spiny at all. They're completely soft and they're inflated by water. They pump themselves up with water pressure and that's what holds them into their given shape. When they want to move, they pump a little water into particular pseudopod or leg and inflate that one and move it and then move other ones with muscle contractions. All of it is about moving water around, so they're kind of a hydraulic system of an organism.

They eat the waste that they find in the sea floor so they're great detritus feeders. When they were first discovered on the deep-sea floor in these various camera surveys they were quickly discovered to sometimes turn up in great profusion literally by the thousands in herds of sea pigs or herds of holothurians thundering across the abyssal plains, maybe not thundering moving kind of slowly, but no one really is quite clear on why they herd together. Perhaps, it's because they find some particularly rich feeding ground or because it's just hard to reproduce and find a mate on the vast abyssal plains so sticking together makes a lot of sense. The holothurians are certainly one of the most abundant organisms on the sea floor.

We've seen that every square inch them, every bit of the muddy sea floor has continuously been worked over by scavenging organisms like these brittle stars and holothurians like the polychaetes or bristle worms and they reprocess all of the available organic matter. Literally every bit of the sea floor has moved through the gut of some organism multiple times over. It's a very efficient scavenging system out there. It's a very diverse one, just tiny little differences in the available resources on the sea floor have led to the evolution of different species in a patchwork all over the planet. There are also isolated zones like the deep sea trenches where at the bottom of the deep sea trench there is one particular set of all these types of organisms, one particular set of species that are different from the ones in a different trench between the Japan Trench, for example, and the Mariana Trench or the Peru-Chile Trench. Similar environments, but not surprisingly, have evolved different organisms because of the great differences in between them.

One of the sets of oases that exist on the deep-sea floor is the existence of detrital falls of windfalls of great amounts of food. One thing that's been discovered just in the era of deep sea exploration by submarines and ROVs is that whale carcasses and presumably other large organisms that die up in the water column somewhere and fall to the bottom are a great source of food. The existence of these whale carcasses has really upended our understanding of how rapidly life can proceed at the bottom of the ocean. When one of these happens and now they've been captured on a video a couple of times and actually dead whales have been submerged by researchers and then watched.

It's found that organisms come out of the woodwork it seems from everywhere around and start to very quickly digest and can completely denude one of these carcasses over the span of just a few days or weeks. Hag fish, specialized worms, the sea cucumbers themselves, and crabs all come in great numbers from the region somehow smelling or sensing that dead organism and digest all the available flesh right down to and including the bones of the whale, which is why we don't find as many fossils as one might expect in deep sea sediments. Even the bones are digested within a matter of weeks.

We've looked at the abyssal plains now and so I want to turn my attention to the really remarkable deep sea vent communities. We've already mentioned them a couple of times now. If we go to the mid-ocean ridges we see these vast profusions of organisms right around those black smokers and the hot hydrothermal vents. All the marine ecosystems we've looked at so far, including the detrital ones, are ultimately based on photosynthesis fueled by the Sun. Until the late 1970s, it was believed by all biologists that all life on earth was based on photosynthesis. That was the only pathway for primary production to take place.

In 1977, the discovery, quite by accident, of the thriving benthic community, the deep sea tubeworms and clams that were living at the hydrothermal vents on the Galapagos rift of the East Pacific Rise showed that this entirely different way of life exists. That's the one we call chemosynthesis or chemoautotrophy. Chemosynthesis is a different pathway than photosynthesis and it uses chemical energy, not sunlight, to basically make the carbohydrates and sugars that life depends on for food. If you have carbon dioxide and oxygen and you combine it with hydrogen sulfide then an organism that can exploit this and can make this reaction take place through chemical pathways that catalyze that reaction can take that hydrogen sulfide, can make glucose, $C_6H_{12}O_6$, and then they use the sulfide, use the energy in the hydrogen sulfide to make the glucose to assemble those molecules and then that produces a whole bunch of free sulfur as well as a bunch of water.

Most of us can't do this in part because we can't deal with the sulfur. That's a poison to us. These organisms have had to develop an ability to resist the toxicity of that sulfur to manage it and get it out of their bodies. The chemosynthesis of the chemoautotrophic bacteria that live at the mid-ocean ridges was an entirely novel concept to science at this time.

The way it works is that hydrogen sulfide, as well as many other chemical species, but in particular hydrogen sulfide comes out in the hot vent water of the black smokers. There are bacteria that can oxidize that sulfide to make the carbohydrates, as I said, and they live freely in the water within some of the mid-ocean ridge vent rocks just adjacent to the hottest of the water, but also within the guts of the larger organisms that are masked around them in these great profusions. There's this symbiotic relationship going on between them.

If we take a look at some video footage of what things look like down there at the mid-ocean ridges, you see that there are these very large tubeworms, what are called the rift tubeworms, Riftia or they're all vestimentiferans is the name for them, they can grow to great lengths, 3 meters or more in length, and you see the actual worm itself sticking out from its chitinous casing, the tube. In the gut of that worm, down inside the tube, are great masses of these bacteria—the bacteria chemosynthesize. They make the food. The worm lives on the food and that's the only food that that worm gets. It can filter feed a little bit out of the water, but it's just filter feeding more of the same bacteria that are floating around that same region that you actually see as that flocculated snow that looks like it's coming out of the black smokers.

Surrounding these worms and surrounding these communities are a number of other organisms as well. They're very large clams that live in the region. They grow very rapidly. They can achieve sizes like this, 10-20 centimeters in length. There are mussels. There are these crabs that live around that are actually feeding off of all of the food generated by the clams, mussels, and tubeworms. The tubeworms, the clams, the mussels all share one really interesting trait. Their flesh is red. It's red because they bare hemoglobin, essentially the thing that makes our blood red, is also present, ubiquitous in all these communities, organisms that live on the chemoautotrophs. The reason is that they need it to bind the sulfur and get it out of their systems. They have red flesh and sort of red blood in a sense. These are clams that you wouldn't want to eat by the way. That red flesh and the actual clam material stinks to high heaven of H_2S if you bring it up to the surface.

There are also shrimp living in this environment that have special organs on the backs of their heads and can sense the heat from the hot vents coming out of the water. They orient themselves around these hot vents. These whole communities of organisms based on a totally symbiotic relationship with the chemosynthetic bacteria are living down there and have been living down there since time immemorial. It seems virtually certain that these communities were evolved early and have been present in the bottom of the ocean for at least hundreds of millions of years.

There are many, many different varieties and species. We've seen that they've been found along rifts now all along the world ocean, not just the Galapagos, but throughout the Atlantic and Pacific and Indian Oceans. More than 900 species associated with the hot vents have been cataloged. One of the interesting ones is a bristle worm called the Pompeii worm because it lives right up adjacent to the hot water. All of these organisms that can live in these hot vent areas are sometimes called hyperthermophiles, they love heat, thermophile. The hyperthermophiles can live, not actually in water that's at 400 degrees, but right up adjacent to it in water in excess of 100° C.

Chemosynthetic communities of other types have been located in a bunch of other non-hydrothermal vent environments. Over the past couple of decades, we've shown that they're far more widespread and varied than was initially recognized. Some of the best-known ones are the communities of what are called cold seeps. Methane or hydrogen sulfide seeps out of the sea floor, on the continental slope and in areas where there are hydrocarbons or petroleum coming out of the sea floor in places like the Gulf of Mexico and elsewhere. Places where those no special heat involved, but just the chemical energy is present.

These cold seep communities are comprised also of clams and tubeworms and some similar organisms, but very different species that can adapt to and exploit the fairly small amount of energy coming out of a cold water seep that just bares a little bit of concentrated H_2S or methane. Remember those *Alvin* dives that I talked about that were my first big project as a graduate student, well this photograph is one these cold seeps, a scraggly little bunch of tubeworms and an octopus living nearby to feast on the clams perhaps, but not much compared to the mid-ocean ridge black smokers, but still a community that thrives in the deep and is living and has been living since time immemorial in places where energy from the interior of Earth, in this case subduction zones, not mid-ocean ridges, is fueling the chemical life that they depend on, the bacteria that they depend on.

At the oil and gas seeps on the sea floor, we see profusions of life because there's more energy coming out in places where those hydrocarbons are leaking out of the seabed. We can't digest oil and fuel ourselves the way our cars do, but these organisms, these tubeworms and clams and the chemosynthetic bacteria they host can do that equally well in places like the Gulf of Mexico where it's seeping out of the seabed in pretty large amounts. Beyond oil spills, there's a lot of natural oil and methane gas seeping out of the sea floor in any of the big petroleum producing basins of the world. They host very similar communities of organisms.

We've seen that although it's deep and dark and cold, the deep-sea floor of the continental slopes and abyssal plains is far from devoid of life. It's really the kingdom of the echinoderms and worms though and the holothurians seem to rule the world, all the way to the greatest depths in the bottom of the ocean and the bottom of the deep trenches. It's characterized by hosting complex ecosystems of low biomass, but very steady productivity and capable of taking advantage of a real windfall though in the form of a whale fall and moving very quickly when it needs to. The chemoautotrophs of the black smokers and the cold seeps are a form of life that is simultaneously, totally new to science, just in the past few decades, but possibly the most ancient of all life on the entire planet.

We've taken a real look through the life that fills up the entire ocean and the nature of the water column as a whole. Next we're going to turn the page and zoom out to look at the ocean in motion, how the processes that govern the ocean include all the currents and the movements of the water through the sea. In order to do that, we're going to have to look at processes at the other edge. We've looked at the extreme bottom of the ocean. We'll have to look at the extreme edge of the ocean in the form of looking into the atmosphere, the surface currents, and how climate and movements of heat on the planet govern those ocean currents and movements in the water.

Trade Winds—The Circulation of Heat and Wind
Lecture 28

T he atmosphere and ocean are intimately linked in their motions, driven by the uneven distribution of heat modified by the Coriolis effect on all movement as Earth rotates on its axis. Uneven heating by the Sun from the equator to the poles causes density differences in air masses, which rise and fall accordingly, creating pressure differences that in turn drive the winds. Wind in general blows due to pressure differences in air; some wind patterns are persistent year after year. Mariners depended on knowledge of wind bands and calm regions for centuries of navigation.

Atmospheric Circulation

- Water is a fluid medium, and it's constantly in motion. Ocean currents cause the large-scale global transport of water that mixes the ocean over long timescales.

- The atmosphere and the ocean are intimately linked in how they move. The ocean wouldn't be in motion if it weren't for atmospheric motions and the wind blowing across the sea. The wind drives the surface currents of the ocean. It's a water planet, but that's partly because it has an atmosphere that moves around and transports heat on the surface.

- The air is approximately 78% nitrogen, 21% oxygen, 1% argon, and a small fraction of 1% carbon dioxide. The largest component after the nitrogen and oxygen is water vapor, which is primarily from evaporation off the surface of the sea.

- What moves the atmosphere around are differences in density that are set in motion by gravity and by differences in pressure. Density of the atmosphere decreases with altitude. Warm air is less dense than cold air, so density varies with temperature

- Humid air—air with more water vapor in it—is actually less dense than dry air because the molecule H_2O is lighter than the nitrogen or oxygen gas that makes up the rest of the air. Warm air can hold more water vapor than cold air can.

- The pressure of the atmosphere is 15 pounds per square inch at sea level, or what we call one atmosphere. That pressure is due to the weight of the entire column of air from sea level up to the top of the atmosphere.

- The pressure decreases as altitude increases. Higher up in the atmosphere, the air expands because the pressure becomes lower, and the expansion causes it to cool off. Conversely, it contracts and also warms when pressure is increased, so the higher the pressure, the warmer the air gets.

- When warm, humid air forms at the surface—just above the sea and the tropical regions—it starts to rise up to the upper atmosphere because of its lower density. The air expands, cools, and then is able to hold less water vapor in gaseous form and tends to form droplets. Therefore, clouds and rainfall are ultimately results of this atmospheric portion of the hydrological cycle.

- Uneven heating from the Sun warms the equatorial regions much more than it warms the polar regions. We think of the tropics as warm and the poles as cool, but this uneven heating drives the circulation of the air in the atmosphere.

- The equatorial region is hotter than the polar region because of the direct heating of the Sun versus the very oblique heating of the Sun in the polar regions or in the far latitudes north and south.

- The uneven heating of Earth—the imbalance of that heating on the surface of the planet—creates a surplus of heat tropically and a lack of heat in the polar regions, and the air starts to move in order to redistribute that heat.

- If there wasn't any movement in the atmosphere, the poles would be much colder and the equatorial regions would be much hotter than they actually are on our planet today.

- There's an uneven heating seasonally that warms the Northern Hemisphere and Southern Hemisphere at different times of the year. Seasons don't exist because Earth gets closer to and farther away from the Sun; they occur because of the angle that Earth makes with the direction to the Sun.

The Coriolis Effect

- We can think of a hypothetical atmospheric circulation on Earth due to uneven solar heating. There would be a giant convection cell in each hemisphere, much like convection in a pot of boiling water. These giant hypothetical convection cells on Earth don't actually exist because there's one more really important complicating factor: the **Coriolis effect**.

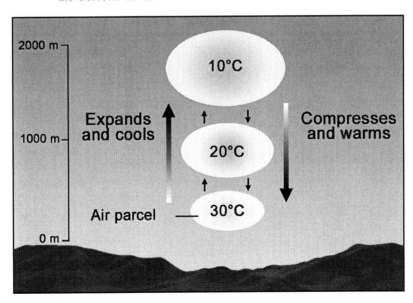

- The Coriolis effect was first described by French physicist Gustave-Gaspard Coriolis in 1835 and states that everything on Earth that's in motion is fundamentally affected by the fact that Earth is always rotating eastward. The Coriolis effect deflects objects.

- It takes 24 hours to complete one full turn on Earth. A place that's far to the north is rotating through a much smaller circle and with a smaller velocity than a place on the equator. Therefore, we're moving at different speeds depending on where we are on the planet.

- Moving objects in the Northern Hemisphere always look like they're veering to the right due to the Coriolis effect. In the Southern Hemisphere, the effect is the same but opposite: Everything looks like it's deflecting to the left.

- Interestingly, the Coriolis effect is zero at the equator. In general, the Coriolis effect is relatively weak when you're near the equatorial regions. This concept is important for understanding the flow of air and water. The Coriolis effect is strongest near the poles due to the rapid change in the amount of rotational velocity.

- The air in motion in the atmosphere is affected by the Coriolis effect as well. It moves poleward, but it's deflected to the right in the Northern Hemisphere and to the left in the Southern Hemisphere. It doesn't make it all the way to the poles.

Atmospheric Circulation Cells

- The atmosphere is broken down into, or develops, a number of different circulation cells. They're driven by convection, but they're not as simple as without the Coriolis effect. We can break down circulation on the planet into some very large, well-developed cells.

- From the equator to about 30° north latitude and 30° south latitude are the symmetrical Hadley cells. From 30° to 60° north are the Ferrel cells, and then above 60° all the way to 90° north or 90° south are the polar cells. These cells govern the generalized airflow pattern for the planet in 30-degree divisions with 3 parts in each hemisphere and 6 sets of cells overall. The Hadley cells, the Ferrel cells, and the polar cells are called **atmospheric circulation cells**.

- The subtropical trade winds, the temperate westerlies, and the polar easterlies are all the low-altitude arms of these major atmospheric cells.

Earth's Wind

- The wind blows because of pressure differences. Air simply flows from zones of high pressure to zones of low pressure. The rising warm and humid air creates a low pressure, the sinking cold and dry air creates a high pressure.

- **Trade winds** are driven by the fact that air rises and sinks. For example, the sinking cold air that's moving eastward comes back toward the rising warm, tropical air that's moving westward.

- Doldrums are regions of calm air where nothing much is happening. These are the places where the warm, humid air is ascending.

- In the boundary between the Hadley and Ferrel cells are the horse latitudes, where the cool, dry air descends. On land, this produces very persistent high-pressure zones that tend to be very dry.

- The big deserts of the world virtually all lie in this 30° to 35° belt north or south. The Sahara and the Gobi deserts are examples, and they are some of the driest places on Earth.

- The zones of intertropical conversions and the horse latitudes are zones where the wind doesn't blow very strongly. The winds in between are the important governing winds that move ocean currents around and also have moved mariners around the sea for a very long time.

- Trade winds come from the east and are called easterlies; in fact, they actually come from the northeast to the southwest. They are the surface winds of the Hadley cells and are centered around 15° north and south latitude. The westerlies, by contrast, are the surface winds of the Ferrel cells and are centered around 45° north and south latitude.

- In the polar regions, up at 70° or more north and south, there are the polar easterlies as well. The geometry becomes very simple: The boundaries are at 30°, 60°, and 90°, and then those strong winds are centered at 15°, 45°, and 75°.

- These wind patterns are persistent on average year after year, which is how the trade winds and the westerlies have gotten the name prevailing winds.

- In the days of sailing ships, mariners depended very specifically on knowledge of these wind bands in the calm regions. This type of knowledge was important not only for getting around, but also as part of their navigational strategy for understanding where they were north and south and moving across the oceans, when they were dependent on winds at all times.

- Columbus, the discoverer of America, actually never set foot in North America. He and his crew headed south along the African coast until they reached the latitude of about 15°, where they got into the trade-wind belt. They rode the trade winds westward across the Atlantic Ocean in order to travel west. When they got to the far side at that latitude, what they hit was not Florida and not the east coast of the United States, but the coast of the island of Hispaniola and other islands in the Caribbean.

atmospheric circulation cells: Large-scale, closed loops of overall mean airflow distributed according to latitude.

Coriolis effect: The tendency of any object in motion on Earth to deviate from a straight-line course due to the rotation of the planet.

trade winds: Prevailing easterly winds centered on 15° latitude north and south.

Suggested Reading

Aguado and Burt, *Understanding Weather and Climate.*

Walker, *An Ocean of Air.*

Questions to Consider

1. What do you think the Coriolis effect is like exactly along the equator?

2. Do prevailing-wind systems such as the trade winds still exert control on human activity and culture as they did in the days of sailing ships, or is that a thing of the past?

Trade Winds—The Circulation of Heat and Wind
Lecture 28—Transcript

Now we're ready to enter a whole new chapter in the course, the ocean in motion. We dealt with the ocean basins and the life that inhabits them, but we treated the water statically. Water is a fluid medium and it's constantly in motion. Even more than that it's in motion in very different ways than just the waves and tides, tsunami that we've already seen, the wavelike motions that transport energy around the planet, but don't move very much water. They don't cause the large-scale global transport of the water that mixes the ocean over long timescales, but ocean currents do exactly that. We're going to take up the great surface and eventually deepwater currents that stir up the sea.

In order to do that, we have to actually step even further out above the skin of the ocean and talk about the atmosphere for one lecture. The reason we have to do this is that the atmosphere and oceans are intimately linked in how they move. The ocean wouldn't be in motion it turns out if it weren't for atmospheric motions and the wind blowing across the sea. Just as the wind moves the waves, we will see that the wind drives the surface currents of the ocean. Just as we had to look at the underpinnings in the ocean basin and step back and look at Earth and the geological cycles and plate tectonics, we also have to look at this outer skin of the planet as a whole. It's a water planet, but that's partly because it has an atmosphere and an atmosphere that move around and transports heat on the surface.

The atmosphere and ocean are linked in a couple of specific ways. One is the uneven distribution of heat on the planet as we'll see and then how that is modified by this mysterious thing that I've mentioned a couple of times now called the Coriolis effect. That affects all movements on Earth as it rotates on its axis. Let's take a look at atmospheric flow.

First of all, what is the atmosphere? It's air, right. What is air? Air is a gas and it's made up of a fairly simple composition of a few gases. If we take dry air and leave the water vapor out, we'll put that back in in a second, then air is basically 78% nitrogen. It's mostly nitrogen, 21% oxygen, about 1% argon, and the rest is just in vanishingly small amounts. There's not much carbon dioxide. It's just a small fraction of 1%, and then various other elements and other gases. Basically it's just nitrogen and oxygen.

Air can also hold water vapor though and up to actually 4% by volume, so a significant component. The largest component after the nitrogen and oxygen is water vapor. This is from evaporation off the surface of the land, but dominantly off the surface of the sea since the ocean is most of the surface of the planet.

Air density varies and so we have to take that into account because what moves the atmosphere around are basically differences in density that are set in motion by gravity and by differences in pressure. Density of the atmosphere decreases with altitude. The higher you go up in the atmosphere, as we'll see, the gases are less compressed and therefore less dense. Warm air is less dense than cold air so density varies with temperature. Think of a hot air balloon, we heat up the air and it expands, but it also rises specifically because it's less dense so therefore it's buoyant through the colder air around it.

Maybe counterintuitively, humid air, air with more water vapor in it is actually less dense than dry air. We think of a humid day as a heavy air kind of day. That's just the feeling it gives us from feeling overheated. Air with more water vapor in it is less dense because H_2O, the molecule is a lighter molecule than the nitrogen or just oxygen, O_2 gas; that makes up the rest of the air. A particular volume of air at a particular pressure has a certain number of molecules of gas in it and water vapor is a lighter gas than those other ones. The more humidity air has the less dense it is and the more it will rise through the other air. Also interestingly, warm air can hold more water vapor than cold air can. Warm air is already less dense and then if it's more humid or holding more water vapor it becomes even more pronounced in its difference in density with colder, drier air that's around it.

We've talked about density, but we usually think about air in terms of pressure and so we have to understand the pressure in the atmosphere. You know that the pressure is apparently 15 pounds per square inch down here at sea level or what we just call one atmosphere or 1 bar or sometimes 1000 millibars if we're meteorologists. That pressure is due to the weight of the entire column of air from sea level up to the top of the atmosphere. That's about 1 kilogram per square centimeter; that's the same as the 15 pounds per square inch, but that air column of course is lighter and lighter as you go higher up in the atmosphere. The pressure decreases as we go up.

The gas, the air that's present then when pressure is reduced'; if you look at a gas higher and higher up in the atmosphere it expands because the pressure becomes lower and if it expands that actually causes it to cool off. We have that reduction in temperature from the expanded gas; the molecules aren't as close together; the heat energy is spread out over a larger area. That means a lower temperature. Conversely it contracts and also warms when pressure is increased, so the higher the pressure the warmer the air gets.

Well, because of the ability of warm air to hold more water vapor than cool air than also when warm, humid air forms at the surface, just above the sea and the tropical regions then it starts to rise because of its lower density and rises up to the upper atmosphere. It expands, it cools off, it then is able to hold less water vapor in gaseous form and it tends to form droplets so we get clouds and ultimately rainfall out of rising warm air that expands in the upper parts of the atmosphere. That's the fundamentals in a nutshell of the atmospheric part of the hydrological cycle. Heat distribution on Earth then, you can probably see is going to be important in terms of understanding what happens to air masses or what happens to the air in the atmosphere and then ultimately how that impacts the ocean and the flow in the ocean and the movement of water around on the surface of the planet.

Let's take a look at the heating of the surface of the planet. The earth has geothermal energy and heat comes out of the interior of Earth, but that's quite minor. That's a tiny fraction of the amount of energy at the surface of Earth relative to the amount that's coming from solar heating. The sun shines on Earth. That's what heats things up. We don't think of our climate as being driven by the heat from the ground. It's driven by the heat from the Sun. That heating is uneven. Uneven heating from the Sun basically warms up the equatorial regions much more than it warms up the Polar Regions. Maybe that's fairly obvious. We think of the tropics as warm and the poles as cool, but that drives a circulation of the air in the atmosphere.

Equal amounts of sunlight might shine on all different parts of Earth, but they shine more directly on the equatorial and tropical regions shining straight at Earth and shine more obliquely as we approach the poles because the surface of Earth is curved and the Sun is off in some direction relative to being essentially perpendicular to the pole of rotation of Earth. You get an oblique sunlight which is more easily reflected away in the Polar Regions. There's also more ice near the poles. That reflects more of the solar energy that reaches the surface there. If you think about it, you wonder maybe why is the equatorial region hotter than the polar region, but that's because of the direct heating of the Sun versus the very oblique heating of the Sun in the Polar Regions or in the far latitudes north and south.

The effect is a net heat gain and a surplus of heat in the tropics and a net heat deficit in the polar areas. The uneven heating of Earth, the imbalance of that heating on the surface of the planet then creates this surplus of heat tropically, lack of heat in the Polar Regions, and the air starts to move in order to redistribute that heat. There's a net transfer of heat poured from the equatorial regions that even out this very uneven insulation or sunshine and heating of Earth at the start. If there wasn't any movement in the atmosphere the poles would be much, much colder and the equatorial regions would be much, much, much hotter than they are actually on our planet today.

There's one more little bit of complication to that story which is that Earth's axis isn't just perpendicular to the plane of the ecliptic and to the direction of the Sun. It's tilted by 23 degrees and so we have summer and winter. We have periods of the year where the Northern Hemisphere is tilted towards the Sun and period s of the year where the Southern Hemisphere is tilted towards the Sun. That changes that obliquity angle and so there are some times of the year where the polar region in the north doesn't get any direct sunshine at all and conversely 6 months later the Southern Hemisphere, Antarctica doesn't get any direct sunshine at all. We have periods of darkness. That's an uneven heating seasonally that warms the Northern Hemisphere and Southern Hemisphere at different times of the year. That's the cause of the seasons. Remember seasons aren't because we get closer to the Sun and further away; they're because of the angle that Earth makes with the direction to the Sun.

We can think of a hypothetical atmospheric circulation on earth due to this uneven solar heating only. You would have rising warm, presumably humid air from evaporation at the tropical regions that would rise up to the upper atmosphere. It would spread towards the polar regions and then it would get colder as it goes to the upper atmosphere and moves toward the poles and then descends back again because the cold air at the poles would become denser and warmer so you have descending air near the poles and then flowing back along somewhere down near the ground surface from the polar region back towards the tropical regions, back towards the equatorial regions.

This would form a giant convection cell in each hemisphere, much like convection in a pot of boiling water or maybe more precisely or more aptly imagine a room that has nothing in it except a radiator on one side of the room and a cold window on the other side of the room. Warm air rises off the radiator, would spread over the top of the ceiling of the room until it got near the cold window, which would cool it back down, and that would cause that cold air to fall and sink and so you'd get a convection current or a convection cell forming inside that room. It turns out that these giant hypothetical convection cells on earth really don't exist. They don't exist because there's one more really important complicating factor and that is the Coriolis effect.

First described by Gustave de Coriolis in 1835, we have the fact that Earth is rotating, modifying any flow of anything, any freely moving object on Earth doesn't flow in a nice, simple direction the way we would maybe like it to, especially if we're in a freshman physics course or something like that. Everything on earth that's in motion is fundamentally affected by the fact that Earth is rotating and it's rotating in a specific direction. It's rotating always eastward. The Coriolis effect deflects objects.

Let's take a look at how that works. First of all, let's imagine a kind of analogy to the planet, something simpler like a merry-go-round on a children's playground with some kids sitting on it and then trying to throw a ball back and forth to each other. The merry-go-round starts to spin. They're in a spinning reference frame, a rotating reference frame, if one throws the ball then the ball already has the angular momentum, the speed of the merry-go-round, so it will fly across to the other side, but of course during the time that it flies across to the other side then the merry-go-round continues to move. To an observer that's outside looking down from the top or something like that, you can see that the ball flies in a straight line path, but to the kids who are on the merry-go-round when the ball is thrown it looks like it veers off to one side, veers off in one direction and flies in a strange and unexpected path. It makes it hard to actually catch the ball. It's not going where you expect it to.

That rotational effect on the path of a moving object is exactly what's happening on Earth. The earth is spinning on its axis and Earth is fat in the middle. The largest diameter is at the equator and then if you think about the way it's rotating then if you imagine an imaginary disk at a constant line of latitude through Earth, any particular place at different lines of latitude the further north or the further south you go from the equator is spinning around a smaller distance, go all the way to the north pole and things are literally just turning around a very tiny, little circle just inches away from the North Pole. It's just inches long.

It takes 24 hours to go all the way around one full turn no matter where you go on earth. The upshot of that is then that a place that's far to the north, let's say Madison, Wisconsin is rotating through a much smaller circle and with a smaller velocity than a place on the equator somewhere. We're moving at different speeds depending on where we are north or south on the planet. What that means is that a moving object is apparently deflected to people on the surface of Earth, much like the merry-go-round because of those different velocities.

If I'm standing there in Madison, Wisconsin and I happen to have an intercontinental ballistic missile at my disposal and I get angry at one of my colleagues in South America somewhere on the equator then I launch my ICBM. If I launch it directly due south at a place that's due south of where I'm located well it won't land there because during the time it's in motion the equatorial region will move further eastward than I will at my high northern latitude spot, 43 degrees north or so. It will apparently look like it's veering off to the right as it moves southward. In that case it would be veering off to the west. If instead the ICBM was launched the other direction it would also look like it veered off to the right because that missile would have that angular momentum and move further eastward than the part to the north of it. You have materials that in the Northern Hemisphere always look like they're veering to the right due to the Coriolis effect on these moving objects.

In the Southern Hemisphere, the effect is the same but opposite. Everything looks like it deflects to the west. If you're moving from south to north in the Northern Hemisphere it goes eastward, but if you're moving from north to south it's still to the right and that means it deflects westward. Interestingly, the Coriolis effect is zero at the equator. If you're absolutely perfectly on the equator and move in a direction that's right along the equator, there is no Coriolis effect. In general, the Coriolis effect is relatively weak when you're near the equatorial regions. This is going to be really important for understanding the flow of air and water. It's strongest near the poles due to the rapid change in the amount of that rotational velocity.

The air in motion then in the atmosphere is affected by the Coriolis effect as well. As the air rises, let's say in the tropical and equatorial regions from the warm air rising phenomenon that I've already described. It moves poleward, but it's deflected to the right in the Northern Hemisphere and to the left in the southern. It doesn't make it all the way to the poles. It makes it up a certain distance then it gets cold enough and then the air starts to sink again. North of that then there's actually another system like that that gets setup from cool air sinking and warm air rising.

The atmosphere is broken down into or is sort of develops a number of different circulation cells. They're driven by convection, it's just they're not as simple as without the Coriolis effect. We basically can break down circulation on the planet into some very large, well-developed cells that have actually been given specific names because they're persistent on the surface of the planet. From the equator to about 30 degrees north latitude and 30 degrees south latitude or the kind of symmetrical Hadley cells. From 30 degrees to 60 degrees north, there are the Ferrel cells and then above 60 all the way to 90 degrees north or 90 degrees south are the Polar cells, so 30 degree divisions, 3 parts in each hemisphere, 6 sets of cells overall, kind of govern the generalized airflow pattern in the planet. We call these atmospheric circulation cells, the Hadley cells, the Ferrel cells, and the Polar cells.

The cells themselves are airflow and so the part of the cells that are at low altitude, the parts of the cells that are along the surface of Earth are the prevailing winds. They're give the names of specific kinds of winds because they're typical winds that flow to move the air to fulfill the circulation, the convection circulation, in these cells. There's also upper atmospheric flow that goes along with it to keep the cells moving. The subtropical trade winds, the temperate westerlies, and the polar easterlies are all the low altitude arms of these major atmospheric cells.

What is wind? I just started talking about wind. We know what it feels like when the wind blows. What's making the wind blow? It's blowing because of pressure differences. It's as simple as that. Air simply flows from zones of high pressure to zones of low pressure so when you see the weather report and you see them talking about a high pressure cell or a low pressure cell if you know there's a high pressure region nearby, especially coming into your area then you're likely in for a windy day. That air is going to flow out of that high pressure region to a lower pressure region.

The rising warm and humid air creates a low pressure; the sinking cold and dry air creates a high pressure. That drives, for example, the sinking cold air that's moved eastward is now coming back towards the rising warm tropical air that's moving westward and so we have the trade winds. We have the air circulation in the subtropical regions that moves from the northeast towards the southwest. Where air is ascending and descending between the cells then we have a different condition because we have regions where calm air prevails, where winds aren't strong. Instead of these prevailing strong trade winds or westerlies that occur associated with the interiors of the Hadley and Ferrel cells, we instead have regions that we call the Intertropical Convergence Zone, ITCZ, or maybe more poetically the equatorial doldrums.

When we're in the doldrums, we're in regions of calm air where nothing much is happening. These are the places where the warm, humid air is ascending. Most of the air flow is relatively slow, but is mostly vertical and so instead of feeling strong prevailing winds, we just feel calm air. There are also regions that have heavy rainfall because of that warm, humid air is dropping a lot of water vapor as it gets aloft, as it gets high.

Similarly then the boundary between the Hadley and Ferrel cells around 30 and 35 degrees north, right in that region around that 30 degree north band lies something that are called the horse latitudes, a place where the cool, dry air descends. On land, this produces very persistent high pressure zones that tend to be very dry. The big deserts of the world virtually all lie in this 30 to 35 degree north or south belt, the Sahara or the Gobi desert in Asia, some of the driest places on earth.

In the ocean, it produces areas where the winds are calm and the salinity can be high because there's very little rainfall. The name horse latitudes actually is a mariners term and at least lore, it's not completely clear whether that's true or not, lore suggests that they're called the horse latitudes because during big ocean crossings in the days of sailing there would be areas both in the northern and Southern Hemisphere where ships would become becalmed for long periods of time. If they were transporting horses then they needed to keep the horses watered; water was a scarce commodity on a ship in those days and so sometimes they couldn't afford to keep the horses and would literally toss them overboard in an effort to basically be humane to the horse that were going to die of thirst out at sea. They needed to save the water for the people to move across the ocean.

We have the zones of intertropical conversions and the horse latitudes as zones where the wind doesn't blow very strongly. The winds in between are the important governing winds that move ocean currents around and also have moved mariners around the sea for a very long time. Just jumping back to those for a second, we call the trade winds easterlies remember, because winds are named by the direction that they come from as opposed to the direction that they blow. That seems confusing to a lot of people. Trade winds come from the east, actually they sort of come from the northeast to the southwest. They're called easterlies. Surface winds are the Hadley cells. They're centered around 15 degrees north and south latitude.

The westerlies by contrast are the surface winds of the Ferrel cells. They're centered around 45 degrees north and south latitude. In the Polar Regions, up at 70 or more north and south, we have the polar easterlies as well. It's becoming very simple geometry. The boundaries are at 30, 60, 90 and then those strong winds are centered at 15, 45, sort of 75. Wind in general blows due to pressure differences in the air. It's actually variable all the time. We know the wind isn't constant, even in the ocean, even in the trade winds regions, it's not constant. It blows in different ways on different days of the year and the wind pattern is a constantly changing, modifying thing on the planet because atmosphere flow is complicated. It has turbulence in it. There are pressure differences all over the place and so the wind blows due to those pressure differences.

Nevertheless, these wind patterns are persistent on average year after year. That's how the trade winds and the westerlies have gotten the name prevailing winds. The winds that prevail most of the time and you can count on to be present more often than not in various parts of the world. In the days of sailing ships, mariners depended very specifically on knowledge of these wind bands in the calm regions, not only to get around, but also as part of their navigational strategy, essentially for understanding where they were north and south and moving across the oceans when they were dependent on winds at all times. We've talked about and heard about ships being becalmed in different locations.

We have a piece of information, the tool to understand why it is that Columbus, the discoverer or America, actually never set foot in North America. As you know, he landed on the island of Hispaniola. He was in the Caribbean, he never came to the mainland of North America in his entire lifetime. He left Portugal and they knew that they had to sail across the Atlantic Ocean. The first thing they did was head south along the African coast until they reached the latitude of about 15 degrees or so where they got into the trade wind belt. They rode the trade winds westward across the Atlantic Ocean in order to just go west. They basically tried to get a line of latitude. They used their navigational tools like their sextants or astronomical observations to stay on that belt, stay in the trade winds and move right across the ocean. When they got to the far side at that latitude, what they hit was not Florida and not the east coast of the United States, but the coast of the island of Hispaniola and other islands in the Caribbean.

Once Columbus' group left and wanted to go back then to Europe they needed to get away from the trade winds because that would be a hard thing to sail against the wind so instead they first moved northward and tracked up north far enough to move out of the trade winds and begin to pick up the westerlies that would give them prevailing winds that would bring them back to Europe. Columbus didn't go very far north and had some trouble on the way back from being in some of the more becalmed seas. Eventually the pattern of trade flow, as we saw in Ben Franklin's map way back in the early part of the course was such that the sailing ships would travel to the south and move across as far south as they could get away with and then catch the gulfstream and then ultimately the prevailing westerlies to make it back to Europe or move to Europe going in that direction. These prevailing winds have been an important part in navigation over very long periods of time.

We've taken a look now at the fundamentals of atmospheric circulation on the planet, but we're going to see very soon that this is the underpinning we need in order to understand all kinds of things about the circulation that actually happens in the ocean. We're going to take a look in the next lecture at major ocean storm events, things like hurricanes and tropical storms, typhoons, and we'll see that those are governed by the interaction of the trade winds with the heat in the ocean. We'll also take a look at big events like El Nino and Southern Oscillation as it's called and see how that's a linkage between the atmospheres and both the currents and the heat flow in the ocean itself.

We'll ultimately find that the great currents of the oceans are driven in a similar way to the waves by the winds that blow at the surface of Earth. Ultimately all of it, atmospheric circulation and oceanic circulation is governed by the transport of heat on the surface of the planet. That transport of heat is going to concern us for several lectures because we'll look at how the ocean is the major player, not just a major player, but the major player in the global climate system that keeps the climate on earth as it is and makes it a temperate place to live for life both in the sea and life on land and ultimately how that climate system in the ocean is changing with changes in the amount of heat input and retained to the global atmospheric system. All of it is linked in an intimate way in terms of understanding the water planet as a whole.

Heavy Weather—Storms and Hurricanes
Lecture 29

Differences in pressure between air masses and differences in heat energy between ocean and atmosphere cause major storms. Extratropical cyclones form at the boundary between Ferrel and polar cells. Tropical cyclones form within one air mass, fueled by the storage and release of latent heat by evaporation and condensation. Hurricanes build in intensity over warm ocean water, dissipate over cooler water and land, and move in predictable ways. The destructive power of hurricanes is in the force of the wind, the intensity of rainfall, and the storm surge that raises local sea level in front of the storm.

Major Atmospheric Storms

- Between the ocean and the atmosphere exist the air masses that drive the major atmospheric storms—from large-scale pressure cells that create gales to various kinds of extratropical cyclones and ultimately even hurricanes and typhoons.

- The sea breezes and land breezes at the coast exist due to a differential amount of temperature change of the land and the ocean during the day when they're both being heated by the Sun equally because of the different thermal capacity and thermal inertia of water versus the land.

- During enormous monsoon seasons of the Himalayas in India and the entire South Asian region, up to 425 inches of rain can fall over areas of India during the summer months.

- **Monsoons** develop for similar reasons as daily sea breezes. The ocean off shore in this subtropical region is relatively warm and very moist. It carries a lot of water vapor. It's being pulled in and then rising up the mountain front, where it's expanding because

Torrential rains that form as a result of the monsoon season cause major flooding during the summer months in India.

of the decrease in pressure as elevation increases and dumping torrential rainfall. It's the changing pressure over the land sucking air in, and all the water that goes with it, off of the ocean.

- Conversely, the pattern reverses in the wintertime. Dry winters occur as dry air sinks off the Himalayan mountains and the Tibetan plateau—the exact same process of differential thermal inertia between the water and the landscape.

Storm Systems

- Storms are disturbances in large-scale flow patterns. Virtually all of the major storms, both winter and summertime storms, that we see in our parts of the world are cyclones, which are rotating masses of low-pressure air.

- All storm systems—hurricanes, northeasters, wintertime gales—have the same characteristics.

- Cyclones can form between 2 different air masses or at the boundaries between different air masses that have very different characteristics. They are bodies of air—with somewhat fuzzy boundaries—that have relatively uniform properties.

- Density drives pressure and therefore drives wind and air flow. Density is a function of the temperature of the air and the humidity in the air. Air masses get either relatively low density or relatively high density and form areas of relatively high pressure or relatively low pressure. Once they acquire these properties, air masses can maintain them for a number of days or weeks.

- The boundaries between the air masses are what meteorologists call fronts, which are areas of a large gradient in density and, therefore, a large gradient or change in pressure. When a front comes through, the wind blows very strongly because the air is rapidly changing in pressure—from low to high or high to low—in a particular region.

Extratropical Cyclones

- **Extratropical cyclones** are the famous winter storms called northeasters; extratropical cyclones form at the boundaries between 2 of the different major atmospheric circulation cells.

- An example of an extratropical cyclone is the record-setting weather that occurred in April of 2007 that affected the entire New England region as well as Canada and regions in Europe.

- Another example of a famous northeaster or extratropical cyclone is the one that became documented by the book *The Perfect Storm*: a 1990 storm that was a convergence of more than one extratropical-style cyclone in the northern Atlantic Ocean.

- In the Ferrel cell, the predominant wind patterns are westerly, which come across the North American continent and move toward the east. The colder air of the polar cell moves predominately from east to west.

- There's a strong front that commonly develops between the westerlies and easterlies at what's called the polar front. In a low region of air pressure, winds will tend to converge in that low. The westerlies will converge toward the low from the south, and the easterlies will converge toward the low from the north, rotating or twisting up the polar front.

- Cyclone storms can dump a lot of water, which is damaging in the form of heavy rainfall or snowfall in a region, but oceanographically speaking, one of the biggest effects is the development of a storm surge.

- As the wind blows across the water, it moves the water. If the wind moves in one direction long enough and strong enough, it will create a pile or hill of water in front of the storm.

Tropical Cyclones

- **Tropical cyclones** begin in tropical regions, and when they become strong enough, they attain the names hurricanes or typhoons.

- Tropical cyclones form within one air mass—not at the boundary between 2—and they're fueled by the tremendous amount of evaporation that's possible in a warm, tropical ocean.

- Tropical cyclones are essentially giant heat engines: They are individual masses of humid, warm, rotating air. They form initially as tropical depressions or low-pressure zones in the trade winds, and they form within one air mass over the ocean between 10° and 25° latitude—either north or south of the equator.

- In order to become full-blown tropical cyclones, these masses have to move over water at a temperature that's greater than about 26°C, which is quite warm water in the ocean.

- As tropical depressions form, they form a little bit of low pressure. Once the low pressure forms, then they can turn into tropical storms and ultimately cyclones.

- Tropical storms occur if the wind speeds are less than about 120 kilometers per hour, but they become hurricanes if the wind speed exceeds 120 kilometers per hour. A hurricane is what we call it in the Atlantic Ocean, but the same type of storm is called a typhoon in the Pacific Ocean.

- Hurricanes have a low-pressure core, and the wind comes in from all directions to try to fill in that low-pressure core. Hurricanes build in intensity over warm ocean water because evaporation continues to keep the pressure at the center low. If hurricanes move over cooler water or land, they will tend to dissipate because they lose that heat field.

- Tropical cyclones form in the tropical Atlantic Ocean—in the middle of the ocean between Africa and the Caribbean region. Tropical cyclones also form in the tropical Pacific Ocean—in the eastern Pacific near Baja, California, and in the western Pacific near the Philippines and Indonesia. Tropical cyclones form in the Southern Hemisphere as well, although they don't form to the same profusion as in the Northern Hemisphere.

- Once they form, tropical cyclones are masses of air that swirl in the Northern Hemisphere in a clockwise manner. As they move with the trade winds, they move in a western direction but will start to turn to the right—just as everything does—due to the Coriolis effect. Tropical cyclones always track westward and in the Northern Hemisphere, turn northward, and bend around.

- In the Northern Hemisphere, tropical cyclones rotate counterclockwise; in the Southern Hemisphere, they rotate clockwise because of the opposite Coriolis forces in that region.

Hurricanes

- The center of a hurricane is the region where an ultralow pressure develops and where water is evaporated off the surface of the ocean very quickly because it's so hot. As this moisture is picked up, it spirals up out of the air mass and exits at the top, dropping massive amounts of water vapor as it reaches the higher altitude levels of the atmosphere.

- The absolute center of the hurricane is called the eye of the hurricane, which is where the weather can actually be calm and clear.

- Hurricanes can have a structure of up to 1000 kilometers in diameter and 15 kilometers tall. The rainbands are rapidly spiraling clouds, copious rain of up to several inches an hour that move with the trade winds east to west.

- The year of Hurricane Katrina, 2005, was the world-record hurricane season for the Atlantic Ocean. This is because the heat generated by an incredibly strong high-temperature zone just happened to be present in the Gulf of Mexico at that particular time of the year in that particular year.

- Hurricane intensity is categorized by using the Saffir-Simpson hurricane scale, which categorizes hurricanes as a 1 through 5, depending on wind strength. A category 1 hurricane has to have winds that travel at speeds higher than 155 miles per hour, and a category 3 has to fall between 111 and 130 miles per hour, for example.

- The destructive power of hurricanes lies in the force of the wind and the intensity of the rainfall. More than anything else, the destructive power of hurricanes is experienced in the storm surge that raises the local sea level in front of the storm.

During Hurricane Ike in 2008, the barrier islands along the region around Galveston, Texas, had tremendous damage from storm surges.

- In the case of Hurricane Katrina, the city of New Orleans, Louisiana, was inundated by flooding as levees failed—not from the direct rainfall of the hurricane, but from the oceanic storm surge that pushed the water in and overwhelmed the city's levee defenses.

- The biggest tsunami are probably more destructive and bigger features than the largest hurricanes. However, hurricanes are somewhat more frequent.

- A storm surge, and the high waves associated with it, drives barrier-island migration over time. A huge amount of sediment transport occurs in the biggest storm events such as hurricanes and typhoons.

- Galveston, Texas, was hit by a hurricane in 1900 that was the worst natural disaster in U.S. history in terms of loss of life, even exceeding the losses that resulted from Hurricane Katrina.

- After 1900, a seawall was built called the Galveston seawall, one of the largest civil-engineering projects that had ever been undertaken at the time it was built. This seawall worked as designed during Hurricane Ike a full century later.

Important Terms

extratropical cyclone: Rotating mass of air formed by the disturbance of the boundary between polar and Ferrell cells; includes the northeasters.

monsoon: Seasonal weather pattern typified by heavy rain resulting from onshore flow of warm, humid air drawn in by rising air heated over mountain ranges in the summer, especially in the Indian subcontinent and Himalayan mountain front.

tropical cyclone: Rotating mass of tropical, low-pressure air with heavy winds and rainfall fueled by sea-surface heat; includes hurricanes and typhoons.

Suggested Reading

Emanuel, *Divine Wind*.

Sheets and Williams, *Hurricane Watch*.

Questions to Consider

1. A storm surge is sometimes called a storm tide. In what sense is it similar to and/or different from a tide?

2. Hurricanes and typhoons can be described as being heat engines. Where is the heat coming from and going to as a hurricane moves through an area of the ocean?

Heavy Weather—Storms and Hurricanes
Lecture 29—Transcript

In the last lecture, I painted the general picture of atmospheric circulation and flow, the prevailing winds, and the stable atmospheric cells of convective circulation. Now let's take a look at what happens when that becomes pathological, when it interacts with the ocean surface to produce all sorts of stormy weather. We're going to see that the differences in pressure between the air masses themselves are packages of air that get some stable characteristics and differences in heat energy. Between the ocean and the atmosphere are the things that really drive the major atmospheric storms from large-scale pressure cells that create gales to various kinds of extra-tropical cyclones and ultimately even hurricanes and typhoons.

Before we get into the storms, let's look a little bit at gentler weather patterns because we need to understand some things about the differential heating of both land and ocean. We can see weather cycles that range from the basic coastal daily breezes that we see at the seashore, the onshore and offshore breezes, to things as large as the tropical monsoon seasons of the Southeast Asian region. All this functions of differential heating of the land and the ocean.

The sea breezes and land breezes that we experience at the coast. Sometimes the thing that makes it so pleasant to be at the beach when just a few miles inland the temperature can be hot and very humid or very uncomfortable. There's a differential amount of temperature change of the land and the ocean during the day when they're both being heated by the Sun equally because of the different thermal capacity and thermal inertia of water versus the soil and the landscape and the vegetation on the land. Remember that we said water had a tremendous heat capacity and also a tremendous amount of thermal inertia so when the Sun shines during the daytime it heats the land up more than it heats the water up. As the land heats up from the Sun shining on it, it heats the air just above the land, the immediate atmosphere above the land. That warming air becomes less dense and starts to rise. It rises up to higher parts of the atmosphere.

If there's an adjacent coastline, the ocean is remaining cooler. It's getting heated by the Sun too, but it doesn't rise in temperature nearly so quickly. As that happens then, the water or the air above the ocean comes streaming in to replace the air that's rising over the land. We pull it air from the ocean. We get a breeze that comes in onto the land, sometimes that cool and perhaps a little bit humid air that's coming in off of the ocean as it meets the land produces the dense sea fogs that we see and San Francisco, for example, is so famous for even during summery weather, this cool and humid and foggy air that's coming in off the sea.

At night, the whole process reverses itself. The sea is warm. The land cools down quickly because it doesn't have very good thermal inertia, very good thermal capacity and so the air sinks. The cool air sinks off of the land, flows down off the land, and moves back out to sea and flows out over the ocean where that cool relatively dry air that's come from the land interacts with the warm air from over the ocean, which then is rising off shore and putting the water vapor in the atmosphere that ultimately turns back into fog for the next day. All this process is driven on a more or less diurnal basis, day to night shifts.

If we look at a much larger scale seasonal instead of daily, we can see something very similar going on driving the enormous monsoon seasons of the Himalayas in India and the entire South Asian region. We've all seen images of the flooding in India during these very seasonal torrential rains of the monsoon, up to 425 inches of rain can fall over areas of India specifically from April to October so essentially during the summer months. What's going on with the monsoons?

They develop for similar reasons as those daily sea breezes. The Himalayan Mountains are a region of both high altitude and also large land area. During the summer months, we see regions where the Sun is warming up the land and it's causing air to flow up over the land of India, up over the mountains of the Himalayans and rise high into the atmosphere. That rising warm air from the land is drawing in air from off shore. Now the ocean off shore in this subtropical region is relatively warm and certainly very moist. It carries a lot of water vapor. It's being pulled in and then rising up the mountain front where it's expanding because of the decrease in pressure as you go to higher elevation and dumping those torrential rain falls. It's the changing pressure over the land sucking air in and all the water that goes with it off of the ocean.

Conversely in the winter time then the pattern reverses. The landscape becomes much cooler. The ocean is still retaining warmth so the rising air over the ocean is what's carrying things out. The air flow reverses essentially. Dry winters happen as dry air sinks off the Himalayan Mountains and the Tibetan plateau. The whole monsoon season then just varies back and forth, but essentially the exact same process of differential thermal inertia between the water and the landscape.

Storms are disturbances in all these large-scale flow patterns. Let's turn our attention to what happens when the atmospheric circulation goes awry. We develop pressure differences in the atmosphere and those pressure differences take on some fairly specific forms that we want to take a look at in a certain amount of detail. Virtually all storms, all of the really major storms that we want to consider, both winter and summertime storms that we see in our parts of the world are cyclones. They're rotating masses of low pressure air. Hurricanes nor'easters, wintertime gales, all of these different storm systems have the same characteristic. When we look at the radar maps, whether it's during summer thunderstorm season or whether it's during the winter and big storm seasons, we often see these cyclonic or rotating, cycling masses of air and bands of clouds that can produce rainfall or snowfall and things like that.

Cyclones can form both between two different air masses, and we'll see what the air masses are in a moment, or they can form at the boundaries within different air masses that have very different characteristics. What is an air mass? We think of air as just a fluid and so it continuously smoothly varies everywhere. Actually they're bodies of air, obviously with somewhat fuzzy boundaries, but bodies of air nonetheless that have relatively uniform properties. By properties, I primarily mean density because that's what as we've seen drives pressure and therefore drives wind and drives air flow.

The density is a function of the temperature of the air and the humidity in the air than that of water vapor in the air. Air masses get either relatively low density or relatively high density and form areas of relatively high pressure or relatively low pressure. Air masses once they acquire those properties can maintain them for longer than you might think, a number of days or even weeks at times when air is not moving all that much because the atmosphere is just so vast certain regions will acquire characteristics like a cold mass of dry air or a warm humid mass of air.

The boundaries between the air masses are what meteorologists call fronts so just simply areas of large gradient in density and therefore large gradient or change in pressure. When we say a front comes through we think of it as the wind blows very strongly because we're rapidly changing in air pressure from low to high or high to low in a particular region. These boundaries can be pretty sharply defined. I mean we've seen them all on radar maps and things like that and that's because the air masses do retain their characteristics and only mix relatively slowly at the scale of weather development.

These cyclones then, we'll talk about 2 different kinds. We'll talk about tropical cyclones, the thing that the name maybe applies more commonly in our minds to, which as the name implies occur in tropical regions, start in tropical regions, and when they get strong enough as we'll see they get the names hurricanes or typhoons or even willy-willies and other strange names like that, but are all really just different names for the same thing. We'll take those up in a second. First we're going to talk about extratropical cyclones, a term we don't maybe hear about so often, but at least here in North America we do hear a lot about the famous winter storms called nor'easters. We'll take a look at how these extratropical cyclones form at the boundaries between 2 different of the major atmospheric circulation cells that I defined in the last lecture.

The extratropical cyclones are great cyclonic or rotating storms, but they really form in a fundamentally different way than the hurricanes and the tropical storms. These can be very damaging, very noticeable storms and they involve both the land and the ocean for their formation. An example of an extratropical cyclone is the record-setting weather that happened in April of 2007. It affected the whole New England region as well as Canada and regions all the way out extending over to Europe as this large extratropical cyclone, nor'easter spun up. It blew huge amounts of snowfall and rainfall and ice storms across the New England region, knocked out power to huge areas and millions of customers, but also brought with it a very large storm surge and wave damage all along the coastline.

We'll take a look at that in just a second. Another example of a famous nor'easter or extratropical cyclone is the one that became documented by the book *The Perfect Storm,* the book and the movie, *Perfect Storm*, which was a 1990 storm that was a convergence of more than one extratropical style cyclone in the northern Atlantic Ocean. How do these things form?

Remember that we have the Ferrel cell where the predominant wind patterns are westerly, so coming across the North American continent and moving towards the east and then the colder air of the Polar cell, which is moving predominately from east to west. It's an easterly current of air flow.

There's a strong front that commonly develops between the 2 regions, the westerlies and easterlies at what's called the polar front and especially in the wintertime that can be a well-developed front with very cold air masses further to the north. That front is not a perfect line of latitude. It tends to have undulations in it and it will tend to also have variability in terms of slight differences in pressure, low and high. As those pressure differences happen and as the front meanders a little bit what can happen is a low region can start to develop and in a low region of air pressure then winds will tend to converge in that low. The westerlies will converge towards the low from the south. The easterlies will converge towards the low from the north and they will start a rotating or start twisting up the polar front itself into a shape that quickly starts to attain this counterclockwise shark fin like shape in the front and then ultimately a kind of spiraling twist.

What happens then is that the cold air masses are dense and they sink in or wedge in below along fronts beneath the warm air mass that's coming from the Ferrel cell westerlies that rises up aloft from that. They'll pick up warm humid air from those westerlies. They'll quickly rise aloft as the cold air wedges in beneath them pushing them up, causing them to decrease in pressure, and drop their moisture, their humidity in the form of rainfall. The rainfall can begin. The extratropical cyclones typically start in either the general gulf coast region or further to the north, but still west across North America for the case of the nor'easters and then they spin up and begin to pick up energy as they move across the continent. If they happen to make it out into the North Atlantic then the relatively warm gulfstream waters will fuel some additional humidity into the system, but it's still dominated by this cold air swirling that's moving downward and encroaching from the Polar cells.

The combination of that humid air with all of this cold air and moving humid air aloft produces the phenomenal amount of rainfall and then low pressure that generates the winds that drive the whole extratropical cyclone and spin it up as it twists the polar front into the cyclonic storm itself. The cyclone storms can dump a lot of water and that's certainly damaging in the form of rainfall or heavy snowfall in the region, but oceanically speaking or oceanographically speaking one of the biggest effects is the development of a storm surge. As the winds blow, we know that winds move water in the form of generating waves and things like that, when the winds develop a very strong pattern in the flow of a cyclonic storm then the winds push the water ahead of the storm system itself. The wind blowing across the water moves water and if it's moving in one direction long enough and strong enough it will create a pile or a hill of water in front of the storm.

When that storm surge, as it's called, reaches the coastline then it can surge up. There're often high waves generated so you have both a general rise in the water level over an area of hundreds or thousands of square miles of ocean surface and then waves on top of that. They broke in in the case of the 2007 storms and did lots of damage to coastal properties and overtopped seawalls all over the New England region along the Maine coast and Massachusetts coast for example. If they come right on top of a high tide as well that just exacerbates the problem. In 2007, that's exactly what happened.

Tropical cyclones, by contrast, are really kind of different animals because they form within one air mass, not at the boundary between 2 and they're really fueled by the tremendous amount of evaporation that's possible in a warm tropical ocean. Tropical cyclones, we can see are essentially giant heat engines. They're using the ocean as a battery that's fueling heat into them and we'll see that that's because of the storage and release of the oceanic latent heat by evaporation and then recondensation when the heat gets up into the atmosphere in the form of generating water droplets and rainfall.

Let's take a closer look at these tropical cyclones then. They are individual masses of humid, warm rotating air as we know. They rotate. They form initially as tropical depressions or low pressure zones in the trade winds and so they form within one air mass over the ocean between 10 degrees and 25 degrees latitude, either north or south of the equator. In order to become full-blown tropical cyclones they have to move over water that's greater in temperature than about 26° C, 79 Fahrenheit, so quite warm water in the ocean. That's because that water facilitates the rapid evaporation of lots of water at the surface, which creates warm, very humid, very low density air that rises aloft quickly and lowers the pressure at the center of the storm. You get a low pressure developing.

Let's take a look at one of these tropical depressions looks like. In this satellite image of the trade wind belt moving across central parts of Africa, we can see that the trade winds are blowing and as they pick up humidity in different places they first just develop areas where maybe you see a little bit of cloud formation and things like that. The small eddies and waves, small variations again in pressure from low to high in those tropical depressions in a way that's a little bit obscure starts forming concentrated zones within that belt of low pressure. They're in the waves of easterly winds and the low pressure and high pressure form what we call the easterly waves in the trade winds or the easterly winds.

As those tropical depressions form they form a little bit of low pressure. Once the low pressure forms then they can turn into tropical storms and ultimately cyclones. We can see a nice satellite image of those storms forming up and spinning up going from tropical depression, which is really just a low pressure meteorological phenomenon into an actual full-blown cyclonic storm. This image happens to come from the Atlantic in 2008 as Hurricanes Ike and Josephine were forming up.

These tropical cyclones form up over this low pressure area and they become just by definition tropical storms if the wind speeds are less than about 120 kilometers an hour, but they become hurricanes if the wind speed exceeds 120 kilometers an hour. A hurricane is what we call it in the Atlantic Ocean. A typhoon in the Pacific Ocean is exactly the same thing. It's just a different name for the same phenomenon. Globally speaking we simply call them tropical cyclones, all these terms are equivalent. The Australian Southern Hemisphere equivalent is the willy-willy, but it all amounts to the same storm phenomenon everywhere.

The hurricanes have a low pressure core and the wind comes in from all directions to try to fill in that low pressure core. The hurricanes build in intensity over the warm ocean water because as long as they're over that warm ocean water, greater than 26 degrees, evaporation will keep the pressure at the center low. We see very low pressures at the centers of all tropical cyclones and the larger the tropical cyclone the lower the pressure tends to be at the center. If they move over cooler water or land then they will tend to dissipate because they lose that heat field. They lose that heat engine at the base of them. They move overall in predictable ways because those directions are governed by the winds at the time and the pressure differences and also the temperature differences at the ocean surface.

Let's take a look at where tropical cyclones form. We have a general idea that yes they form in the tropical Atlantic Ocean out in the middle of the ocean somewhere between Africa and the Caribbean region. Again, that's in these disturbances in the easterly wind areas. They also do the same thing in the tropical Pacific Ocean in the eastern Pacific near Baja, California let's say and the Mexican mainland and also in the western Pacific near the Philippines and Indonesia and so on. They're formed in the Southern Hemisphere as well although not to the same profusion as in the Northern Hemisphere, just for reasons of meteorological differences with less land in the Southern Hemisphere. They're certainly present in the south Pacific and to the Australian region or even in the Indian Ocean affecting the eastern coast of Africa.

All of them once they form are masses of air that are swirling like this in the Northern Hemisphere in a clockwise way. As they move with the trade winds they move in a western direction, but unless they're moving perfectly west, if they're veering at all in latitude then they will start to turn to the right just as everything does with the Coriolis forces. When we look at the track lines of many different hurricanes over time, or many different tropical storms. They always track westward and in the Northern Hemisphere turn northward and bend around. They'll either come into the Gulf of Mexico and Texas region or bend northwards across the mid-continent or sometimes come up along Florida and right back out to the Atlantic Ocean affecting the east coast either more or less depending on how rapidly they're moving and therefore how rapidly they're turning to the right as they go.

They have very specific storm tracks. The typhoons in the western Pacific do exactly the same thing. They're spawned in the western Pacific region and they have very constant tracks that carry them up past the Philippines, Taiwan, and into the Japanese islands region very typically. Many typhoons per season are generated in that region just as a number of hurricanes per season tend to be generated in the Atlantic region. They're specifically formed though in the areas where the water can be warm enough to generate them. They're also not spawned within a few degrees of the equator north or south because the Coriolis forces are too weak in those regions to actually get the storm rotating and generate that ultra low pressure zone at the center of the storm.

That raises a question then, why do they rotate in the directions that they do? Northern Hemisphere tropical cyclones rotate counterclockwise. It seems like this is the wrong direction of rotation if we say that things always sort of bend to the right. That looks like a backwards rotation. The Coriolis force actually controls it as well, but it's in a way that might not be immediately obvious. If you have a low pressure zone at the center of the storm then what's happening to air masses around it is that the air is all trying to rush in to fill that low pressure. As the air rushes towards the low pressure though it always bends to the right with the Coriolis. That air coming in will veer essentially away from the center of the storm as it gets close. If it's coming from the south it'll veer eastward. If it's coming from the north it'll veer westward and so it starts that rotation that's going counterclockwise in the Northern Hemisphere. It's clockwise in the Southern Hemisphere because of the opposite Coriolis forcing in that region.

What's the internal anatomy of a hurricane actually look like? The center of the hurricane is the region where this ultra-low pressure develops, water's being evaporated off the surface of the ocean very quickly because it's so hot. The winds are blowing as they try to move into rush to fill that area so wind that has relatively low humidity is coming in, it's quite warm and it's being heated up even more. It's picking up moisture from the ocean. As it picks up that moisture, it then spirals up out of the spiraling air mass and exits at the top dropping massive amounts of water vapor as it reaches the higher altitude levels of the atmosphere.

The rain bands that form are the water vapor that was generated close to the center and then are dropped as rain and form these large convection cells that spiral around that central region. The absolute center of the hurricane as we all know is the eye of the hurricane where the weather can actually be calm and clear. As these winds are spiraling around that center, there's a point obviously that has to be right at the center where the wind is essentially not blowing at all and so we have calm, gentle winds. The only flow may be vertical; there may even be some down flow within that region of air from aloft that drops into the center and is more air that fuels that cell overall. Largely, the hurricane's eye is a very confined feature of just maybe a few miles or few tens of miles across compared to the hundreds or even thousand mile scale dimension of a really large hurricane.

They can have this kind of structure of up to 1000 kilometer diameter, 15 kilometers tall. The rain bands are these rapidly spiraling clouds, copious rain of up to several inches an hour and they're moving with the trade winds east to west. They're losing that energy if they move over land, but as long as they're over warm water, they're still fueled, the battery is still running the engine of the hurricane itself.

If we look at Hurricane Katrina as an example, 2005 was the world record hurricane season for the Atlantic Ocean, many named storms. They actually ran out of names at Z and had to start over again with the alphas and the zetas at the end of the season. Hurricane Katrina was the biggest one and certainly the most famous one that moved in from the Atlantic Ocean into the Caribbean region. It formed up into a Category 1 hurricane by the time it was east of the Florida Keys. It moved northward far enough to move just a little bit over Florida, made its way out into the Gulf of Mexico and then it rapidly intensified in strength. It moved up to a Category 3, 4, and 5 hurricane as it moved over the Gulf of Mexico.

The reason for that was the heat generated by an incredibly strong high temperature zone that was present in the Gulf of Mexico just by bad luck at that particular time of the year in that particular year. In the Gulf, there is a current that's called the Gulf Loop current. We'll take a look at that later on. It has a very high surface temperature and an especially high surface temperature in the summer of 2005. The satellite mapping of this temperature of the surface of the water in that Gulf Loop current shows you exactly where Hurricane Katrina picked up its excess strength and grew into a monstrous storm where near record sea surface temperatures were present at that time. Those warm surface temperatures directed it and veered it off towards the north where it went directly at essentially New Orleans or just to the east of New Orleans as opposed to heading off into Texas like some later hurricanes did, Rita for example.

I've just talked about the categories of different storms. Hurricane intensity is categorized; the Saffir-Simpson Scale is the name of the scale that we use that's 1 through 5. The details are maybe not important to us right now, but just recognize that the scale is directly based on a measurement of the wind strength of the hurricane. A category has to have more than 155 mile an hour winds, 135 knot winds at sea. A Cat 3 is 111 to 130. All of this is dependent though on the degree to which the center is low pressure and how low the pressure gets, at the center of the hurricane compared to the surrounding air masses, will determine the wind speed that's swirling up within that cyclonic storm. The destructive power of hurricanes then is in the force of the wind and the intensity of the rainfall. More than anything else, the destructive power of hurricanes is in the storm surge that raises the local sea level right there in front of the storm just as it is with the coastal effects of the nor'easters.

When Katrina came in and veered to the north and seemed to be heading directly for New Orleans there was the worry about a direct hit on the city of the center of the hurricane itself with the full fury of the rainfall. It veered a little bit north and eastward as it made landfall and initially there was actually a little bit of a sigh of relief if you remember that this hurricane hadn't quite hit the city, but it veered just a little bit to the east of the city. However, that initial sigh of relief just within a few hours was replaced by dismay as the full effects of the storm surge were seen. If we look at the sea surface of the mapping of the height of the sea surface at the time of the storm we can see from satellite imagery again that there was up to an 8 meter storm surge pushed by the winds on the leading edge of the hurricane.

If the hurricane is rotating in this counterclockwise fashion, that means compared to the eye, the right side is pushing water in front of it to the north. The left side was pushing water out to sea, to the south, so that water can circle around the hurricane out in the open ocean, but as it moved in towards the land that water that was being pushed by the right-hand or eastern side of the hurricane piled up against the coastline. It produced this very large storm surge that then sloshed westward into Lake Pontchartrain and so the city was inundated by flooding as the levies failed, not from the rainfall directly of the hurricane, but from the oceanic storm surge that pushed that water in and overwhelmed the city's levee defenses. The rainfall was really a secondary feature. That storm surge was even stronger further to the east as Pass Christian, Mississippi. It reached a height of something like 11.3 meters, a 37 foot storm surge.

Remember we talked about tsunami and the height of tsunami. An 11 meter tsunami would be quite a high one and only the largest and most destructive like the Indonesian tsunami or the Japan tsunami produced runups that are even higher than that. We saw as much as 30 to 38 meters of runup at the coastline in that Japan tsunami in 2011. This has been larger than the storm surges from even the largest hurricanes. On the other hand, they affect fairly comparable areas with their worst damage. Probably the biggest tsunami are more destructive and bigger features than the largest of hurricanes. But, hurricanes are somewhat more frequent.

If we look at storm surges then from other recent events, we've seen that the barrier islands that mark the Gulf coast so strongly, that are so well-developed along the Gulf coast also have been affected by storm surges from many, many hurricanes time and time again. That applies of course to the Florida Keys and other regions as well. The barrier islands that I showed you in the previous lecture along the region around Galveston and what's called the Bolivar Peninsula, just north of Galveston, had tremendous damage from storm surges especially in Hurricane Ike in 2008. We've probably seen these images from the news that show that the storm surge literally just washed right over the very low elevations of those barrier islands. It eroded away the coastal area.

If we take a look at these before and after images of that region around Gilchrist, Texas you can see not only that the waves washed over the land because of the storm surge and the high waves associated with it and washed away a lot of houses, but also moved a lot of sand up into areas that were formerly not beach. This would be the kind of event that drives barrier island migration over time. Barrier islands, in general, as sea level rises and things happen don't necessarily migrate absolutely steadily. The big sediment transport happens in the biggest storm events like the hurricanes and typhoons.

The region just to the south of that area that we just looked at is Galveston, Texas. Galveston had a hurricane in 1900. It didn't have a name; hurricanes weren't named at that time. There was little or no warning of hurricanes at that time because we didn't have the meteorology we have today. People were trapped in the city and many thousands of citizens were killed. It was actually the worst natural disaster in U.S. history in terms of loss of life, even exceeding what happened in Hurricane Katrina.

After that time, there was a seawall built, a very high seawall constructed over the 10 years or so after the 1900 hurricane in order to keep the storm surge out from Galveston Island. We've talked about some of the problems with seawalls and those problems are certainly still true, but in terms of protecting against the storm surge from a very large hurricane the Galveston seawall, one of the largest civil engineering projects that had ever been undertaken at the time it was built, pretty much worked as designed during Hurricane Ike a full century later. Many of the houses or all the houses that were behind the seawall were essentially okay. Some waves came over the top, but the real storm surge didn't erode away the island over the top of the seawall in Galveston.

By combining our understanding of the atmosphere, the surface waters, and how the heat energy is channeled in them, we've gained insight into the major weather patterns and storms on the planet. Now we have all these tools to see how heat drives flow in the atmosphere and the ocean, we're going to take a look next at how all these forces drive the oceanic scale currents out in the open sea.

The Gulf Stream to Gyres—Vast Surface Currents
Lecture 30

T
he major ocean currents move vast quantities of water and are driven by the persistent westerly and trade winds of the atmospheric cells. The phenomenon of Ekman transport induces rotary current systems in each ocean basin called gyres. Western boundary currents (e.g., Gulf Stream and Kuroshio) are the deepest and largest; they move warm, tropical water poleward in both hemispheres. Eastern boundary currents (e.g., Canary and California) are wider and shallower and move cold water toward the equator. Gyre currents affect only the uppermost few hundred meters of the ocean.

Ocean Currents

- Ocean currents can be broken down into surface currents and much slower deepwater transport.

- The major currents—the Gulf Stream and its counterparts, for example—are surface currents of the ocean that are caused mainly by wind friction directly on the sea surface and by differences in the density of different water masses.

- Surface currents affect the uppermost 10% of the world's ocean. The shallow, warmer, lower-density waters are the places where the surface currents live.

- Surface currents are induced primarily by the prevailing winds. The westerlies and the trade winds are the most important ones for understanding the big currents on the surface of the ocean. The trade winds blow from the northeast toward the southwest, and the westerlies blow from the southwest toward the northeast. Both are in different latitudinal bands.

- The water moves with the trade winds, but it doesn't move in the direction the trade winds blow, and the same goes for the westerlies. This is because of the Coriolis effect.

- The water moves much slower than the wind. When water moves either north or south, Earth rotates beneath it and causes Coriolis bending. If the water moves slower than the wind, Earth is rotating more for a given unit of time and causes the water to bend much more than the wind.

Direction of Surface Water Flow

- If the wind blows in a given direction, the water is deflected and starts moving at about a 45° angle to the overall direction of the surface wind. The wind sets the surface water in motion, but it sets the water in motion at an angle to the overall wind direction. **Ekman transport** describes the phenomenon in which the surface water blows with the wind at a 45° angle.

- As we look deeper and deeper in the water over the upper hundred meters, each successive depth moves in a different direction that keeps changing in a characteristic way that produces what's called an Ekman spiral. The water itself is not actually spiraling, but the vector, or the direction, that shows the way the water is moving starts out at an angle to the wind that with successive depths moves in slightly different directions.

- The overall effect is that there's a spiraling direction of transport of the water such that at approximately 100 meters depth, the water moves much more slowly than at the surface, but it's moving in the opposite direction.

- For the surface waters down to about 100 meters, the net direction of the transport is perpendicular to the wind direction. This is what sets the surface-ocean currents in motion.

- As they move, they bend to the right very sharply, developing these loops called oceanic gyres—the major loops of the ocean circulation pattern of the surface currents that are persistent and very large scale.

- There is one major gyre for the North Atlantic Ocean, one major gyre for the South Atlantic Ocean, and a couple of major gyres in the Pacific Ocean.

- The current flow and the Coriolis effect combined in the form of an Ekman spiral drives all the water toward the center of the gyre, forming a dynamically balanced hill in the water.

- The fact that gyres are dynamically balanced means that water is piled up by the Coriolis forces of the currents, but it wants to flow back down because gravity wants to even the water out and maintain a constant water level. The competing effects of Ekman transport and gravity balance out.

- The oceanic gyres that are in this balanced flow system that causes the flow to move right around the gyre and stably maintain this dynamically balanced hill are called **geostrophic gyres**.

- The hill of water that sits in the Atlantic Ocean is called the Sargasso Sea, and it's a region where the water is relatively calm. This oceanic gyre in the North Atlantic has an elevation that is 2 meters high—higher than the average sea level for the Atlantic as a whole.

Major Geostrophic Gyres

- There are 5 major geostrophic gyres that are planetary-scale surface-current features: the North Atlantic gyre, the South Atlantic gyre, the North Pacific gyre, the South Pacific gyre, and the Indian Ocean gyre.

- The Antarctic Circumpolar Current is driven by the westerlies, hence the name it is also known as: West Wind Drift. It's the place that generates the biggest winds and the biggest storms on the planet because the wind blows continuously right around Antarctica.

- Within oceanic gyres, there are a number of types of major surface currents. The western boundary currents are the fastest and deepest currents on Earth. They move warm water from tropical regions to higher latitudes.

- The largest and most famous of the western boundary currents is the Gulf Stream, which moves at about 2 meters per second or as much as 5 miles per hour. It moves like a river that is out in the ocean.

- The Gulf Stream is about 70 kilometers wide and about 450 meters deep; it's a relatively deep trough extending down to the lowermost parts of the thermocline and pycnocline in that region. The Gulf Stream flows at a rate of 55 million cubic meters of water per second—55 times the flow of all the rivers in the entire planet.

- Eddies can spin off of the main western boundary current and persist for weeks at a time, even in the ocean, before they finally dissipate and remix. This is a major way in which the surface waters of the ocean get mixed across large areas of the sea surface.

Studying Currents

- Oceanographers study major surface currents of the ocean by using CTDs, which measure current velocity, temperature, and salinity with depth.

- Another way is to put special kinds of floating beacons or sensors out in the ocean that will drop down to a particular depth and take measurements.

- The most modern way to study surface currents is the use of robotic vehicles called AUVs, autonomous underwater vehicles. One example is called a Slocum glider.

- AUVs are special devices that are battery powered and use sensors to measure temperature and current speed. They can dive down to certain depths in the water, and they can change buoyancy and altitude in the water. Periodically, they are programmed to rise up to the surface and beam the information they're carrying to a satellite and the oceanographers on shore.

Western and Eastern Boundary Currents

- The second biggest and most famous example of the western boundary currents is the Kuroshio off the coast of Japan. The Kuroshio is important for tuna fishing and for all of the fisheries of the Japanese islands.

- There are also many eastern boundary currents in the world. Some examples include the Canary Current in the Atlantic Ocean and the California Current in the Pacific Ocean. They move mostly cold water toward the equator.

- Eastern boundary currents are shallow and very broad, and they're more diffused and move slower than western boundary currents. They might be as much as hundreds to thousands of kilometers wide but only a hundred meters in depth.

- The major eastern boundary currents of the world are the Canary Current in the North Atlantic Ocean, the Benguela Current of the South Atlantic, the California Current, the Peru Current in the South Pacific, and the current of Western Australia.

- The westward currents are intense, fast, and deep, and the eastern currents are spread out because of the Coriolis interaction with these geostrophic gyres.

Mapped by Benjamin Franklin in the 1760s, the Gulf Stream is like a river out in the ocean.

Transverse Currents

- The boundary currents on the west and east are linked together by **transverse currents** that move water from east to west and west to east.

- In the middle latitudes, the westerlies drive the transverse flow—such as the Northern Pacific transverse current and the North Atlantic transverse current. In the Southern Ocean, the West Wind Drift dominates, so the far southern transverse currents are not very strongly developed. In the equatorial regions, the trade winds drive the north and south equatorial currents.

- The trade winds drive the equatorial currents because there's a meteorological equator on Earth that's different from the geographic equator. This has to do with the fact that there's a lot more land mass in the Northern Hemisphere and a lot more ocean area in the Southern Hemisphere.

- Oceanographers use many different kinds of information to learn about the ocean currents: drift cards, notes in bottles, and even serendipity.

- In 1990, a ship dumped several containers that contained 61,000 pairs of brand new Nike tennis shoes overboard in the middle of the Pacific Ocean. Some oceanographers found out about this and talked to the people involved with that ship to map out where the shoes had shown up—where they had been carried to by currents.

- In 1992, another spill put 29,000 bathtub toys into the Pacific Ocean, starting another flurry of activity to study how these toys could become oceanographic markers.

- All of these very important surface currents influence the climate of the entire planet because they're moving heat around on the planet. They're also influencing and making the large-scale mixing of the surface ocean water possible.

Important Terms

Ekman transport: The tendency of wind-driven surface currents to move at an oblique angle to the wind direction, caused by the Coriolis effect acting on the water. The effect increases with depth, creating the variation in motion direction known as the Ekman spiral.

geostrophic gyre: The hemisphere-scale surface-current loops set up in each ocean basin that are dynamically balanced by competing effects of Ekman transport and gravity.

transverse current: The generally east-west flowing surface currents that link the boundary currents and also account for the Antarctic Circumpolar Current (also known as the West Wind Drift).

Suggested Reading

Hohn, *Moby-Duck*.

Ulanski, *The Gulf Stream*.

Questions to Consider

1. Try to imagine the surface currents on a planet with no continents—only one big ocean. What form might they take? (Hint: Think of the Antarctic Circumpolar Current and extrapolate.)

2. Why don't the currents simply follow the prevailing wind cells?

The Gulf Stream to Gyres—Vast Surface Currents
Lecture 30—Transcript

Now that we've taken a look at the major circulation of the atmosphere and in particular the persistent and prevailing winds of the atmospheric cells like the westerly winds, the trade winds. We're going to see how those same winds are also driving the major ocean surface currents. We would like to understand how the ocean circulates as a whole. In order to do that, we have to link the prevailing winds to the sea itself.

We're going to look in this lecture then at ocean currents and we can breakdown ocean currents into surface currents and then much slower deepwater transport. The deepwater transport we'll take up in a later lecture, but the really big currents that we think about, like the Gulf Stream, are surface currents of the ocean that are caused mainly by wind friction directly on the sea surface, just as the waves are, and then also by differences in the density of different water masses and difference in the heat and density characteristics of those water masses. The surface currents themselves affects the uppermost, just 10% or so of the world's ocean. Basically above the thermocline and above the pycnocline, remember those 2 equivalents of temperature and density that change rapidly in the ocean. The shallow, warmer, lower density waters are the places where the surface currents actually live.

Surface currents are induced primarily by the prevailing winds. The westerlies and the trade winds are the most important ones for understanding the big currents on the surface of the ocean itself. We've seen that the trade winds blow from the northeast towards the southwest. The westerlies blow more from the southwest towards the northeast and they're in different latitudinal bands. The wind changes direction every day, but because the winds are prevailing winds they set the water in motion. They set the waves in motion in all sorts of different directions that change from day to day. The averaging out of the flow of air in the westerlies and the trade winds sets the water in larger scale motions that move it across the ocean surface as a whole and ultimately set these surface currents in motion.

The water moves with the trade winds, but it doesn't move in the direction that the trade winds blow and the same goes for the westerlies. That, again, is because of our old friend Coriolis. As the trade winds blow, they tend to blow at an angle in latitude from northeast to southwest and they curve with the Coriolis forces, but they drag across the water surface. Water doesn't move nearly as quickly as the winds. When the wind blows at 10s of knots over the water, it just sets the water in motion at most a couple of knots, usually much less than that. The water is moving much slower than the wind.

If the wind is affected by the Coriolis bending then, remember that the Coriolis bending is as something moves either north or south Earth rotates beneath it and causes the bending. If it's moving more slowly Earth is rotating more for a given unit of time and causes it to bend much more than the thing that is setting in motion or in something that's moving faster like the wind. If the wind blows in a given direction, the water actually is deflected and starts moving at about a 45 degree to the overall surface wind direction. The wind sets the surface water in motion, but it sets the water in motion at an angle to the overall wind direction.

The water movement is even more complicated than this due to a strange phenomenon, but one that's active all over the world where wind sets water in motion and that's something called Ekman transport. What happens in Ekman transport is that if we look at the very surface water it blows with the wind, but it blows at this 45 degree angle. As we look deeper and deeper in the water over about the upper hundred meters or so of the water, each successive depth is moving in a different direction and it's moving in a different direction that keeps changing in a characteristic way that produces what's called this Ekman spiral.

The water itself is not actually spiraling. There's no spirally motion of the water, but the vector or the direction that shows the way the water is moving starts out at an angle to the wind that with successive depths gets to be moving in slightly different directions at each depth. That's because essentially the surface layer of the water starts moving and it drags on the water below. That water moves a little bit slower than the surface water so its Coriolis deflected to the right. That in turn drags on the water even below that and so that in turn is deflected a bit more to the right and so on right down through the water column.

The overall effect then is that there's this spiraling direction of transport of the water such that at something like 100 meters depth, the water is moving much more slowly than at the surface, but it's moving literally in the opposite direction. The net direction or the direction of water transport at that depth, because of the wind blowing over the surface plus the Coriolis effect can actually be exactly in the opposite direction. It's very strange isn't it?

If we integrate the water over that whole hundred meter depth or average out its motion and come up with a net direction of transport of all of this water, we find that for the surface waters down to 100 meters or so, the net direction of that transport is exactly perpendicular to the wind direction, not exactly, but it averages out to 90 degrees to the wind direction. Again very strange; the wind blows in this direction and causes the water to move off to the right at a 90 degree angle. This is what sets the surface ocean currents in motion.

As they move then they bend to the right and they bend to the right very sharply and it causes the water underneath the trade winds in the regions that are at 15 or so degrees north and south to get moved westward across the ocean basin and pile up against whatever continents or obstacles are in the way and then turn even more sharply to the right and move up along the coastline and then out towards the sea and back towards the east again. This develops these loops that we call the oceanic gyres, the major loops of the ocean circulation pattern of the surface currents that are persistent and also are very large-scale such that there's just a few in the whole world because they're centered on 30 degrees approximately north or south, so there's one big gyre for the North Atlantic, one big gyre for the South Atlantic, just a couple of big gyres in the Pacific Ocean and then some complications in some other parts of the world in smaller ocean basin what we'll look at.

The North Atlantic gyre system, for example, is a linkup of the flow of all of the various surface currents. We'll take a look at those currents in a moment. It involves flow that's north of the equator along the trade wind belt, but at a high angle to the trade winds that brings warm water into the Caribbean region and flows it northward along North America, ultimately over towards

Europe and then back down southward again to get picked up by the trade winds again.

With these gyres happening, the current flow and the Coriolis effect combined in the form of this Ekman spiral drives all the water towards the center of the gyre. If you imagine the flow is always turning around the gyre then it's pushing the water at that high angle to the wind direction and high angle to the overall current flow direction into a hill in the middle of the ocean. It's not much of a hill; it has a height of just a meter or a few meters at most relative to regions that are thousands of kilometers away. A ship would never notice it as a hill, but it's a dynamically balanced high in the water.

Dynamically balanced means that water is piled up by the Coriolis forces of the currents, but it wants to flow back down because gravity wants to even the water out and maintain a nice constant water level. The competing effects of the Ekman transport and the gravity balance out such that the net water transport direction is along the hillside so the net water transport is actually right along the line of constant elevation of this very subtle but very real hill of water. The oceanic gyres that are in this balanced flow system that causes the flow to go right around the gyre and stably maintain this dynamically balanced hill are called geostrophic gyres. That's just the terminology for these large-scale globally driven gyre systems in the global ocean.

We can actually see these hills. They exist and they're visible in satellite data. For example, the satellite I mentioned a long time ago when we were mapping altimetry of the sea; the TOPEX Poseidon Satellite image, that hill of water that sits in the Atlantic Ocean is called the Sargasso Sea. It's a region where the water is relatively calm. The winds are very calm. It's in between the trade winds and westerlies in the horse latitudes. It's named Sargasso Sea because there was great amounts of what was called Sargassum seaweed that grow floating in this relatively stable region of the ocean. This oceanic gyre in the North Atlantic has got an elevation 2 meters high, higher than average sea level for the Atlantic as a whole.

There are a number, in fact 5 major geostrophic gyres like this, plus one oddball that we'll talk about in just a second. That's it for the whole planet. These are huge scale, planetary scale surface current features. There's the

North Atlantic gyre, the South Atlantic gyre, as I mentioned, the North Pacific gyre, and the South Pacific gyre and then there's the Indian Ocean gyre. All of them behave in exactly the way I just described and we'll break them down into their component surface currents in just second.

The one oddball is what's called the West Wind Drift or the Antarctic Circumpolar Current. The Antarctic Circumpolar Current is driven by the westerlies, hence the name the West Wind Drift, but it's driven in a region of the ocean where there's no land to get in the way and so there's no piling up against anything because the southern ocean between Antarctica and South America or Australia or Africa is open ocean as we've already seen. It's the place that generates the biggest winds and the biggest storms on the planet because the wind can just blow continuously right around Antarctica. That West Wind Drift, that continuous west wind also whips up this strong flowing current in the ocean and so one of the strongest ocean currents is this Antarctic Circumpolar Current that just ceaselessly and endlessly circles around Antarctica in a particular direction.

Within these oceanic gyres then there's a number of major surface current types. We can break them down in their individual components. We have the western boundary currents. We have the eastern boundary currents and by west and east now remember we're talking about west and east parts of the ocean. The east coast of the U.S. just off shore has a western boundary current because it's the western side of the Atlantic Ocean. Linking the western boundary currents and the eastern boundary currents which largely transport water either north to south or south to north in each hemisphere, linking them are the transverse currents, the currents that basically just hook them up and move water between east to west.

First let's take a look at the western boundary currents. These are the fastest and deepest currents on earth and we'll see why in just a second. They move warm water from the tropical regions to higher latitudes so they're a major component in the heat redistribution on the planet redistributing that heat generated in the equatorial regions to the high latitudes. The largest and most famous to us in the western boundary currents is the Gulf Stream. The Gulf Stream mapped by Ben Franklin way back in the 1760s and still ever present year end and year out all the time in the ocean. The Gulf Stream is truly phenomenal. It moves at something like 2 meters per second or as much as 5 miles per hour. It's literally like a river out in the ocean.

It's narrow and it's relatively deep and it's relatively well-defined in terms of its boundaries. It's about 70 kilometers wide typically and if you're on a ship at sea you can be outside the Gulf Stream in water that's barely moving at all and then just cross just a few knots and suddenly be in water that's moving 5 miles an hour. It's up to about 450 meters deep so it's relatively narrow, but it's a relatively deep trough extending down to the lowermost parts of the thermocline and pycnocline in that region.

The Gulf Stream is a phenomenal volume of water. It flows at a rate of 55 million cubic meters of water per second. That's such a large number, cubic meter of water is a large volume of water, and 55 million of them per second past any given point, if we put a screen across the Gulf Stream and measured the flow. That's such a large number that 1 million cubic meters of water per second as a measure of volume of flow has been given an oceanographic named 55 sverdrup in honor of a famous oceanographer. The sverdrup is 1 million cubic meters of water per second. The Gulf Stream is flowing at a rate of 55 sverdrup. Just for perspective, the entire global input of fresh water from all the rivers in the whole world to the ocean is approximately 1 sverdrup. The Gulf Stream is moving 55 times the flow of all the rivers in the entire planet and it's doing that year in and year out.

We can see this Gulf Stream flowing and its sharp boundaries mean that the rapid flow and the big temperature difference keeps the current mostly intact. When we look at a thermal image, an infrared image of the surface of the ocean, we can actually see the Gulf Stream in these satellite images very well defined very often. We can see that it comes up from the region of the Caribbean and offshore Florida, moves up the southeastern coast of the Atlantic seaboard and then around Cape Hatteras detaches from North America and moves out across in the North Atlantic Ocean.

As it goes, it tends to form meanders. Those meanders can bend and open up loops and ultimately even form turbulent eddies that detach from the mainstream as either the cold water gets entrained into the warm water of the Gulf Stream, in which case we get something that's called a cold core eddy.

Conversely some of the warm water of the Gulf Stream gets wrapped up in a loop that circulates in the opposite direction, typically north of the Gulf Stream, such that we have a warm core eddy, meaning warm water that was originally in the stream gets swirled in by the cold water coming down from off of Labrador in the North Atlantic. These eddies can spin off of the main western boundary current and persist for weeks at a time even in the ocean before they finally dissipate and remix. This is a major way in which the surface waters of the ocean get mixed across large areas of the sea surface, the formation that these vortex or spinning eddies and then their mixing of different water masses together.

You might wonder how do we study these major surface currents of the ocean. There's an interesting current studying story. One way is to simply go out there and make measurements with a ship, lower a CTD down, remember the CTDs that measure current velocity and temperature and salinity and things like that with depth. Another way is to put special kinds of essentially floating beacons or sensors out in the ocean that will drop down to a particular depth, but aren't attached to anything and they'll pop back up to the surface to be recollected by a ship. The most modern way is the use of true robotic vehicles in the sense that they're called AUVs, autonomous underwater vehicles. One example is something called a Slocum glider.

These are special devices that are battery powered and a bunch of sensors so they can measure temperature and current speed and a lot of other things. They can dive down to certain depths in the water. They have chambers they can either fill with gas or move weights around so that they can change buoyancy in the water and they can change their attitude. They have wings so they'll fly upward or downward within a given zone of the ocean. They're dropped into the water and then steer themselves essentially measuring everything along the way, but periodically are programmed to rise up to the surface and beam the information they're carrying to a satellite back to the oceanographers on shore.

The oceanographer can sit in his or her office and get the data every few days from one of these gliders that may spend weeks or even months at sea measuring data. They use a very small amount of power so their batteries can last a long time. These have really revolutionized our understanding of currents in some ways.

Let's return to the western boundary currents one more time and look at a few more around the world. This second biggest and most famous example to us in western boundary currents is the Kuroshio current off the coast of Japan. It's famous in the Taiwan, Japan region. Kuroshio means the black current. It carries this very dark looking nutrient rich water up from the Philippines and Taiwanese region and again flows up along the Japanese coastline and ultimately detaches and hugs across the open Pacific Ocean.

The Kuroshio current is actually important for tuna fishing and for all of the fisheries of the Japanese islands too because seas can only carry so many nutrients that it becomes a fertile feeding ground for a lot of different materials. These western boundary currents are important oceanographically. They're important for understanding the mixing in the ocean and many other features. They've been the subject of some really intensive work with detailed computer simulation. What I'd like to show you now is actually a simulation of the Kuroshio current in the Pacific Ocean where it's been flowing over a lot of time. There's a lot of data for a period in the 1990s and these are one of the largest computers in the world that temperature and pressure and wind gradients of the ocean were used as input and then a simulation or a calculation of the Kuroshio current was run.

As you look as this simulation, you'll see that it shows us the temperature of the water surface in the color coding. You see warm water in red and warm colors. The surface elevation looks like it's changing because in a very exaggerated way it's showing us the surface elevations of the water. Then the spinning and moving current which you can see meandering and also spinning eddies off just as we described for the Gulf Stream, is constantly in motion and it speeds up and slows down with the seasons, but it shows you the degree and power over these month by month simulations that we're seeing of these major surface ocean currents like a fire hose moving warm water from tropical regions to much more temperate regions of the ocean.

If there's western boundary currents then there have to also be eastern boundary currents. There are many eastern boundary currents of the world.

Some example include the Canary Current in the Atlantic or the California Current in the Pacific Ocean that move water from northern regions to southern regions along the west coast of the continents in that case. They move mostly cold water equatorward. They're quite different from the western boundary currents. Eastern boundary currents are shallow and they're very broad and they're more diffused, slower moving currents. They occupy a larger area of the ocean surface, but they don't have the kind of concentrated power, that fire hose power of something like the Gulf Stream or the Kuroshio.

They might be as much as hundreds to thousands of kilometers wide, but just a hundred meters or so in depth. Individual parts of them carry less water than the western boundary currents, but overall they have to match the western boundary currents. The water doesn't gradually build up in one area or another. It has to all balance out in the geostrophic gyre.

If we look at the major eastern boundary currents of the world, we have the Canary Current in the North Atlantic, the Benguela Current of the South Atlantic, California Current, the Peru Current in the South Pacific, the Western Australia current, all of them representing that return flow path on the oceanic gyres. Let's take a look at why the western boundary currents, like the Kuroshio, like the Gulf Stream, like the Benguela Current or the Aqulhas Current are so different from the eastern boundary currents.

There's a process that we call westward intensification. Remember the map of the Sargasso Sea; you notice that it wasn't in the center of the Atlantic Ocean. It was hugging more of the North American side of the Atlantic Ocean so it was displaced towards the west. The reason for that is as the water flows around these geostrophic gyres. It pools up to form the western boundary currents because of a very strong intensification or flow of the water towards the west side of the basins. Remember Coriolis forcing, it's less strong at the equatorial regions, in fact it's zero right at the equator, but its relatively weak forcing in the low latitudes and it becomes a very strong Coriolis forcing in the high latitudes, high to the north or high to the south.

What happens is the trade winds push the water over to the west side of the Atlantic Ocean let's say and the Coriolis doesn't turn them very rapidly.

They tend to actually move all the way west and accumulate and there's so much warm water pooling there that it pushes the thermocline down. It builds up that deep current, that 400 plus meter deep source for the Gulf Stream. It runs into the continent. The continent gets in the way so as the continent gets in the way then the current turns and it's kind of sloshing over and then where it meets that obstacle starts to move northward.

As it moves northward it picks up very much stronger Coriolis forces so it starts to turn in the North Atlantic and the Coriolis is strong so the water spreads out and turns more efficiently towards the south again. So what happens is it starts turning before it ever gets over to Europe. It doesn't pool on the east side of the basis in the north the way it does on the west side of the basin in the south. This produces the broadening and shallowing of the overall current to move the water back. The westward currents are intense and fast and deep and the eastern currents are spread out and it's all again because of Coriolis interaction with these geostrophic gyres.

If we have the boundary currents on the west and the east then we have to have something that links them up and those are called the transverse currents moving water east to west and west to east. At the mid-latitudes the westerlies drive the transverse flow and then the equatorial region things are a little bit different. If we look at the transverse currents in the westerly regions, in the northern parts of the ocean or the high southern parts of the ocean we have things like the Northern Pacific transverse current or the North Atlantic transverse current, which is really the Gulf Stream just turns into or gradually grades into the North Atlantic transverse current, which then quickly turns into the return flow of the Canary Current.

In the southern ocean, things are dominated by that West Wind Drift so the far southern transverse currents are not so strongly developed although they're certainly present. In the equatorial regions, the trade winds actually drive the north and south equatorial currents and those are not at the geographic equator, they're offset somewhat from the geographic equator to the north. The north and south equatorial currents don't just hug the equator at equal latitudes north and south, but they're moved northward such that the south one is right about at the equatorial position and the north one is significantly further north in kind of a 5 to 10 degrees north range.

That's because there's a meteorological equator on earth that's different from the geographic equator. This has to do with the fact that there's a lot more land mass in the Northern Hemisphere and a lot more ocean area in the Southern Hemisphere. The air flow patterns based on the seasons and everything are unequally distributed. Without getting too complicated about it we'll just say that the meteorological equator doesn't really correspond to the true geographic equator. At any rate, the north and south equatorial currents move a lot of water, about 30 sverdrup are transported in the Atlantic and also in the Pacific. They move water right across the equatorial region. They don't turn very sharply due to Coriolis forcing because Coriolis forcing is relatively weak at the equator. They pile water up at the western side especially in the Pacific Ocean. The western Pacific around Indonesia has a pile of water that's being pulled away from Peru and the equatorial South American region.

In the Atlantic, a little bit less so because the ocean basis is not quite as big. In both cases, the west side of the tropical regions of an ocean basin have a sea level that's several meters higher than the east side of those same basins. Sea level in Indonesia is not really the same level as sea level in Peru and that's because of the drying of this water, dynamically maintaining that across the Pacific Ocean. Because that water piles up at the western side then, it drives something called the equatorial counter-currents and these are currents that are flowing water back across the ocean in the direction utterly counter to the main equatorial currents. It's almost like you sloshed all the water in your bathtub in one direction and then a bunch of it has to flow back except that they're all happening at the same time in a dynamic balance.

In the Pacific equatorial counter-current, in particular, is a very important phenomenon that we're going to take a closer look at in the next lecture when we talk about El Nino a little bit. We want to look at ocean currents in general so we have our neat oceanographic tools like the floats, the CTDs, even the Slocum gliders measuring the surface currents and mapping them out all over the world. There's only so many of those and technology is expensive and oceanographers' time is also expensive at times.

Oceanographers will use all sorts of information, whatever is available to learn something about the ocean currents. For a very long time, over the course of a century, there were sometimes controlled releases of what are called drift cards, little wooden cards that float and have printed or painted on them some information that basically says if you find this card on the beach send it back to let's say University of Washington School of Oceanography and gives an address and says write down the exact location you found it and the date you found it on. Those are ways of being released in the ocean almost like a tracer dye into the water and then found in different locations to talk about where they drifted. Even bottles, literally notes in bottles, were used for a long time.

Sometimes it's just serendipity that finds these oceanographic experiments. On May 27, in 1990, a big container ship was travelling across the sea and if you've ever had to ship something by container this may be disconcerting, but because ships at sea encounter big waves and storms all the time. containers fall off those ships actually fairly regularly and in 1990 this particular ship dumped several containers that happen to contain 61 thousand pairs of brand new Nike tennis shoes overboard in the middle of the Pacific Ocean. The exact location where they went overboard is known and the exact date. Six months later, huge numbers of shoes started showing up on Pacific northwest beaches around the U.S. and Canada. In fact, beachcombers started literally getting together to try to find pairs that matched up, left and right and the same size, so they could use them. The shoes were in great condition although they'd floated at sea for a long time.

Some oceanographers caught wind of this and started to talk to them and map out where the shoes had shown up. It turned out to be a significant experiment in understanding the exact state of current flow in the North Pacific Ocean at that particular time because 61,000 individual pairs of markers, many of which were actually recovered came back from that experiment. In 1992, another spill put 29,000 bathtub toys into the Pacific Ocean starting another flurry of activity to study how they were oceanographic markers ultimately leading to the publication of a recent book called *Moby Duck* chronicling that event.

All of these very important surface currents as we're going to see influence the climate of the whole planet because they're really moving heat around on the planet wholesale. They're obviously influencing and making the large-scale mixing of the surface ocean water possible. They mix the ocean at relatively rapid timescales giving us this even distribution of salinity. They move water all about the surface of the ocean. All of that horizontal flow interestingly enough also drives some very important vertical flows. We're going to see how these horizontal currents create vertical distribution of water, which is incredibly important to the productivity in the sea as well as coastal climates all over the world.

Upwelling, Downwelling, and El Niño
Lecture 31

Vertical movement of near-surface waters driven by the wind, called upwelling and downwelling, is important in oceanic biological productivity and also plays a key role in the global climate phenomenon known as El Niño. Upwelling brings deeper, nutrient-rich water to the surface along the equator and many coastal areas, supporting major fisheries. Downwelling causes surface waters to sink, pushing the thermocline down, which reduces productivity. El Niño is a cyclical climatic effect in which the trade winds slacken, equatorial currents reverse, and downwelling replaces upwelling off the coast of Peru with climatic effects felt around the world.

Upwelling and Downwelling

- Vertical movement of near-surface waters, and even of waters significantly deeper than that, can be driven by the wind and by oceanic surface currents. These vertical movements are important in oceanic biological productivity and play a key role in the global climate phenomenon known as El Niño.

- **Upwelling** brings deep water, or water that's currently not at the surface, up to the surface. **Downwelling** causes surface waters to sink.

- Downwelling can have important coastal effects and is important for the formation of the deep water that fills up most of the ocean basins—called high-latitude cold-water formation.

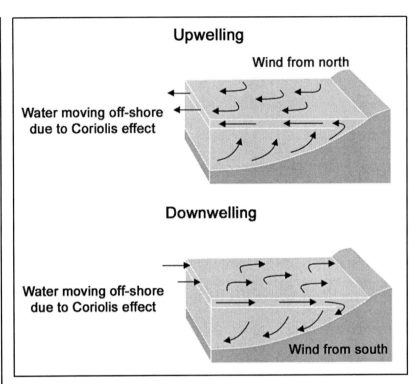

Upwelling

Wind from north

Water moving off-shore
due to Coriolis effect

Downwelling

Water moving off-shore
due to Coriolis effect

Wind from south

- The south equatorial current moves water from east to west across both major ocean basins and flows essentially right along, or slightly diagonally across, the geographical equator. Meanwhile, the trade winds in the Northern Hemisphere and the Southern Hemisphere also blow east to west because they drive that current along the equator.

- In the Northern Hemisphere, the water turns away from the equator and toward more northerly waters. The water that's just a bit to the south of the equator turns to the left because it is in the Southern Hemisphere.

- The net effect is that the water at the surface is parting, and we call that process divergence. The south equatorial current parts the water, so deeper water wells up to fill in the gap. This parting of the surface waters pulls up colder water.

- The Coriolis effect causes the water to turn in opposite directions across the equator and, therefore, causes **equatorial divergence**, which in turn is the cause of equatorial upwelling.

- Most of the tropical regions of the euphotic zone are relatively barren of primary productivity because those warm surface waters are depleted in the key nutrients for photosynthetic activity.

- There's a very strongly developed thermocline in tropical regions— warm surface water, cold deep water, and a strong gradient between the 2. Surface waters are depleted in carbon dioxide because the photosynthesizers use it up.

- In deeper water, there exists the detrital food web, in which zooplankton and all the other consumers break down organic matter and re-release nutrients along with a lot of carbon dioxide.

- In deeper water, an upwelling takes place, the waters part, and deeper water wells up, bringing dissolved carbon dioxide–rich water and other nutrients to the surface, which facilitates great masses of phytoplankton blooming along the equatorial region.

Upwelling and Productivity

- Phytoplankton blooms can be seen from space. The SeaWiFS satellite measures ocean color, which is directly converted to a measure of the presence of chlorophyll for these phytoplankton. The phytoplankton feed a localized food web along the tropical region.

- Upwelling is induced by the combination of the equatorial current and the trade winds. Coastal upwelling is another process that is very important for biological productivity.

- In the California Current, for example, a combination of wind blowing and water flowing along the coastline causes Ekman transport to take place. Ekman transport actually means that as the wind blows along the coast, the water moves perpendicular to the coast and off shore.

- If there's a barrier in the form of a coastline, then the water moves away. There's no surface water to replace it, so it draws deep water up—in the same way as with equatorial water.

- In places such as California and Peru, coastal upwelling is a very important process that moves a large amount of water from great depths up to shallow areas. This deep water is drawn up from even thousands of meters deep in the water and replaces the surface water, producing a voluminous amount of nutrient-rich water that arrives at the surface and fuels major phytoplankton blooms.

- The phytoplankton in these areas are the basis of a highly productive food chain. The famous fisheries of California, Peru, and the areas in South America of anchovy and sardine—as well as fisheries in rich Antarctic waters that have the same kinds of coastal upwelling—are all fueled by upwelling productivity.

- The converse to upwelling is downwelling, which is the process that works in the same way due to the Coriolis effect and Ekman transport, but it occurs when the wind is blowing in the opposite direction along the coastline.

- In the Northern Hemisphere, if the coast is on the east side, the open ocean is on the west side, and the wind is blowing from south to north, the wind pushes the water to the right, causing the surface waters to pile up against the coastline as the wind blows.

- The surface waters don't actually pileup; they are actually forced to sink because there's nowhere for them to go. They depress the thermocline and push the pycnocline down, which can suppress primary productivity.

- The surface waters are rich in oxygen because phytoplankton makes oxygen, but the deep waters are depleted in oxygen. Downwelling mixes the oxygenated-rich surface water into the deep water. Oxygen is an important nutrient for all the organisms that are in the deep pelagic and benthic zones of the ocean.

El Niño

- Upwelling and downwelling also has pathological effects, especially with the phenomenon called El Niño or, oceanographically, the Southern Oscillation.

- In the 1890s, Peruvian fishermen noticed that in certain years there was the arrival of an unusually warm current on the coastline. It happened to come typically around Christmastime, so they started to call it the Corriente del Niño, meaning the current of the Christ child in Spanish. In those years, their fisheries failed.

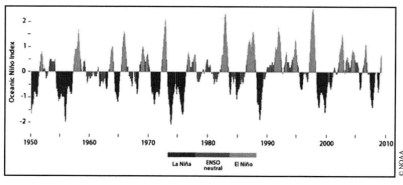

In 2009, El Niño spread across the Pacific Ocean and hit the Peruvian coastline, damaging the fisheries there.

- The bird guano (fertilizer) industry was strongly affected during the El Niño years. The fisheries were no good, the guano was no good, and the local economy would crash. In fact, especially in earlier times, the whole region would go into a state of potential famine because of the lack of food.

- In a normal year, the surface winds are strong, so they create equatorial upwelling and blow the equatorial currents strongly over toward the western Pacific.

- Meanwhile, there's been strong upwelling off the Peruvian coast because the water is pulling away from the edge of the continent. The Peru current is coming from the south, so great upwelling is occurring, leading to happy fish, happy fishermen, and happy guano miners as a result.

- In an El Niño year, the fisheries fail because of an atmospheric phenomenon that is a persistent high-pressure zone in the tropical western Pacific. That change to a high-pressure system is called the Southern Oscillation.

- Because winds blow away from high pressure toward low pressure, the trade winds weaken and die out. The water moves back across the Pacific and suppresses the upwelling on the Peruvian side; in fact, downwelling is generated in the other direction on the Peruvian side.

- The strongest El Niños have been in recent times—specifically, in 1982–1983 and 1997–1998. One of the best-recorded occurrences was a more recent one in 2009–2010.

- Some of the effects of El Niño and the Southern Oscillation are sea level rises in the eastern Pacific by as much as 20 centimeters; water temperature rises by up to 7°; more evaporation occurs; low pressure intensifies over the eastern Pacific; and heavy precipitation often occurs in coastal South America along with torrential rains and landslides.

- All around the world in the trade-wind belts, there are major modifications due to El Niño that affect the amount of rainfall. El Niño has caused major droughts in Africa and in India at times, while causing torrential rain in other parts of the world—all disrupting local climate and local economic activity in many cases.

- Eventually, the reestablishment and redevelopment of equatorial upwelling occurs in a process called La Niña, which is the absence of an El Niño—or the opposite effect of an El Niño.

- In a La Niña year, there are very dry, sometimes very drought-like conditions across the southwest and California. There are more effects all over the world, in fact.

- The NOAA, the National Oceanographic and Atmospheric Administration, keeps the Oceanic Niño Index (ONI), which is a record of sea-surface temperatures measured in a particular place in the central Pacific Ocean.

Important Terms

downwelling: The movement of surface water downward, depressing the thermocline due to either high density or Ekman-transport effects.

equatorial divergence: The tendency of wind-driven surface waters to move in opposite directions just across the equator because of the opposite Coriolis effect in the Northern and Southern hemispheres.

upwelling: The movement of cold, deeper water upward to the sea surface when surface waters are drawn away by divergence or Ekman-transport effects.

Suggested Reading

Fagan, *Floods, Famines, and Emperors*.

Nash, *El Niño*.

1. How might upwelling at the surface influence the pattern of sediment types that are deposited on the ocean floor? (Hint: Think biogenous sediments and where you might expect to find more of them than other places.)

2. Could El Niño also have an effect on equatorial upwelling in the Pacific Ocean, besides the effect on coastal South America, based on the mechanism of how it is thought to be generated?

Upwelling, Downwelling, and El Niño
Lecture 31—Transcript

Let's continue our examination now of the really big scale movements of water in the oceans, the things that mix the ocean efficiently and set all the water travelling around the entire globe. We've already explored the surface currents that move water horizontally around the planet in these great oceanic gyres and we've seen that they're driven by prevailing winds, by the trade winds and westerlies and winds like that. It turns out that vertical movement of near surface waters and even of waters significantly deeper than that can also be driven by the wind and can be driven by oceanic currents, the surface currents themselves. These vertical movements are things that are going to be important in oceanic biological productivity and play a key role in the global climate phenomenon that we know as El Niño.

Let's take a look at vertical movements of water driven by horizontal flows. The vertical circulation of water that's induced by this horizontal flow, but in currents and in wind is known as upwelling and downwelling. These are fundamental processes going on mixing the water in the ocean. Upwelling brings deep water up to the surface or water that's currently not at the surface from depth. It takes 2 forms. There's basically an equatorial upwelling and coastal upwelling and we'll look at both of those in a few minutes. Then its converse is downwelling, not surprisingly downwelling causes surface waters to sink and downwelling can have important coastal effects and also, as we'll see in the next lecture, is important for the formation of the deep water that fills up most of the ocean basins, what we call the high latitude cold water formation.

First let's consider equatorial upwelling. This is a phenomenon that goes on in both the Atlantic basin and the Pacific basin and it has to do with the position of the equatorial currents and also the trade winds. Remember that I said that the northern and southern equatorial currents are a pair of congruent currents in the northern and Southern Hemispheres in the ocean. They straddle the equator, but they don't straddle the geographical equator I should say. They're not on either side of the geographical equator. For reasons of meteorology and the difference in land and ocean balance in the 2 hemispheres, the south equatorial current is more or less right on the equator and the north equatorial current is significantly further north in the northern tropical belt.

This south equatorial current moves water from east to west across both ocean basins, both major ocean basins and it flows essentially right along or slightly diagonally across the actual geographical equator. Meanwhile the trade winds in the Northern Hemisphere and the Southern Hemisphere also blow east to west because they're driving that current along the equator. Remember the Coriolis effect. Absolutely at the equator, the Coriolis effect is zero, but as soon as we move off the equator, either north or south, it's non-zero. It's weak in the equatorial regions, but it's certainly present.

The water that's moving along the equatorial region, along the equator itself driven by that south equatorial current, if it's just a bit to the north of the equator, even a degree or less to north of the equator it's going to turn to the right. We're in the Northern Hemisphere so it'll turn away from the equator and towards more northerly waters. On the other hand, the water that's just a bit to the south of the equator is going to turn to the left because it's in the Southern Hemisphere. The net effect then is that the water at the surface is parting and we call that process divergence. The south equatorial current parts the water literally like Moses parting the Red Sea. The water, unlike in Moses' case can't just create a hole, it moves away from the equator itself and so deeper water wells up to fill in the gap. This parting of the surface waters pulls up colder water that's actually maybe more dense because it's colder, but has to fill up the space that's left behind by the motion of the surface waters away, by the pressure drop of the surface waters moving away.

The Coriolis effect causes the water to turn in opposite directions across the equator and therefore cause equatorial divergence. That equatorial divergence in turn is the cause of equatorial upwelling. We can actually see this divergence in satellite imagery of Earth. If we look at a satellite image of the sea surface temperature, map from space, then cold water sort of fingers, very narrow running right along the equator meandering a little, but essentially running right along the equator in the narrow band, extends across the Pacific Ocean basin. You can see it in the image as the cooler colors because that's the way the map is colored by temperature so the yellows and greens are that cold upwelled equatorial water.

It's cold because the water comes from several hundred meters deep. It's actually associated with something called the equatorial undercurrent or equatorial counter-current that I mentioned before. That colder, deeper water is welling up to the surface and showing up as a sea surface temperature anomaly in satellite imagery year in, year out. We call that most of the tropical regions of the euphotic zone are relatively barren of primary productivity. When we looked at our maps of global productivity at the sea surface of phytoplankton, photosynthesizers that are responsible for all the primary productivity, for the most part the tropical regions of the open Pacific Ocean and the open Atlantic Ocean were kind of barren. There's not much going on. The reason there's not much going on is that those warm surface waters, the waters that are very well-warmed by the Sun, they are depleted in the key nutrients for photosynthetic activity.

That's due to the fact that there's that very strongly developed thermocline that we described earlier in the tropical regions, warm surface water, cold deep water and a strong gradient between the 2. Remember that the thermocline is also a pycnocline or a density gradient. The warm surface waters are low density; the deep waters are high density, so they don't mix very well with each other. Surface waters are depleted in carbon dioxide because the photosynthesizers use that up. They're also depleted in other important nutrients that photosynthesizers need to fix nitrogen and to use carbon to build carbohydrates and carbon compounds, the phosphorous and the iron and other things that they need.

In the deeper water, remember we have the detrital food web and so the stuff that dives in the surface water falls down there, other organisms scoop it up. All the zooplankton and all the other consumers and they basically break down all that organic matter and re-release those nutrients and also re-release a lot of carbon dioxide. They re-spire carbon dioxide. The carbon dioxide is trapped as depth when there's a strongly developed pycnocline and thermocline. An upwelling takes place then the waters part, deeper water wells up, it brings carbon dioxide, dissolved CO_2 rich water to the surface and it also brings those other nutrients to the surface and that facilitates great masses of phytoplankton blooming along the equatorial region. The equator has lots of sunshine so it's great for photosynthesis and these organisms are essentially nutrient limited. As soon as they get enough nutrients they become very productive.

We can actually see those phytoplankton blooms as well from space. In a different satellite image, from the NASA satellite called SeaWiFs, measures the surface color of the ocean water. It's just a measurement of color, but in the open ocean because the water's very clear, the only thing that really changes the color of the water is the presence of the color of the photosynthetic plankton. Basically the presence of the chlorophyll in their bodies makes the water a little bit greener. The SeaWiFs satellite measures ocean color and that's directly converted to a measure of the presence of what's called chlorophyll a, the most common type of chlorophyll for these phytoplankton. We're looking at a global scale map of the SeaWiFs measurement averaging out 6 years of data, winter, summer, spring, and fall in both hemispheres. Again you can see that narrow finger, almost a pencil it looks like, across the equatorial region, especially well-developed in the Pacific, but certainly also present in the Atlantic that represents the productivity, the actual phytoplankton productivity of chlorophyll along this zone of equatorial upwelling.

The phytoplankton in turn then feed a localized food web along the tropical region. Most of the tropics are relatively barren. You see the large areas of deep blue; that's very low chlorophyll concentration, but the equatorial waters have the phytoplankton. They have fish and zooplankton that feed on them and ultimately they have large fish like the tuna fisheries of the tropical regions that are living in this dense, highly productive zone.

Those measurements in turn, the combination of the sea surface temperature measurements and then the chlorophyll measurements can be used with some calculations of the rate at which the water has to be replaced to maintain a certain temperature profile and a certain color profile based on the productivity of phytoplankton. It can be converted into a map of global wind induced upwelling. How much of the upwelling is there? I should say its wind induced because the trade winds drive the equatorial currents. It's really truly induced by the combination of the equatorial current and the trade winds themselves.

That wind induced upwelling measured in centimeters per day shows this very highly productive zone of high upwelling. The upwelling in this image goes up to as much as 50 or 60 centimeters per day. Water is coming up moving much, much slower than the currents are flowing. Remember some of the currents flow at several knots, meaning several miles per hour and this upwelling is proceeding at rates of tens of centimeters, a couple of feet per day of vertical movement of the water. Nonetheless that's enough to bring this cold nutrient rich water up to the surface and fertilize the equatorial region and cause these phytoplankton blooms. That's equatorial upwelling.

As I said there's another process also very important for biological productivity, maybe even more important for biological productivity. That's called coastal upwelling. We have a coastal region. You have ocean water on one side and land on the other and we very often have currents that flow parallel to the shore. For example, along the west coast of the United States there's the California Current. It's the eastern boundary current bringing water from northern latitudes up in the Gulf of Alaska and off Canada down along the U.S., California and then eventually merging with the equatorial region.

As that water moves from north to south and also prevailing winds tend to move from north to south for the same reasons basically. Higher pressure zone in the north and to the south, so prevailing winds move in the same direction. That combination of wind blowing and water flowing along the coastline causes Ekman transport to take place. Remember Ekman transport, whatever direction the wind is going and the water is going the water beneath it is moving at a direction off to the right at least in the Northern Hemisphere to that water. Ekman transport actually means that as the wind blows along the coast the water moves perpendicular to the coast and off shore. The surface water moves off to the right of the wind direction and normally that might mean that it would just pull water in behind, but if there's a barrier there in the form of a coastline then that water moves away. There's no surface water to replace it so it draws deep water up once again just like we did with the equatorial water.

It's now adjacent to the coastline; deep water is welling up and replacing that surface water. In places like California and Peru which has the equivalent situation for the Southern Hemisphere, this coastal upwelling is a really important process moving a great deal of water from deep to shallow. It's also kind of magnified by the fact that if you recall the continental shelf is very narrow in California and things drop off the continental slope. If you're standing in coastal central California, if you were to go off shore you'd be in very deep water very quickly. There's very little continental shelf unlike the east coast. It means that deep water can efficiently well up off shore the continental slope and fill in that area. This deep water is drawn up from even thousands of meters deep in the water. It replaces the surface water and once again, just like with the equatorial system it produces a very voluminous amount of nutrient rich water arriving at the surface and fueling major phytoplankton blooms.

If we look now at sea surface temperature and chlorophyll, the 2 images that we are familiar with from the equatorial region at this point. For the region off shore of central California, from the San Francisco Bay to Monterrey Bay and down on towards Santa Barbara you can see in the sea surface temperature the signal of this phenomenal amount of coastal upwelling, very cold water at the surface right at the coast. If you've ever been to the beach in any of those regions you know that you're in for a shock if you expect water temperatures similar to the same latitudes along the east coast because even in the middle of summer in central California the water is freezing.

I used to live in Santa Cruz where I did my PhD and wore a wet suit even in the middle of summer just to go swimming in the ocean. But, what's bad for swimmers is great for productivity of the biology in the water. The color image on the side is again a chlorophyll image and it shows that there's this massive concentrations of chlorophyll where that upwelling fuels biological productivity and that's phytoplankton productivity once again. That phytoplankton is the basis of a very highly productive food chain. The famous fisheries of California and also of Peru and the areas in South America like this of anchovy and sardine, as well as fisheries in rich Antarctic waters that have the same kinds of coastal upwelling are all fueled by that upwelling productivity. Again, we've referred once or twice to Cannery Row in the Steinbeck era, those canneries of Monterrey and the canneries of San Francisco Bay were all based on these productive fisheries of sardines and other fish that were fueled by phytoplankton productivity due to coastal upwelling.

The most productive fishery in the world per square meter is the anchovy fishery of coastal Peru regions and so that's the same kind of story in the Southern Hemisphere. There's other regions of the world as well that have significant amounts of upwelling productivity. One notable area or parts of the Mediterranean where you have a lot of coastline, you have this enclosed ocean basin, and so prevailing winds drive very strong upwelling in localized areas around the Mediterranean producing high productivity.

The converse to upwelling is downwelling and downwelling is the process that works in the same way due to Coriolis effect and Ekman transport, but if the wind is blowing the opposite direction along the coastline. If we use our example of the Northern Hemisphere, if the coast is on the east side and the open ocean is on the west side the wind is blowing from south to north than it pushes the water to the right that means as the wind blows the surface waters pile up against the coastline. They don't actually pileup, what they do is those surface waters are forced to sink, even though they're low density they're forced to sink because there's nowhere for them to go. They depress the thermocline, they push it down, they push the pycnocline down and this can suppress primary productivity because now you have all these warm nutrient depleted surface waters that are making it to great depths. That's not good obviously for the potential fisheries and things like that. Some areas of the world's oceans are relatively unproductive because of strongly developed downwelling.

Downwelling has some position benefits too because ultimately the same problem in terms of mixing goes the other direction. The surface waters are rich in oxygen because phytoplankton makes oxygen, but the deep waters are depleted in oxygen. Downwelling mixes that oxygenated rich surface water into the deep water and that is an important nutrient for all the organisms that are in the deep pelagic and even benthic zones of the ocean. If it weren't for downwelling going on over the world quickly the stratification of the ocean would become very extreme and all the deep waters would be oxygen depleted. They would become anoxic zones and much of the zooplankton and larger organisms that live down there wouldn't be able to live because they wouldn't have enough oxygen to fuel respiration.

All of this upwelling and downwelling then is something that's going on all the time and plays a major role in productivity in general, but it also has, to continue a theme we've already developed, some pathological effects at times. Let's take a look at the phenomenon called El Niño or as we also call it sometimes oceanographically the Southern Oscillation, and I'll explain why. Sometimes it's even abbreviated ENSO El Niño Southern Oscillation, ENSO. What is El Niño?

Actually where does the name come from even? In the 1890s, Peruvian fishermen, the fishermen who are exploiting that big anchovy fishery off the shore, noticed that in certain years there was the arrival of an unusually warm current on the coastline. The water got warmer than it normally was. It happened to come typically around Christmastime. They started to call it the Corriente de El Niño, meaning the current of the Christ Child. El Niño is the Christ Child in Spanish. It just means the boy literally. This Christmas current Corriente de El Niño would show up in certain years and in those years their fisheries failed. They would see that they would go out fishing and they just weren't catching anything nearly as productive as in a normal year.

In fact, it was worse than just the fisheries because there were so few anchovies and so few fish that the sea gulls had not much to eat and the other birds that were there. That particular region has for a long time had a very large bird guano mining industry. Why do you need guano? It's fertilizer of course. The bird guano industry was really strongly affected during the El Niño years. The fisheries were no good, the guano was no good, and the local economy would crash. In fact, this caused especially in earlier times the whole region would go into a state of potential famine because of the lack of food. It's not much of a Christmas present is it?

Let's take a look at what happens and why the Peruvian fisheries actually fail. First off, let's start with the pattern in a normal or non El Niño year. If we think about the equatorial currents, the trade winds and the whole Pacific basin, in a normal year what goes on is the surface winds are strong, they create the equatorial upwelling and they also blow the equatorial currents strongly over towards the western Pacific. The Coriolis turning is not as strong as we said before at the equatorial region so the water makes it all the way across the Pacific until it's in the region of Indonesia and New Guinea,

Philippines over there, and all this warm surface water that's been warmed by being in the tropics piles up. It actually has a higher elevation than the water on the other side. It depresses the thermocline in that region so you get a warm water pool.

Meanwhile back off the Peruvian coast, there's been strong upwelling because that water is pulling away from the edge of the continent, the Peru Current is coming along from the south so great upwelling is going on, the fish are happy so the fishermen are happy and the guano miners are happy too. It drives a lot of rainfall in those years and so you get a lot of evaporation in the western Pacific, the west side of the Pacific, away from Peru. Rainfall takes place and the water keeps moving and the equatorial upwelling zone is strong and everything is pretty comfortable. In a year like this, if we look at a profile of the temperature of the water with depth, this false color image is a profile down through the water column to several hundred feet. You can see this warm water pool in the western edge of the Pacific Ocean, obviously greatly vertically exaggerated on the planet, but the cool water over on the Peruvian side of the equatorial region of the ocean.

What happens in an El Niño year? Why do the fisheries fail? There's a diminishment for reasons that are somewhat unclear in the trade winds in the equatorial Pacific Ocean. It starts with an atmospheric phenomenon that is a persistent high pressure zone in the tropical western Pacific. In that region over by the Philippines, Indonesia, New Guinea area, high pressure develops and stays around in the atmosphere, not in the ocean but in the atmosphere. That change to a high pressure system is called the Southern Oscillation, so that's the SO part of ENSO.

When that happens you get high pressure over there and what happens is the trade winds don't blow towards it because winds blow away from high pressure towards low pressure. The trade winds weaken and die out. That means the equatorial surface current kind of dies out or weakens and instead all that warm water pool, that is dynamically maintained by the wind blowing over to that region starts to slosh back across to Pacific. It flows eastward from the western Pacific and it suppresses that upwelling.

If we look at the El Niño year then, we see that the thermocline starts to rise up in the west Pacific where it's drought conditions and high pressure air is over there. The water moves back, a ton of water moves back across the Pacific and suppresses the upwelling on the Peruvian side, in fact it even generates downwelling going the other direction on the Peruvian side. This is Pacific wide. Remember that's a third of the circumference of Earth is participating in this whole phenomenon. The water is warmer only by a degree or 2, but that's a significant amount in oceanographic circulation. The trade winds die out, the equatorial currents die out, and the water moves around. A cross section through the water column shows us that that warm water of the thermocline has progressed far to the east.

The strongest El Niño's have been in recent times. They've been in 1982-83 and 1997-98. One of the best recorded ones was a more recent one in 2009 and 2010 when lots of satellite data measured all sorts of things about the progress of this El Niño. We'll take a look now at this animation or time lapse series of all the satellite data. It's actually a measure in color coding of sea surface height. What we see is as it progresses we start off with sort of normal equatorial conditions. The sea surface is low; it's colored blue, that's a direct proxy for temperature, directly analogous to temperature. In the fall of 2009 as El Niño gets going you see this red pool of warm water that started out over there in the western Pacific, starts spreading back across to the eastern Pacific and hit the Peruvian coastline and suppressed that upwelling. Do the fisheries real damage.

As the process continues then, we move into 2010, we eventually see the reestablishment and redevelopment of equatorial upwelling going on. That's the process that we call La Niña. The currents eventually reestablish themselves once that high pressure has dissipated and the warm water pool has spread out over the ocean. Now we see a ton of blue water, blue color-coded water, meaning cold surface temperatures again reestablish itself. The Peruvian fishing industry is happy once again. If we look at 2 timed snapshots out of that we see this very strong, warm water equatorial situation totally opposite to the normal in the late fall and December of 2009, contrasting directly with the water situation along the equator in the La Niña case 6 month later or 7 months later.

What are some of the effects of the El Niño and the Southern Oscillation? First of all because of that sloshing of the water, the sea level actually rises in the eastern Pacific by as much as 20 centimeters or so. Normally, the western Pacific is a little higher than the eastern Pacific by as much as a meter. They kind of level out. Remember that's over 10,000 kilometer span we're seeing these differences of a meter. These are small values. The water is a fluid medium and so it moves around. More importantly than that, in the eastern Pacific the water temperature rises by up to 7 degrees. It causes more evaporation, low pressure over the eastern Pacific intensifies, and there's often heavy precipitation in coastal South America, torrential rains, landslides.

In the 1997 and 1998 El Niño 250,000 people were left homeless and every port in the country was closed by torrential rain and bad weather and landslides for over a month actually. It was a tremendously devastating event locally in that region. The climate effects are felt all around the world especially in the trade wind belt, but also to a lesser extent in other areas including North America. All around the world in the trade wind belts we see major modifications due to ENSO of the amount of rainfall. It's caused major droughts in Africa and in India at times, while causing torrential rain in other parts of the world all disrupting local climate and local economic activity in many cases.

As I said 1982-83 and '97-98 were some of the worst ones. The events in California in 1997-98 were pretty bad as well. We saw even in the Northern Hemisphere record snowfall in the mountains, torrential rains and landslides hitting the coast there and that was because of modification of the whole global pattern of airflow and high/low pressure systems in both hemispheres. If we take a look at some of the global effects, basically during an El Niño year the Pacific jet stream is suppressed down to a relatively southern area by persistent low pressure in the Gulf of Alaska and so that brings warm, wet air. The so-called Pineapple Express across California and the southern part of the U.S. has called major storm event all the way across to the eastern U.S. It doesn't affect the northern parts of the country as much, but it allows a certain amount of warm air to settle in over the northern United States and southern Canada because it moves the polar jet streams further to the north. I referred to La Niña just a second ago so let me define that. La Niña is the absence of an El Niño or the opposite effect of an El Niño. When there's an especially wet and warm time in the far western Pacific and the Peruvian currents are especially well-developed. In a sense, which just means the girl is just the counterbalanced El Niño. The world oscillates back and forth between the 2 conditions with relatively few years that are neither, at least a weal La Niña or a weak El Niño and then every once in awhile there's a really strong one.

In a La Niña year, to contrast it with that El Niño year that I just talked about, we see the Pacific jet stream goes farther to the north. It can even merge with the polar jet stream. We get persistent high pressure up in the Canadian Arctic that brings very cold air across the central part of the United States and we have very dry, sometimes very drought-like conditions across the southwest and California. More affects going on all over the world in fact.

If we look at the ratio of El Niño to La Niña years, we can really see this oscillatory nature of it. NOAA, the National Oceanographic Atmospheric Administration keeps a thing called the Oceanic Niño Index, which is sea surface temperatures measured in a particular place in the central Pacific Ocean. You see that it just bounces back and forth between strong and weak El Niño, which is above the line and La Niña, which is below the line in the curve, 1950 to 2009. Not a lot of change necessarily and they come and go and they're periodically very strong ones. You can see the `82 and the `97 spikes there in El Niño. Often the strong ones are followed by strong La Niña conditions, but the magnitudes oscillate up and down for reasons that are really not clear today in climatology.

We've seen then that vertical motions, upwelling and downwelling of the surface waters can be driven by both winds and the surface currents. They pull deep water up to the surface in the case of upwelling controlling the location of especially productive zones of the world's oceans in the point of view of biology. There are cyclical disturbances to those patterns in the form of El Niño/La Niña cycles that cause major disruptions in the fisheries in the global circulation of water and of the air and even cause natural disasters. In the next lecture, we're going to follow the upwelling and downwelling down deep, deeper into the ocean to see how the water moves right beneath the thermocline and the density barrier we call the pycnocline.

The Deepest, Slowest River—Polar Bottom Water
Lecture 32

M̲ost of the volume of the ocean participates in very slow deepwater circulation driven by density differences called thermohaline circulation, which depends on temperature and salinity variations. Cold, salty water formed in the northern and southern polar regions sinks to form deepwater masses and spreads throughout the entire ocean. Flow is very slow relative to surface currents but involves enormous masses of water and is responsible for the global-scale mixing of the ocean. Surface currents and deep circulation together make up the global conveyor belt for water and heat in the ocean.

Deep-Ocean Transport

- Ocean circulation at the grandest scale is the circulation that occurs in the great bulk of the water that represents the deep ocean.

- The ocean is stratified, or layered, with the main boundary being the thermocline—the difference between the warm surface waters and the cold, deep waters. Stratification also indicates a density difference.

- Most of the volume of the ocean participates in a very slow and even majestic deepwater circulation. It takes place in specific patterns that are driven by the atmospheric circulation on the planet, the climate, the differences between the poles and the equator, and the Coriolis forces.

- The deep ocean is in motion due to—specifically and exclusively—density differences. Ultimately, it is gravity-driven flow; denser water sinks, and water that is not as dense rises.

- Density varies specifically with 2 major features: temperature and salinity, which is the amount of dissolved solids in the water. Water becomes denser as it becomes more saline, and colder water is denser than warmer water.

- Sometimes temperature is the dominant density variation in the water, and sometimes salinity is the dominant density variation—and sometimes it's a combination of the 2.

- **Thermohaline circulation** is heat-salt circulation. In fact, it's because those 2 things are the variables that govern density in the water that thermohaline circulation is density circulation.

Water Masses

- There are different water masses in the ocean. Even though the ocean is a fluid medium, there are still vast volumes, or parcels, of the water that acquire certain persistent characteristics.

  - Down to the beginnings of the thermocline, the surface waters exist from zero to about 200 meters.

  - Below that is the central water that extends from about 200 meters to the base of the thermocline.

  - Below that is a very important water mass called the intermediate water, which extends down to about 1500 meters.

  - From 1500 meters down to close to the bottom of the ocean is called the deep water of the ocean.

  - Below the deep water, there is a layer of water in some parts of the ocean called bottom water, which is water that is in contact with the bottom of the ocean and occupies the lowermost few hundred meters.

- Water masses form due to processes that occur exclusively at the surface. Even the water at the very bottom of the ocean acquired its characteristics—its density, salinity, and temperature structure—at the surface of Earth.

- The density-dependent layering of the ocean is a function of these different water masses. As water becomes denser or less dense, it sinks or rises until it's in some kind of equilibrium. Whenever water moves in the ocean, other water has to come in and fill in the space that it displaced.

- The surface water is the least dense, not surprisingly. It's typically warm water, and it's low in salinity because there's rainfall on the surface of the ocean that dilutes it.

- Conversely, the deep water is the densest, so it's very cold and very saline at the same time. It forms at the surface in high-latitude polar regions.

- The intermediate waters are intermediate in density and, therefore, intermediate in the salinity and temperature profile to the surface and deep waters. Intermediate waters also form at the surface but in very specific areas of the world's oceans.

- The cold regions, naturally, are the northern and southern polar regions. The water forms and sinks to form the deepwater masses in a downwelling process due to density differences. Ultimately, from the polar regions, the water spreads throughout the entire ocean.

- In the areas off Antarctica in the Arctic Ocean, the air temperature is cold; the ocean is losing heat to the atmosphere, so the water is getting colder, which is making it denser. At the same time, sea ice is forming.

- When water freezes and ice forms in the ocean, it makes freshwater ice. If the ice that has formed floating on the ocean surface is freshwater, then it has excluded the salts that were in that volume of water that turned into ice. Therefore, adjacent water around the ice has to take up those excess salts. The water becomes more saline and colder, which causes that water to sink.

- As that water forms, it sinks down and starts to spread through the ocean. This process is the basis for a conceptual model of pure thermohaline circulation.

- If water sinks, it has to be replaced, so the surface water is drawn northward or southward from the equator. Therefore, water has to well up in equatorial regions.

- This conceptual model of pure thermohaline circulation is a major part of the heat transfer from equator to pole on the planet that smoothes out the temperature differences between equatorial regions, which have an excess input of heat, and polar regions, which have a deficit of input of heat.

Deep-Measurement Methods

- Physical oceanographers measure the complicated temperature-depth-salinity profiles of the ocean using the CTD, the conductivity, temperature, depth profiler that has Niskin bottles attached to it. Many different bottles are lowered off the ship and are triggered at different depths to sample the water's chemistry.

- Swallow floats drift along with the currents, and they have sonar paintings that send their data out to a ship with a sonar sensor on the bottom of the hull that constantly receives data.

- A more sophisticated sensor system is something called an **Acoustic Doppler Current Profiler (ADCP)**, which can make a profile of the speed of movement of the water at different depths from the surface.

- In addition, gliders such as the Slocum glider are autonomous devices sent out in the water that can measure and then come to the surface and beam their data to satellites.

- There was a major program in the 1990s called the World Ocean Circulation Experiment that revolutionized our knowledge of deep circulation with millions of measurements.

- Today, the Ocean Observatories Initiative promises to put sensors on the ocean floor and in the water looking up through the water column that send data through fiber-optic cables to land so that real-time measurements can be kept.

Using Niskin bottles, oceanographic ships generate temperature and salinity profiles at given locations and depths.

- Another method uses chemical tracers in the water. In the 1950s and 1960s, it was the atmospheric nuclear bomb–testing era that generated a large amount of the isotope tritium, which has a half-life of 12.5 years.

- For a long time, water samples were taken and the amount of tritium was measured, which could be used to determine the signature of water that had been at the surface and had been displaced in the deep subsurface.

- Today, chlorofluorocarbons that were released through the industrial production of CFCs are being used as deep-ocean tracers.

Antarctic Bottom Water and North Atlantic Deep Water

- As the sea ice forms off Antarctica, it leaves behind the coldest and highest-salinity water in the ocean. It obtains the salinity of about 34.8/mil and a water temperature that is below zero. Because it is saline, it can get down to $-1/2°C$. It's forming at a prodigious rate, with 20–50 million cubic meters forming every second off Antarctica.

- The sea ice rapidly sinks off the Antarctic shelf and down the continental slope. It's so dense and so cold that it sinks all the way to the bottom of the ocean and then spreads along the ocean floor, hugging the ocean floor of the Atlantic all the way to the equator in the widest and slowest-moving river on the planet. It takes about 500 to 1000 years to reach the equator while travelling at a rate of 10–20 kilometers per year.

- The North Atlantic also generates cold, deep water of similar salinity— 34.9/mil. It generates water that's a little bit warmer at 2–4°C, which sinks and moves southward. **North Atlantic Deep Water** comes in and layers on top of the **Antarctic Bottom Water**.

© UCSB, Univ. S. Carolina, NOAA, WHOI.

Niskin bottles are lowered off ships and are triggered at various depths to obtain samples of ocean water.

- Most of the bulk of the Atlantic water in the ocean is made up of North Atlantic Deep Water.

- Intermediate water forms in a couple of different locations in the world ,and it's an important part of the overall mixing of the ocean—especially the mixing that governs how strongly stratified the thermocline is.

Intermediate Water

- Antarctic Intermediate Water forms near the continent of Antarctica and is at about 5°C and 34/mil. It is layered in a sort of tongue that sits on top of the North Atlantic Deep Water.

- In the Northern Hemisphere, a very important source of intermediate water is the Mediterranean Sea, which evaporates a lot of water, so the water is pretty salty at 37.3/mil—quite a bit saltier than the rest of the water in most of the ocean.

- The Mediterranean Sea is also pretty warm at 13°C. It comes out of the Strait of Gibraltar and mixes with some Atlantic waters. It sinks to about 1000 meters depth, and that's where it finds its buoyancy neutral point—its balance point—and spreads out.

The Pacific Ocean

- The Pacific Ocean doesn't have a significant source of Arctic cold water in the way that the Atlantic does because the Bering Sea and the Aleutian Islands form a shallow-water barrier.

- The deep water in the Pacific is the slowest-moving water on the planet, and the conditions are quite uniform below about 2000 meters. There isn't a real source for distinct intermediate water, so it has more of a less-featured, slow-steady gradient in the water.

- The water in the Pacific Ocean is the oldest water at depth, which is measured by the time since it left the surface region. This concept is related to the residence time of water in the ocean, which is how long it takes to come back to the surface water and acquire new characteristics. In the Pacific, the residence time is at least several thousand years.

- All of these deep circulatory systems in the ocean link up in some way with the surface currents. The surface currents and the deep circulation together make up what is called the global conveyor belt for water and heat in the ocean.

- Through the 1990s and into the 21st century, we have a much more nuanced and complex view of circulation within the world's ocean.

- The surface waters and the deep waters are circulating on very different kinds of timescales. There's only a limited amount of exchange between the 2 of them—especially from the point of view of deep water turning into surface water.

- Surface water acquires its characteristics in the tropics, generally where there's warm water and a lot of rainfall. Everywhere where it is warm, there's water slowly diffusing upward—about a centimeter per day.

- The equatorial and coastal upwelling zones also contribute to surface-water formation by bringing deep water up. The wind-driven downwelling zones bring shallow water down, and the mixing of these systems is occurring especially around the continental margins all over the world all the time in a complex pattern of exchange.

Acoustic Doppler Current Profiler (ADCP): A device that measures current speed by measuring the Doppler frequency shift of sound waves reflected back from particles in the water.

Antarctic Bottom Water: The coldest, saltiest, and densest water mass in the ocean that forms off the Antarctic continental shelf and spreads over the base of the entire Atlantic Ocean.

North Atlantic Deep Water: The cold, saline water mass that forms in the North Atlantic and Arctic oceans that is responsible for most of the volume of the deep ocean.

thermohaline circulation: Gravity-driven movement of deepwater masses due to the density differences controlled by salinity and temperature.

Suggested Reading

Garrison, *Essentials of Oceanography*, chap. 8.

Open University, *Ocean Circulation*.

Questions to Consider

1. Do you imagine that it is likely that Coriolis motions affect deepwater circulation? Why or why not?

2. What factors about deep circulation might allow water masses to retain their characteristics so persistently for even thousands of years?

The Deepest, Slowest River—Polar Bottom Water
Lecture 32—Transcript

We've taken a look at the surface currents and how they transport water across the upper part of the ocean and even how they bring some deep water up through upwelling and downwelling processes. Now it's time to take a look at ocean circulation at the grandest scale of all, the circulation that goes on in that great bulk of the water that represents the deep ocean. We've seen that the ocean is stratified or layered with the main boundary being the thermocline, the difference between the warm surface waters and the cold, deep waters. Remember that that stratification is also a density difference. It turns out that the thermocline is not the only boundary in the ocean. There are others as well that we'll see in just a moment deeper down within the deepwater mass.

Most of the volume of the ocean participates in a very slow and even majestic deepwater circulation. It takes place in specific patterns that are driven by the atmospheric circulation on the planet, climate, the differences between the poles and the equator, Coriolis forces, and everything else. Let's take a closer look at that global scale, deep, slow motion ocean.

To talk about the deep ocean below the thermocline, we could call them deep ocean currents, but in fact that's kind of a misnomer. They move so slowly and involve such large volumes of the ocean water that they're not really currents so much as just transport of water. Maybe the right way to really put it is that it's ocean circulation, slow, steady mixing. The flow that happens in the deep ocean is different from the flow in the surface water. The surface currents as you recall were driven by the wind blowing. The wind blows and Ekman transport takes place, and water moves about the surface of the ocean. That's fundamentally driven by the drag of the wind on the surface.

By contrast, the deep ocean, which is not of course in contact with the wind or any force like that, is in motion due specifically and exclusively to density differences. Ultimately, it's gravity driven flow, denser water sinks and less dense water rises relative to each other. Density, I'll remind you, varies specifically with 2 major things, temperature and salinity, the amount of dissolved solids in the water is the salinity. That makes the water more dense as it gets more saline and colder water is denser than warmer water. Water expands a little bit when it warms and that makes it less dense.

The two have similar scales of effect on that water density so sometimes temperature is the dominant density variation in the water, sometimes salinity is the dominant, sometimes it's the combination of the two. The water in the deep ocean then acquired different temperature and salinity characteristics that drives density differences and the density differences in turn through gravity driven circulation. We call that circulation thermohaline circulation. Thermohaline, what does that big word mean? Thermal, so heat, and haline, remember halite, or geological term for salt crystal. Thermohaline circulation is just heat salt circulation. In fact, it's because those two things are the variables that govern density in the water, thermohaline circulation, density circulation.

There are different water masses in the ocean just in the way we talked about air masses meteorologically speaking that even though it's a fluid medium, there is still volumes or parcels of the water of vast scale that acquire certain persistent characteristics. They're not persistent forever, but as we'll see water moves a lot more slowly than the atmosphere does so water masses can retain certain characteristics and be identifiable for longer periods of time than the atmosphere does. There are different water masses and we define them largely by depth at least at the most basic level of definition. We can talk about the surface waters.

We've already mentioned them quite a lot. That's basically down to the beginnings of the thermocline; the surface waters from zero to about 200 meters give or take, sometimes shallower, sometimes deeper than the thermocline varies around the world. Below that over the span of the thermocline is a water mass that is less clearly identifiable and even a term that's not always used, but sometimes called the central water from that 200 meters or so to the base of the thermocline. Below that is a very important water mass that is simply called intermediate water and that's down to about 1500 meters or so and we'll see why that's an important number a little later on. Then from 1500 meter on down to nearly the bottom of the ocean, remember the average depth of the ocean spread over large areas is about

4000 meters. From 1500 down to close to the bottom is called deep water, simple term, the deep water in the ocean.

Below the deep water, there's one more layer of water, at least in some parts of the ocean, we call that bottom water, so water that's just simply in contact with the bottom and just maybe occupies the lowermost few hundred meters in some cases, maybe even a thousand meters, maybe less. That's the deepest water of all. Surface water, intermediate water, deep water, and bottom water are the important ones we want to remember. These water masses form due to processes that happen exclusively at the surface. It turns out that even the water at the very bottom of the ocean actually acquired its characteristics, its density, salinity, temperature structure, at the surface of Earth. It acquired due to processes of heating and cooling, freezing and precipitation.

Let's take a look at those. The density dependent layering then is a function of these different water masses and as water becomes denser or less dense it will sink or rise until it's in some kind of equilibrium, just like our old analogy of the hot air balloon. You put some heat into the balloon; it rises in the atmosphere until it's at a equilibrated buoyancy or density structure. Add a little more heat, it goes up, let it cool off for awhile it starts to sink. The same goes for masses of water. They get certain density properties. We're going to see that that process is just an upscale version or a larger scale version of our upwelling and downwelling that we've already discussed.

The one important principle behind all of this density dependent layering is the concept of something called continuity of flow, and I already described that when we talked about upwelling, that the ocean you know any time water moves in the ocean other water has to come in and fill in the space that it displaced. You can't create holes in the ocean. The volume of the ocean isn't changing over time, certainly not significantly for our purposes here so you're always displacing other water whenever you move one mass of water around.

What are the differences among these layers or masses of water? The surface water is the least dense, not surprisingly. It's typically warm water. It's low in salinity because there's rainfall on the surface of the ocean that dilutes it. There's even in some areas enough river runoff to dilute the water a little bit. The surface water of the ocean basically forms tropically in high precipitation areas. Places where the water gets the warmest and it gets rained on a lot, you generate water of relatively low salinity and high temperature.

Conversely the deep water is the most dense, not surprisingly, so it's very cold and very saline at the same time. It forms at the surface though as I said. It forms, it turns out, in high latitude polar regions and we'll take a look at that in just a moment. In between are these intermediate waters and even the central waters and they're just what they sound like. The intermediate waters are intermediate in density and therefore intermediate in the salinity and temperature profile to the surface and deep waters; they also form at the surface, but in very specific areas of the world's oceans, as we'll see.

How does this deep water and even the bottom water form? You need to generate that cold salty water somewhere in the ocean. The cold regions naturally are the north and south polar regions and the water forms and sinks to form those deepwater masses so it sinks to a downwelling process due those density differences. Ultimately it turns out that from the polar regions it spreads throughout the entire ocean as we'll see.

Let's take a look at how that formation process takes place. If you go to the North Atlantic in the Arctic Ocean or in the areas offshore Greenland or if you go to the far Antarctic in the areas off Antarctica, then what's going on there is that the air temperature is cold, the ocean it losing heat to the atmosphere so the water is getting colder. That's making it denser. At the same time, sea ice is forming. When water freezes and ice forms, as we said a long time ago in this course, you make fresh water ice. If the ice that's formed floating on the ocean surface is fresh water then that means its excluded the salts that were in that volume of water that turned into ice. Adjacent water around it that's still liquid has to take up those excess salts. The water becomes more saline so it simultaneously is getting more saline and getting colder and therefore that water starts to sink.

We have voluminous amounts of downwelling going on, not by any kind of wind currents, but just by the formation of dense water in the Northern Atlantic and Arctic regions and then offshore Antarctica. As that water forms, it sinks down and starts to spread through the ocean so we can come up with a conceptual model of pure thermohaline circulation. When that takes place the water sinks in the polar regions and remember that one of the functions of the polar regions is that there's very little thermocline. It's cold water at the surface. It's cold water deep and the sinking water is happening and so therefore the temperature structure in the water is pretty much constant or near constant with depth, weak thermocline. Water moves through it very easily. The water is not particularly layered or stratified, but it spreads across the ocean towards the equator and then ultimately it has to be filled in by surface water that flows towards the North or South Pole.

If water sinks it has to be replaced so the surface water is drawn northward or southward from the equator and therefore water has to well up in equatorial regions. In a much, much smaller or broader and more diffuse upwelling then what we saw with actual equatorial divergent upwelling, but nonetheless it's an upwelling and so water moves across the well-developed thermocline very slowly in equatorial regions. This conceptual model of pure thermohaline circulation is a major part of the heat transfer from equator to pole on the planet that we talked about already that smoothes out the temperature differences between equatorial regions, which have this excess input of heat and polar regions which have a deficit of input of heat.

The real situation is a lot more complicated than a simple diagram like that of the conceptual model of thermohaline circulation. If we look at the Atlantic Ocean, there are all kinds of water masses in there. We'll take a look at that shortly and see what the actual differences are in these deepwater masses, intermediate water masses, bottom water masse. But, first I'd like to spend a couple of minutes just talking about how this detail is known, how do physical oceanographers find out the complicated temperature depth salinity profiles of the ocean.

We talked already about some of the methods so I've introduced you to the idea of the CTD, the Conductivity Temperature Depth profiler with the Niskin bottles on it, many different bottles lowered off the ship triggered at different depths that sample the water so they can get a water chemistry sample and continuously measure temperature and salinity because of the electrical conductivity against depth. Oceanographic ships have been going around the ocean for decades now making tens of thousands of these measurements and they generate a temperature profile at a given location with depth. They also generate a salinity profile with depth.

Go around the ocean in enough different places and you can build up all those data sets and start to draw contours around areas of constant salinity or temperature or the combination which is density. That's a laborious process. It takes a long time to lower down a sampler and do all of that and so other ways of trying to get more data faster have been devised, especially in recent decades. For example, floats have been dropped into the ocean that basically drop in the water and they're weighted in such a way so they'll be neutrally buoyant at a predetermined certain depth position. Then they drift along with the currents and they actually have sonar paintings that send their data out to a ship with a sonar sensor on the bottom of the hull or something or sometimes a moored buoy that's just constantly getting their data.

They can be cheap and so lots of them can be thrown in the water. They drift passively, but they allow lots of measurements to be made in lots of different places. Sometimes they last a very long time. One of them sent data for over 9 years this way. Another method that's even a more sophisticated sensor system is something called an Acoustic Doppler Current Profiler, ADCP. This is a transducer on the bottom of a ship that's sort of like an echo sounder, but it's designed with frequencies that instead of bouncing off the bottom and coming back actually go down in the water and are reflected back from the suspended particles of plankton and things like that in the water. It turns out that the Doppler shift of frequency, the same thing that makes a train sound louder when it's coming towards you and quieter when it's going away from you, allows you to calculate the velocity that the water is moving.

The different frequencies allow you to calculate that at different depths so an ADCP without lowering anything down in the water can actually make a profile of the speed of movement of the water at different depths from the surface. That's pretty good. That gets you a lot of data quickly. There's also gliders. I showed you the Slocum Glider in a previous lecture so things that are autonomous devices sent out in the water that can measure and then come to the surface and beam their data to satellites. Another type is actually towed behind the ship on a cable, like a sort of underwater kite, and it has control of the wings so it can go up and down and measure values in different levels of the water.

All of these sorts of things and many others were put together increasingly in recent years to really profile the whole oceans. There's a major program in the `90s called the World Ocean Circulation Experiment that revolutionized our knowledge of the deep circulation with millions, literally, of measurements like this. Today even more measurements like that are going on including the development of something called the Ocean Observatory Initiative, which promises to put sensors on the seabed and in the water looking up through the water column and then sending their data through fiber optic cables back to land so that real time measurements can be kept.

One other interesting method uses literally chemical tracers in the water. The story is a fascinating one because it's another place where science has serendipitously benefited from other things that happened. In the 1950s and 1960s, there was the atmospheric nuclear bomb testing era. That generated a lot of the isotope called tritium, which has a half-life of 12-1/2 years. If there's tritium in the water you know it came from the bombs. Over the course of those decades now the tritium is basically depleted because there's no more testing going on atmospherically or on atolls in the Pacific.

For a long time, water samples were taken, the amount of tritium was measured and so it could determine the signature of water that had been at the surface and had displaced in the deep subsurface. Carbon-14 with a longer half-life is also used actually in a similar way. Nowadays chlorofluorocarbons that don't occur naturally, but were released through industrial production of CFCs are being used as a deep ocean tracer. Chemistry of these things that get in the water inadvertently starts to tell us about ocean currents.

Let's go back to our deepwater formation now. We can see that persistent and identifiable water masses form and two really important ones are the North Atlantic deep water and the Antarctic bottom water. First the Antarctic bottom water, as the sea ice forms off Antarctica it leaves behind the coldest and highest salinity water of all in the ocean. The conditions are so extreme down there and rapidly forming sea ice. It gets the salinity of something like 34.8/mil and a water temperature actually below zero. Because it's saline, it can get down to -1/2° C is typical for this water. It's forming at a prodigious rate 20-50 million cubic meters forming every second off Antarctica.

It rapidly sinks off the Antarctic shelf and down the continental slope. The Antarctic bottom water spreads slowly northward and it actually tongues in along the deep sea floor. It's so dense and so cold that it sinks all the way to the bottom of the ocean and then spreads along the sea floor hugging the sea floor of the Atlantic all the way to the equator in the widest and slowest moving river of them all on the planet let's just say. It takes something like 500 to 1000 years to reach the equator travelling at a rate of 10-20 kilometers per year.

Remember our surface currents traveled at a rate of miles per hour, 1 to 5 let's say; this is 10-20 kilometers per year. It's been shown through these chemical signatures and through other kinds of phenomena like that that it retains it characteristics for as much as 1600 or even 2000 years. This Antarctic bottom water, once it gets down there, stays down there for a very long time before it ultimately mixes with water around it.

The North Atlantic, the Northern Hemisphere who also generates cold deep water, the same process occurs in the Arctic off of Greenland and in the North Atlantic in that region. It forms water of similar salinity, 34.9/mil. Remember the average is between 33 and 34. It generates water that's a little bit warmer, 2-4° C and that water sinks and moves southward. The water's a little bit less dense because of that little bit higher temperature than the Antarctic bottom water so the North Atlantic deep water kind of comes in and layers in on top of the Antarctic bottom water.

The bottom water is down here, the North Atlantic deep water; they're coming from opposite directions on the planet and converging in the middle of the ocean. It turns out that most of the bulk of the Atlantic water in the ocean; most of that entire region of deep water is made up of North Atlantic deep water. This is where huge amts of water are generated and huge amounts of water sink and fill in the ocean. A cross section through the Atlantic Ocean all the way from north to south shows this intertonguing of the 2 types of deep water that are being generated at the opposite poles of the planet.

What about the intermediate water then? I said we would talk about intermediate water. It forms in a couple of different locations in the world and it's an important part of the overall mixing of the ocean especially the mixing that governs how strongly stratified the thermocline is. In the Southern Hemisphere basically in the Antarctic region water also forms that's cold and salty, but not nearly as cold and salty as the really high concentration stuff and so Antarctic intermediate water forms, AIW, near the continent and it's at about 5° C and 34/mil and kind of layered in a tongue sitting in on top of the North Atlantic deep water. We have yet another sheet of water spreading out, but balancing out at a particular depth of just between 1000 and 1500 meters or so depth in the Atlantic Ocean.

In the Northern Hemisphere, a very important source of intermediate water is actually the Mediterranean Sea. The Mediterranean is an enclosed basin, it evaporates a lot of water and so the water gets pretty salty, 37.3/mil, quite a bit saltier than the rest of the water in most of the ocean, but it's also pretty warm 13° C. This water has an intermediate density and forms intermediate water. It comes out of the Straits of Gibraltar over the shallow water shelf at the Straits there, comes out of the Mediterranean; it mixes with some Atlantic waters and grows in volume and becomes a little less distinct density wise, but it sinks to about a thousand meters depth and that's where it finds its buoyancy neutral point, it's balance point, and so it spreads out.

This Mediterranean intermediate water can be traced as much as 2500 kilometers away from Gibraltar and identified as a persistent water mass once again out in the Atlantic Ocean. If we take a look at the profile of the entire Atlantic Ocean—a profile running from north to south, which shows Antarctica at 80 degrees south on one side and 60 degrees north and the the Arctic basin on the other side, the equator right in the middle—we can look at what the density and temperature structure is of the ocean itself. It's based on all those millions of measurements that were made by all the different sensors that we talked about.

In the contours you see that they outline zones of particular, kind of constant, density, or constant salinity and constant temperature. We see the very low temperature waters associated with the region just off shore of Antarctica, even less than zero in places. Then the waters associated with north Atlantic deep water, forming this large tongue surrounded by the 3 or 4 degree contours in the north Atlantic. If we actually looked at the same profile but really mapped to the entire Atlantic basin, then we can identify these persistent water masses that I've been talking about—the North Atlantic deep water tonguing in and crossing right across the equator, with its constant salinity and 2–4 degree temperature filling in most of the volume of the ocean; the Antarctic bottom water layering in below that, with its extreme temperature and high salinity; and then the water that's coming out of the straits of Gibraltar and filling in as intermediate water in the North Atlantic, filling in the center of the North Atlantic basin and extending down to about the equatorial region.

What about the Pacific Ocean? The Pacific is a little bit different story. It's the biggest ocean so it should be the biggest player. The Pacific doesn't really have a significant source of Arctic cold water in the way that the Atlantic does because the Bering Sea and the Aleutian Islands are kind of in the way and form a shallow water barrier. There's no source of Arctic cold water. There's no real equivalent of North Atlantic deepwater formation. There's some weak deepwater formation, Gulf of Alaska and off the Bering Sea, but it doesn't amount to anything like the Atlantic. There's also, just for oceanographic reasons, lesser amounts of the Antarctic bottom water forming in the Pacific Basin area off of Antarctica.

There's not much deep water being generated in the Pacific. It's slowly trickling down there. There is Atlantic deep water coming in getting entrained in the deepwater region that's underneath the West Wind Drift circulating around Antarctica that moves into the Indian Ocean and very slowly moves into the Pacific Basin. The deep water in the Pacific is actually the slowest moving water on the planet and the conditions are quite uniform below about 2000 meters. There's not a real source for very distinct intermediate water either so it's got more of a less-featured and slow stead gradient in the water.

It does mean though that the water in the Pacific Ocean is the oldest water at depth and by age I mean the time since it left the surface region and therefore related to the residence time of water in the ocean, how long it takes to come back to the surface water again and acquire new characteristics in the Pacific is at least several thousand years. It can be 3-4 or more thousand years for deep water to actually end up as surface water in the Pacific Basin. If we look at that same contour cross section of the Pacific Basin again vertically exaggerated, but we see that the stratification is simpler and the structure is less complex in general than the Atlantic, but it shares some characteristics with the coldest water being in the southern ocean adjacent more or less to Antarctica.

All of these deep circulatory systems in the ocean, let's call us, link up in some way with the surface currents and so the surface currents and the deep circulation together make up something that's been referred to as the global conveyor belt for water and heat in the ocean. The North Atlantic deepwater formation takes place up there and it hugs the continental slope as it goes down and fills in the Atlantic. The same is happening in the Antarctic. The water is filling in the Atlantic Basin and it's spreading, as I said, south of Africa, south of the Indian Ocean, south of Australia, and eventually adding some of the deep water to the Pacific Basin.

Ultimately that water moves through the Pacific Basin as well. There's been this diagram that became popular in the 1980s showing what was called the global conveyor belt and the idea that the surface waters move through the ocean in a certain way, the deep waters move through the ocean, they were linked in the North Atlantic and in the Antarctic and not much of anywhere else really in order to link them up and form that deep water and create a global circulation pattern. The implication is that global conveyor belt is not just transporting water, but transporting a great deal of heat around the ocean, again smoothing out the heat gradient on the planet, making it a pleasant place to live for us and for the denizens of the sea.

That diagram was probably always an oversimplification even in the time it was made and it certainly it was recognized as an oversimplification at that time. On the other hand, measurements that have been made since then, the WOCE and the recent measurements have shown that the situation is considerably more complex than was even recognized in the 1980s. Through the `90s and into the 21^{sr} century, we have a much more nuanced and complex view of world ocean circulation. There may be one way that the global conveyor belt diagram really doesn't do world circulation pattern justice is in the idea of the linkage because the surface waters and the deep waters are circulating at very different kinds of timescales. There's only a limited amount of exchange between the two of them especially in the point of view of deep water turning into surface water.

Remember surface water flows at meters per second. Deep water flows at kilometers per year barely and can live down there for thousands of years. By contrast, water that gets entrained into the surface oceanic gyre of the Atlantic, the Gulf Stream, and the North Atlantic current, and the Canary Current and back down to the equatorial currents, that can make an entire circuit around the ocean, one molecule of water might make it all the way around in not much more than a year or so. The residence time of surface water might be relatively high, but it moves around a lot. The deepwater residence time, by contrast, how long it stays down there and circulates in the deep waters anywhere from 250, say in the Indian Ocean, to 3500 years or more in the Pacific Ocean. These are very different systems operating at different scales.

I talked a lot about deepwater formation so what about surface water formation. You must be wondering where's the surface water coming from. We said that surface water acquires its characteristics in the tropics generally where there's warm water and a lot of rainfall and that's essentially true. It's true in a diffuse and slow upwelling going on all over most of the ocean surface in the tropical regions. Everywhere where it is warm there's water diffusing upward slowly, about a centimeter per day spread out over large areas of the ocean, not insignificant, a centimeter per day is something you can potentially measure, and that's filling in the gap left behind by the surface water that's entrained and forms deep water in the high latitudes north and south.

The equatorial and especially the coastal upwelling zones also contribute to surface water formation bring deep water up. The downwelling zones, wind driven downwelling zones bring shallow water down and so mixing of these systems is occurring especially around the continental margins all over the world all the time in a complex pattern of exchange that the conveyor belt model doesn't quite do complete justice to. You have to think of these wheels within wheels going on at the scale of the whole ocean.

Our global scale and density driven thermohaline circulation now we've seen is what moves the great bulk of the ocean slowly, but inexorably transferring the water and heat around the planet. Those deepwater masses form exclusively in the polar regions and exclusively at the surface and so they're all part of this massive heat redistribution engine that is the ocean and is intimately linked, in fact inextricably linked, with the atmosphere and its heat redistribution system. These are the things that control Earth's surface climate. In the next lecture, we're going to take a look at that heat system and all of its interlinkages and understand a little better why Earth is a habitable planet today.

The Ocean and Global Climate
Lecture 33

Earth's climate is a balance among solar radiation, the redistribution of heat by ocean and atmosphere, and the natural greenhouse effect that traps heat due to the chemical composition of the atmosphere. Most of the heat in the climate system is stored in the ocean. Water vapor, carbon dioxide, and methane are the main heat-trapping gases in the atmosphere responsible for the greenhouse effect; without them, Earth would be a frozen wasteland. Ice and sediment cores are records of the past climate and show how rapidly Earth's climate has changed through time.

Earth's Climate System

- The natural state of Earth's climate is a balance among solar radiation as the heat and energy input, the redistribution of that heat by the ocean and the atmosphere, and the envelope of the atmosphere itself, which contains the naturally occurring greenhouse gases that make up the chemical composition of the atmosphere.

- The ocean plays an absolutely central role in the maintenance of the overall thermostat and climate control of the planet due to its tremendous heat capacity.

- The oceans contain the vast majority of the overall heat in the ocean-atmosphere system; the oceans are the great heat sinks for the planet.

- The Sun shines down on the planet and warms it, but an equal amount of heat is radiated back to space. The planet surface overall is in a balance; it has a heat budget, and the budget is balanced.

- The heat that's radiated out to space has to exactly equal the heat that's coming in—or else the planet would slowly (or rapidly) warm up, or it would slowly (or rapidly) cool down. Over millions and millions of years, it has maintained equilibrium.

- Of the incoming solar energy, 31% of it reflects back off of the atmosphere. Basically, clouds are reflective, and the light immediately bounces back into space. **Albedo** is a measure of how reflective the surface is.

- In addition, 47.5% of the incoming solar energy is absorbed at the surface of Earth and ultimately gets reradiated back as heat instead of light, so it warms things up and radiates into the atmosphere.

- Almost all of the remaining balance, 17.5%, is absorbed within the atmosphere directly.

The Natural Greenhouse Effect

- The **greenhouse effect** is the fact that certain gases in the atmosphere are able to absorb heat and basically maintain that heat. The atmosphere doesn't radiate through those gases; instead, it heats them up.

- Water vapor is the primary greenhouse gas on the planet. The atmosphere can take up to 4% water to get to high humidity.

- The second greenhouse gas that's important is carbon dioxide, which occurs in very small amounts—much less than 1%—but it absorbs heat very efficiently.

- The other important greenhouse gas is methane, which is naturally emitted by the planet due to biological processes—specifically, the decomposition of living things.

- Currently, Earth's average surface temperature is between 15°C and 16°C—or 59°F and 60°F—which is a reasonably comfortable average for life.

- If there were no water vapor, carbon dioxide, or methane in the atmosphere and no ocean on the planet—no giant heat trap—people have calculated that the actual surface temperature of Earth on average would be about $-18°C$, or just below $0°F$.

- On our planet, the day-to-night range is just a few tens of degrees, and the annual range from winter to summer—even in the high latitudes—is measured in tens of degrees and not hundreds. That's a good thing.

- Life depends on the greenhouse effect in the sense that if it weren't occurring, the world would be frozen over. We wouldn't be able to live here; there wouldn't be any free water present.

- In 1824, French mathematician and physicist Joseph Fourier recognized the fundamental heat-trapping nature of Earth's atmosphere.

- In 1857, British physicist John Tyndall demonstrated the atmospheric greenhouse effect quantitatively through experiments and identified the specific gases carbon dioxide and water vapor as the key gases that played the role in generating this greenhouse effect.

- By 1896, Swedish chemist Svante Arrhenius proposed that the burning of fossil fuels—coal in particular—would increase the amount of carbon dioxide in the atmosphere, trap heat, and prevent the next ice age.

- In 1906, Arrhenius calculated the warming effect of a doubling of carbon dioxide as $1.6°C$ or more. He thought that this would take 3000 years, but we're actually approaching the doubling level already. It won't be that many more decades before we reach the doubling level—at least at current rates of increase of carbon dioxide in the atmosphere that are being measured today.

In the 1990s, Mount Pinatubo erupted in Indonesia and put massive amounts of dust and sulfur dioxide into the stratosphere.

Natural Climate Change

- Climates certainly change. The ice ages are examples of long-term scales of climate change, but there are also short-term scales such as the medieval warm period—a period in the middle ages when Europe enjoyed especially clement weather.

- There was a period in the 1700s of the Little Ice Age, when the climate was especially cold and harsh in Europe and even in North America.

- Large-scale volcanic eruptions, such as Mount Pinatubo in Indonesia in the 1990s, put massive amounts of dust and sulfur dioxide by way of the ash that comes out of the volcano into the stratosphere. These eruptions reduce warming over a period of time, and the global climate and global temperatures take a noticeable dip.

Measuring Long-Term Climate Change

- How do we know about longer term climate change, such as the changes between the ice ages and over the past million years?

- The fundamental record for long-term climate change are ice cores—particularly those from Antarctica and Greenland—which provide data for over 600,000 years on temperature and on the content of the atmosphere at any given time in history or prehistory.

- The record that comes from ice cores shows that there's been a cyclicity of changing parent surface temperature of the atmosphere in which the rise and fall of temperature exhibits a gradual growth of the glaciers and ice sheets and a cooling of the atmosphere—and then a sudden drop-off coming out of each glacial period.

- Currently, Earth is experiencing an interglacial period. There have been major glacial periods, and the carbon dioxide and temperature in the atmosphere and the apparent sea level have increased and decreased together. There is a linkage between these systems.

- Sediment cores from the ocean floor also provide a record that goes back much farther in geological time—before there were any glaciers on the planet.

- Oxygen isotopes and other proxies show us what the temperature conditions of the ocean were at different times. There were periods that were much warmer than today, and they were associated with different chemistries of both the ocean and the atmosphere. There were also periods that were much cooler during the glacial stages.

- We can obtain a much longer-term record in the ocean-floor sediment cores than we can obtain from the ice cores.

Modern-Day Global Warming

- We hear about the atmospheric warming, but we don't hear about the ocean warming as much because that's quite well known now. The measurements are robust and can be shown from many different kinds of data—from both surface and satellite measurements. In fact, ocean heating is actually taking up most of the change in heat on the planet.

- The climate system is going through a modification that is different from what was happening prior to the late 1800s with a signal that started to strongly emerge in the early part of the 20th century.

- The heat content of the ocean is rising rapidly, and it is a reflection of the excess temperature in the atmosphere on the land surface and at the ocean surface.

- We also know from measurements that were made starting in the 1950s that the concentration of carbon dioxide in the atmosphere has been rising over time. At no time from the geological record in the last 10 million years has the concentration been as high as present-day levels.

- Temperature and carbon dioxide levels are changing in lockstep on the planet. That's one of the fundamental observations that causes people to draw the conclusion that the change in temperature that we observe on the planet is related to the change in the amount of carbon dioxide in the atmosphere that's being put there by the burning of fossil fuels—as noted by Arrhenius in the 1800s.

- The atmospheric level of carbon is changing. Carbon dioxide has changed from a preindustrial level of 280 parts per million to a level of 390 parts per million in 2010.

- Methane is another greenhouse gas that is going into the atmosphere at greater rates, and this is primarily due to agriculture.

- Besides the greenhouse heat-retaining effect, carbon dioxide plays a huge role in the ocean system: The more carbon dioxide that gets dissolved in the ocean, it has an effect on the chemical balance of the ocean, which is detrimental for much of the life that's present in the ocean today.

The Ozone Layer

- The ozone layer story is kind of salutary because it shows that there can be successes in global-scale modification of what we do chemically to the atmosphere.

- In 1990, there was an international agreement to ban CFCs, and it seems to be working.

- The concentration of chlorofluorocarbons in the atmosphere is declining rapidly. The ozone depletion has flattened out from a very rapid change and may reverse soon.

- Maybe this is a model for global-scale cooperation on carbon emissions and the change in the natural state of the climate system that is represented by additional heat-trapping gases going into the atmosphere today.

- On the other hand, there is the possibility of finding ways to chemically remove carbon dioxide from the atmosphere by a process called carbon sequestration.

Important Terms

albedo: The fraction of solar energy reflected by a surface (as opposed to energy absorbed).

greenhouse effect: The physical property of some atmospheric gases to absorb and trap heat from the Sun's radiation shining on Earth.

Broecker, *How to Build a Habitable Planet.*

Murphy, *To Follow the Water.*

Questions to Consider

1. The average temperature of the ocean as a whole is just a few degrees above freezing. Given that, how is it that most of the heat in the climate system resides in the ocean?

2. Based on what you know about water and heat capacity, if the concentration of greenhouse gases in the atmosphere somehow suddenly returned to preindustrial levels, how rapidly or slowly might the global ocean heat content return to previous levels as well?

The Ocean and Global Climate
Lecture 33—Transcript

In recent lectures, we've taken a close look at circulation of both the atmosphere and the ocean and we've seen how intimately the two are linked, one driving the other and one affecting the other. One of the most important ways in which they're linked to each other is Earth's natural climate systems. The natural state of Earth's climate is a balance among solar radiation as the heat input and the energy input, the redistribution of that heat as we've seen by the ocean and the atmosphere, and the envelope of the atmosphere itself, which contains the gases that trap that heat on the surface of Earth. The naturally occurring greenhouse gases that make up the chemical composition of the atmosphere.

The ocean plays an absolutely central role in the maintenance of the overall thermostat and climate control of the planet due its tremendous heat capacity. Let's explore that in this lecture. Most of the heat in the climate system is in the ocean. In fact, the vast majority of the thermal energy in the overall climate, the atmosphere ocean/land climate system is in the water. That's because the heat capacity of ocean water is a thousand times that of the atmosphere. The gases can't hold much heat. Water can. It has that great thermal capacity that we've been talking about. The oceans contain the vast majority of the overall heat in the ocean atmosphere system. They're the great heat sink for the planet.

The currents in the ocean that we've seen in the last couple of lectures redistribute that heat making both the tropics and the high latitude polar regions relatively hospitable for life, and the reason why things have been able to adapt to life and we have open water oceans and reasonable air temperatures all over this planet. Let's take a look at Earth's heat budge in a little bit more detail then. Fundamentally the heat budget is very simple.

The sun shines down on the planet and warms things up, but an equal amount of heat is radiated back out to space. The planet surface overall is in a balance. It has a heat budget and the budget is balanced in fact. Remember we said the geothermal energy was not contributing significant amounts of heat to our surface climate. It's all about the Sun and the solar radiation shining on the planet.

As that happens then, the heat that's radiated out to space has to exactly equal the heat that's coming in or else the planet would slowly warm up or maybe rapidly warm up or it would slowly cool down or rapidly cool down. Over millions and millions of years, it's maintained equilibrium. It goes up and down over a small range, but that small range is within the comfort zone for life as we've been talking about. The oceans have never boiled away, the oceans have never frozen solid, and generally things have stayed within this narrow range. We've already explored some of the reasons why that is.

Of the incoming solar energy, if we take 100% of the incoming solar radiation shining on the planet, it's partitioned then into different things, 31% of it reflects back right off of the atmosphere. Basically clouds are reflective and the light just bounces back into space. It doesn't really warm the planet up at all. That reflectivity, by the way, is given a name scientifically and it's called albedo. Albedo is just how reflective the surface is. It ranges from 0 to 1, high albedo 1 means perfectly reflective, a mirror has an albedo like that; 0 means something that's black and just absorbs all the heat that's coming in, all the light that's coming in and converts it to heat.

Albedo is an important concept. Clouds have reasonably high albedo. Ice has reasonably high albedo because it's white, it's bright, it reflects the Sun back out. Open water, by contrast, if we're talking about the oceans has relatively low albedo. The sun shines on the water. It penetrates into the water. From space the water looks dark and that's because it's absorbing that solar energy and converting it into heat.

So, 31% reflects off the atmosphere, 47.5% of that incoming solar energy is absorbed at the surface of Earth. The vast majority of that absorbed in the ocean because the ocean is good at absorbing heat, the land also warms up obviously from the Sun shining on it. That 47.5% that is absorbed at the surface ultimately gets re-radiated back as heat instead of light so it warms things up and it radiates into the atmosphere; 17.5%, so the balance, is absorbed within the atmosphere directly. The sun shines in and the molecules of gas in the atmosphere are warmed directly by the Sun shining on the gas itself, the air itself. All of these things ultimately are either reflected out to space or converted into heat, which is then eventually just radiated back out into space by its heat loss at the top of the atmosphere. It's all in balance overall.

We have something then that is the natural greenhouse effect and that is the fact that certain gases in the atmosphere are well-known through long time known chemistry and physics to be able to absorb heat and basically maintain that heat so it doesn't radiate through those gases it heats them up instead. Water vapor is actually the primary greenhouse gas on the planet. The gases that go into the atmosphere include water as a gas, water vapor, and that water vapor absorbs heat very efficiently. There's a fair amount of water vapor. We said the atmosphere can take up to 4% water remember to get to high humidity.

The second greenhouse gas that's important is carbon dioxide. It's a naturally occurring gas. It's part of the atmosphere. It only occurs in very small amounts, much, much less than a%, in fact we measure in parts per million, a few hundred parts per million, but it absorbs heat very efficiently. The other important one is methane, which is naturally emitted by the planet due to biological processes, decomposition of things, and that's another important greenhouse gas as well. These are the 3 that are creating the natural greenhouse effect.

Right now Earth's surface average temperature is between 15 and 16 degrees C, 59 and 60 degrees Fahrenheit, a reasonably comfortable average for life and that's not a surprise. We've evolved to live under this condition so naturally that's what we like. If there were no water vapor in the atmosphere or CO_2 or methane, if there was no ocean on the planet, no giant heat trap, people have calculated that the actual surface temperature of Earth on average would be about -18 degrees C or just below zero, I should say, Fahrenheit. The surface temperature of Earth overall would be enough to freeze everything pretty much solid.

We certainly see that this effect of having these heat trapping gases on the planet is important for life on the planet as a whole. They trap that heat energy before it's re-radiated into space. It's a temporary trapping again. The earth's not warming up quickly or cooling down quickly, but it traps enough heat to maintain that particular set of temperatures; that 15 or 16 degrees C as the dominant condition on the surface of the planet. Most of that heat as I said is stored in the ocean and so that buffers the atmospheric changes. Remember the atmosphere can change a lot, the comparison to Mars was that the day and night range can be 150 degrees difference from day to night on a planet with no ocean. On our planet the day to night is really just a few tens of degrees and the year to year range or the annual range from winter to summer, even in the high latitudes, is measured in tens of degrees and not hundreds. That's a good thing.

We like that because it means that this whole natural process exists, life depends on the greenhouse effect in the sense that if it weren't happening the world would be frozen over. We wouldn't be able to live here. There wouldn't be any free water present.

The link between these gases carbon dioxide, methane, and water vapor because they are so fundamentally important to the nature of the climate system on the planet through their heat trapping properties has been recognized for a really long time, over 150 years, and it's because of that role that it plays. In 1824, the French famous mathematician and physicist Joseph Fourier recognized the fundamental heat trapping nature of Earth's atmosphere. The atmosphere itself kept things warmer on the planet than in the absence of an atmosphere.

In 1857, John Tyndall, an Englishman, demonstrated the atmospheric greenhouse effect quantitatively through experiments and identified the specific gases carbon dioxide and water vapor as the key ones that played the role in generating this greenhouse effect. By 1896, a chemist Svante Arrhenius proposed that the burning of fossil fuels, in particular coal in his day, would actually increase the amount of carbon dioxide in the atmosphere, trap heat, and as he was thinking about, prevent the next Ice age. This was actually the first clear statement of not just greenhouse gases as a fundamental process on earth and a natural process, but things that human beings were doing might modify the amount of those greenhouse gases. The first clear statement of what we would call anthropogenic global warming all the way back in 1896.

In 1906, Arrhenius calculated the warming effect of a doubling of CO_2 as 1.6 or more degrees C. He thought that this would take 3000 years, but actually we're getting pretty close to the doubling level already. It won't be that many more decades before we're there, at least at current rates of increase of CO_2 in the atmosphere that are being measured today.

The earth's climate varies. It's not just a constant. I said it's in equilibrium, but I also said that that equilibrium changes over time within a narrow band. We certainly know that over geological time climate has varied. We know that there's been an alternation of ice ages and warm periods over timescales of tens of thousands of years to millions of years. there's even megacycles of periods where there were no ice ages for millions of years and other periods like the recent past, geologically speaking, where the ice came and went on a timescale of tens or hundreds of thousands of years. We know that climate is highly variable.

We also know that it varies over much shorter timescales, even decadal scales, because of events that have taken place within recorded history. History and then beyond history, ice and ocean sediment cores that are those kinds of records, as I discussed with the ocean sediments way back when we were talking about sediments, give us a tape recorder or a tree ring system, so to speak, of past climate. They show us how some of that change has occurred over time, both the very gradual and long geological process change and increasingly people are recognizing from detailed analysis of year by year layers in the ice cores and the sediment cores, but sometimes it's been rapid natural climate change even in the distant geological past.

As we said climates certainly change. I talked about the long scales, like the ice ages, but there are also these short-term scales, the medieval warm period, a period in the middle ages when Europe enjoyed especially clement weather. On the other hand, there was a period a little later on in the 1700s of the little ice age when climate was especially cold and harsh weather in Europe and even in North America at that time. These were long thought to be gradual changes would occur, but as you recognition that all of these even short-term changes are driven by geological factors of different kinds and sometimes the rapid changes are pretty clear and it's pretty clear what causes them.

For example, big-scale volcanic eruptions like Mt. Pinatubo in the 1990s, which was a big volcano that erupted in Indonesia put massive amounts of dust and sulfur dioxide and all kinds of stuff, the ash that comes out of the volcano into the stratosphere. A big enough volcanic eruption can spread enough of those particles in the stratosphere that they actually cause, and Pinatubo caused, a noticeable dimming of the amount of sunlight reaching the surface of Earth and reaching the lower parts of the atmosphere. That reduced warming over a period of time and the global climate and global temperatures took a noticeable dip due to that volcanic input of material.

In the more geological past, there've been times when very large-scale volcanic eruptions had taken place like the super volcano explosion of Yellowstone for example. Those kinds of things where a Crater Lake explosion that took place several years ago; those kinds of events have also had even greater effects over short periods of time, say decades on climate. That kind of thing is linked to periods like a potentially little ice age and Medieval periods so these variations over centuries and decades. How do we know about the longer term climate change, the changes between the ice ages and over the past several hundred thousand, even one or more million years?

The fundamental record for that is ice cores and ice cores particularly from Antarctica and Greenland where drillers have gone out and sampled ice going right down through the ice sheets and found that they could find literally down to annual scale cycles of snowfall and then compaction and then it's not snow anymore by the time it compacts for an ice core that's thousands of feet deep. It becomes bands that are very dense and very narrow, but individual cycles can be found. They provide data over 600,000 years on temperature and also the content of the atmosphere because the ice tracks tiny bubbles, microscopic bubbles of ancient air and those can be analyzed with a mass spectrometer and you can get the carbon dioxide content, the methane content, and even the isotopic ratios of some of those carbon and oxygen and other compounds that tell you about the chemistry of the air at any given time in history or in pre-history, and also even proxies for what the temperature of the air or the ocean water itself was.

If we look at the record that comes from ice cores, we see that there's been a cyclicity of changing parent surface temperature of the atmosphere which partitions the oxygen isotopes and therefore causes a signal in the ratio of different isotopes of oxygen going up and down. That pairs with the time period such that you can see the rise and fall of temperature in a saw tooth pattern where we see a gradual growth of the glaciers and ice sheets and a cooling of the atmosphere and then a sudden drop-off as we come out of each glacial period. It turns out that we can map those directly to the kinds of sea level curves that we see and have already looked at coming from mostly ocean sediment cores that tell us where eustatic sea level was at any given time over the past several hundred thousand years.

Remember we said we're at a high now. It was in the not that distant past between 10 and 18 thousand years ago down 120 or more meters below its current level and then gradually sea level was higher and higher. That's the same saw tooth pattern that we actually see in the ice cores and it shows us that sea level went up and down in lockstep with the changes in oxygen isotopes that tell us about the temperature and the changes in carbon dioxide over all of that time through the waxing and waning of the different glacial periods. Remember we're in an interglacial now and there've been major glacial periods and the CO_2 in the atmosphere and the temperature in the atmosphere and the apparent ocean sea level have gone up and down together. We see this linkage of all of these systems.

The sediment cores actually from the ocean also provide us a record that goes back much, much further in geological time, back before there were any glaciers on the planet, for example, into a period that was much warmer than today, several tens of millions of years ago, between 40 and 60 million years ago in the early part of the Cenozoic era or after the dinosaurs were gone. Again oxygen isotopes and other proxies are showing us what the temperature conditions of the ocean were at those different times and so there were periods that were much warmer than today and they were associated with different chemistry of both the ocean and apparently the atmosphere; high carbon dioxide, and then periods that were much cooler during the glacial stages. We see a much longer term record in the ocean floor sediment cores that we can actually get from the ice cores

What causes all these ice age changes? What caused all this natural climate variability over time? These were caused by an external process to Earth or at least an external process to the climate system that has to do with Earth in orbit around the Sun. Remember that Earth goes around the Sun once per year and its orbit is tilted. We have a rotation axis that's tilted. That tilt changes a little bit over time and it's like a spinning top on a table and wobbles just a little bit. That's called the precession of Earth's axial tilt and then the tilt changes, it precesses, and at the same time Earth doesn't go around the Sun in a perfect circle. It goes around in an ellipse and that ellipse gets more squashed and then more circular on a rhythmic cycle that just has to do with gravity in the solar system. That's called the eccentricity. There are 3 different things that change on different time scales that are very long scales about Earth and the Sun.

Astronomers are able to calculate these very precisely and so the precession, the so-called obliquity, which is the tilt, and the eccentricity all cycle back and forth on different periodic signals. Some of them cause more solar energy to reach the surface of Earth and others cause less. You have to put them together and they create constructive and destructive interference that creates changes in solar forcing. A calculation of all those Milankovitch cycles when compared to the stages of the glaciation show that they're linked when there's more solar forcing, more sun energy on Earth. We come out of the glacial stages when there's less. We go into a glacial stage and that's driven by the external process. It's accompanied by the big changes in atmospheric carbon content among other things.

This is all the process of the natural climate system on the planet. If we take a look at what's going on in the present day climate system on the planet, we have to look at the warming that's evident that we see. We have to try to understand how it fits into this natural set of cycles of the planet as a whole. I can show you some data in just a second that suggests that the ocean is warming up. We hear about the atmospheric warming. We don't hear about the ocean warming as much, but that's quite well-known now. The measurements are robust and showing it from many different kinds of data, both surface and depth profile measurements as well as satellites. In fact, ocean heating is actually taking up most of the change in heat again on the planet as we'll see.

The climate system is going through a modification that is different from what was happening prior to the late 1800s with a signal that started to really strongly emerge in the early part of the 20th century. If we look at the heat content of the ocean as measured by averaging by temperature measurements all throughout the ocean, all over the planet, then we have a signal that we can see and use and look at the average trends in that heat content of the ocean. We don't talk about the average temperature of the ocean because temperature is so variable between surface waters and different latitudes across the planet, but that's a difficult number to find very meaningful.

The heat content is a more direct map of the integrated temperature, really heat energy that's being stored in the ocean at any given time. If we look at the actual data for the heat content of the ocean based on field measurements and then also satellite measurements all of them integrated together from 1955 to about 2009, we see that there have been fluctuations up and down. There's lot of variability in the measurements, but in general there's a rising trend and in fact there's an accelerated rising trend after about 1970 or so in this length of the time series. We don't have the direct measures of the heat content going back any further than that. The global ocean heat content and this summary is made for 0 to 700 meters depth, that's where virtually all of the changing heat is stored and it's showing that the heat content of the ocean is rising and is rising rapidly.

In any given set of years, it goes up and down a little bit. Short-term changes are due to major fluctuations in ocean currents, things like El Niño and the Southern Oscillation, cause rises and falls in given periods. For example, it fell around the period of 2007-08 as a strong El Niño system developed, but overall there's a very strong trend of growing heat content of the ocean and it's unequivocal at this point. That heat content in the ocean is directly a reflection with sort of the same trends and the same ups and downs as the global surface temperatures measured from space by satellites of the recent global surface temperature of the land and the entire planet integrated everywhere. The heat content of the ocean is a reflection of the excess temperature in the atmosphere on the land surface and at the ocean surface.

We also know from measurements that were made directly starting in the 1950s that the concentration of carbon dioxide in the atmosphere has been rising over time. In fact, we can look at the carbon dioxide variations again from those ice core records and we can see that they have that saw tooth pattern that's so characteristic for the ice cores. We were at the high point of those saw tooth's at the beginning essentially of the industrial revolution and certainly by the time the strong data started to be put together in the middle part of the 20th century and then CO_2 concentration has goes to much higher levels since then and people are familiar with this kind of diagram that shows that the CO_2 concentrations are rising and rising relatively rapidly today and in recent decades and at no time it turns out from the geological record in the last 10 million years has the concentration been as high as the present day.

We have a warming gas in the atmosphere at a level that hasn't been present throughout the entire glacial-interglacial period and going back to that much warmer era much earlier in the Cenozoic. Looking at that in detail then we also see that the changes in the carbon dioxide greenhouse gas shows the same acceleration after about the 1960s or so that we saw in some of world temperature records. The temperature and the carbon dioxide are changing in lockstep on the planet. That's one of the fundamental observations that causes people to draw the conclusion that the global warming is related, that the change in temperature that we observe on the planet is related to the change in the amount of carbon dioxide in the atmosphere that's being put there by the burning of fossil fuels as noted by Arrhenius way back in the 1800s.

Further corroborating evidence that goes along with that is that global climate simulation, so the computer models that are run over time, we'll look at this a little bit more later on, show that if you leave out the extra CO_2 in the atmosphere and run those global simulations, you can't get the kind of warming trends with reasonable assumptions about the planet's climate. These are models that are somewhat like weather models that we use for the weather forecasting but run over much larger area scales and much larger time scales. They're not meant to predict day to day or year to year variations, but long-term trends. You have to have the excess warming generated by the blanket of the extra CO_2 and methane in the atmosphere to get the models to run even for the past century. We're not talking about the future, but just for the past century to get the level of warming we've already seen.

I want to give you a little quotation that's from a report of a blue ribbon commission to the president. It says this. It says, "Through his worldwide industrial civilization, Man is unwittingly conducting a vast geophysical experiment. Within a few generations he is burning the fossil fuels that slowly accumulated in Earth over the past 500 million years. By the year 2000," a clue that my quote is a little bit old, "the increase in atmospheric CO2 will be close to 25% and this may be sufficient to produce measurable and perhaps marked changes in climate."

That report was actually written all the way back in 1965. It was a report of the scientific community to President Johnson. They recognized that global warming was going on and was going to change the climate and the change in atmospheric CO_2 by the year 2000 was somewhat greater than 25%, more like 29% or more based on the preindustrial baseline because we're putting more of it in the atmosphere faster than they recognized in 1965. The atmospheric level of carbon is changing. We see CO_2 having gone from a preindustrial level of 280 parts per million to a 2010 level of 390 parts per million. A rate of increase that's increasing in the past 2 decades over the rate it was going before and that's just very simple. We are burning it. We're taking it out of the ground. We're burning it and it goes in the atmosphere. There's no magic to that.

Methane is another greenhouse gas that is going into the atmosphere at greater rates primarily due to agriculture and there are a lot of cows that emit methane on the planet and so that's increasing at a fast rate too. That's another important greenhouse gas. Besides the greenhouse heat retaining effect, carbon dioxide plays a huge role in the ocean system for another reason.

CO_2 is the very rapidly exchanged gas between the atmosphere and the ocean. Actually that's good because most of the CO_2 we're putting in the atmosphere is being dissolved into the ocean water and so therefore it's not trapping heat in the atmosphere at as rapid an increased rate as it would be otherwise. On the other hand, that's bad because the more CO_2 that gets dissolved in the ocean as we'll see a little later on it has an effect on the chemical balance of the ocean and this is bad news for a lot of the life that's present in the sea today.

I want to draw a little bit of a comparison maybe to the ozone layer because we hear a lot about global warming and greenhouse gases and it may seem that it's very hard to see how we can do anything about it. The ozone layer story is kind of salutary though because it shows that there can be successes in global scale modification of what we do chemically to the atmosphere. Remember the ozone layer, the ozone hole, the depletion of the ozone layer due to the release of chlorofluorocarbons going back through the industrial era and right up until the 1970s into the 1980s is not the same thing as the greenhouse effect. In fact, they're not linked at all. The ozone hole has no particular effect on global warming.

People often confuse the two. The ozone layer story is that the natural ozone in the stratosphere absorbs the ultraviolet coming in. That protects us an all other life on the planet from DNA damage. It actually has an oceanic effect in the reduction of productivity of plankton when too much ultraviolet gets to the surface along with the effects like skin cancer and eye damage that we feel. The chlorofluorocarbons, the CFCs that we produce react with that and break it down. There's a small depletion over the U.S., about 3%, but over the Polar Regions it was depleted, the ozone layer itself was depleted by 50% or more. In 1990, there was this international agreement to ban the CFCs and it seems to be working.

The concentration of chlorofluorocarbons in the atmosphere is declining rapidly. The ozone depletion has flattened out from a very rapid change and may reverse soon. If we look at a graph going up to the most updated numbers we have available now, ozone depletion was rapidly increasing and then it kind of flattened out. It hasn't really started to go down yet, but the computer simulation suggests that it will start to go down in the coming years and decades and so we'll probably avert the worst effects of that.

Maybe this is a model for global scale cooperation on carbon emissions and the change in the natural state of the climate system that is represented by additional extra heat trapping gases going into the atmosphere today. It's a thornier problem than the ozone hole because chlorofluorocarbons could be replaced by other industrial chemicals. It's less easy to see how we replace the fossil fuels and the carbon dioxide that we emit unless we come up with ways to generate significant and I really mean truly significant amounts of our energy from non-fossil fuel burning sources. That's proved to be a thorny problem.

On the other hand, one possibility is being examined today is the possibility of actually finding ways to chemically remove carbon dioxide from the atmosphere so some of what's already been emitted take it back out of the atmosphere, a process called carbon sequestration. There are pilot projects on now in terms of pumping CO_2 into the ground on land and there's some very interesting proposals to look at pumping carbon dioxide into the deep ocean where it might sink to the bottom and stay there or drilling holes and pumping it back into the deep sea in the same regions where petroleum carbon is being taken out of the ground in the ocean.

We've looked at the natural climate system. We've looked at how it's starting to change in the present day post-industrial era. In the next lecture, we're going to take a look at the effect of those climate changes on sea level and the ocean itself and the ice volume and we'll look at the effect that all of these things have and are going to have perhaps on life in the sea.

The Warming, Rising Sea
Lecture 34

T he global warming phenomenon is a modification of the natural greenhouse system due to the rapid addition of carbon compounds to the atmosphere over the past 150 years, primarily from the burning of fossil fuels. The link between carbon dioxide, methane, and greenhouse warming has been known for over a century. About 80% of the extra heat retained through anthropogenic greenhouse warming is stored in the ocean. Effects that are already in existence include sea-level rise, changes in ocean acidity, and loss of sea ice—especially in the Arctic region.

Heat Content of the Ocean

- The largest effects of the modified heat-trapping nature of the atmosphere from the increased carbon dioxide content are already being seen in the ocean and are probably going to continue to be seen in the ocean.

- The heat content is rising in the ocean at an accelerating pace, and it's going to have an effect on all sorts of aspects of the ocean as a whole—from sea level to the movement of ocean currents over time.

- Future decades are likely to see the rise of heat content accelerating in nature and in intensity. The first most important change that we're seeing on the planet is that global-scale sea level, or the eustatic average, is clearly rising.

- From 1930 to the turn of the 21st century, the sea level has been rising at an average rate of about 1.8 millimeters per year.

- Once there was satellite data that could measure the height anomalies in the sea surface directly, it became possible to calculate sea-level change with even greater precision.

- For the period from 1993 to the end of 2008, the slope of the curve showing change in sea level shows about 3.1 millimeters per year of sea-level change—a much steeper slope than it had been.

- Sea-level rise closely tracks the overall global average temperature rise over time. When the global temperature increases, land ice starts to melt. Glaciers are currently in retreat on the planet.

- Even more importantly, the Greenland Ice Sheet is one of the major ice caps of the planet, and if it melted, sea level would rise tremendously.

- Greenland and Antarctica are losing volume; they're losing land ice, and it's turning into water. That water is being introduced into the ocean as new mass, so there's an increase in the volume of water in the ocean.

- The sea-level rise is also partly due to the **thermal expansion** of the water. As the water heats up, the water gets a little bigger, filling the basin a little higher than it did before.

© Patrick Kelley, U.S. Coast Guard.

Since the 1970s, there has been a rapid decrease in the amount of ice in the Arctic due to the addition of carbon dioxide to the atmosphere by humans.

- Of the overall change in sea level—at least 3.1 millimeters per year—about 2/3 is the effect of land ice melting and about 1/3 is thermal expansion in that short window of time (from 1993 to 2008).

- The ocean is a great heat sink, and 80% of the heat comes from the contribution of anthropogenic carbon dioxide that's added to the atmosphere through human activity that makes it into the ocean.

- Probably the most significant effect of carbon dioxide being added to the atmosphere is the warming of the Arctic region; in particular, the annual melting of sea ice in the Arctic Ocean is rapidly increasing.

- The reduction of sea ice is a problem for many of the organisms that live in the Arctic Ocean that depend on the sea ice. There are a number of Arctic marine ecosystems that are dependent on sea ice being present on top of the ocean to provide various habitats and to limit the amount of water mixing and wave action.

Projections of Earth's Future Climate

- At the current rate of change, by about 2030 the sea ice is projected to be less than 1/3 of its average level that existed during the 1979–1990 time period.

- In 2007, for the first time ever, navigable waters for ships that were not icebreaker-class ships, which are ships that are specifically designed to be able to cut channels through ice, opened up through the Arctic Ocean.

- When the Arctic sea ice melts, the freshwater will return to the ocean, but it won't change sea level directly. More importantly, the melting of sea ice contributes to a positive feedback in the ocean-climate system—and that is the albedo change.

- When you melt ice and turn it into open water, then more energy is absorbed from the Sun, and that warms the water up more, which can feed back into melting more ice. Therefore, there's a positive feedback in which melting the ice warms the Arctic Ocean, which causes more ice to melt—and the process continues. It's pretty clear that this process is under way in the Arctic already.

- Land ice can contribute to sea-level rise because it adds water that was on land to the ocean. This change in land ice is dominated by Greenland and Antarctica: Approximately 50%–80% of the total sea-level rise that comes from ice melting is coming from Antarctica and Greenland together, but Antarctica in particular.

- The present-day sea level is near the highest it's been over all the glacial and interglacial cycles. There's only been one point in the last 250,000 years during which sea level was higher than the present-day level.

- The melting of the sea ice and the partial—not complete—melting of some of the polar icepacks could induce and ultimately raise sea level 4 to 6 meters, or even more if the land-ice melting goes even further than expected.

- Besides sea level, the salinity in the ocean is also starting to be modified by this whole process of melting sea ice.

- If ice melts and is put back into the ocean as freshwater, it's going to cause the surface waters in the Arctic region, the region off Greenland, and the region in which the North Atlantic Deep Water forms to become fresher.

- As a result, deepwater formation could begin to slow down and could begin to go into a new state in which it's not being generated as robustly as it is today.

Modeling Earth's Climate

- One piece of somewhat good news from climate modelers is that current models suggest that the likelihood that this freshwater effect could be so strong as to significantly impact the Gulf Stream, change the climate in Europe, and paradoxically throw it into a new ice age looks very unlikely.

- In order to project into the future, we have to start to speculate more, and the way that scientists speculate is to run numerical models—global-scale computer simulations of the climate.

- Scientists use the best-available physics and understanding of how the ocean and the atmosphere flow, interact, and respond to heat input in order make the best projections. They use the biggest computers in the world to run what are called **general circulation models**, or GCMs.

- All the simulations suggest that if we stopped emitting carbon dioxide today, what's already in the atmosphere and what's already in the ocean in terms of the heat is going to continue to warm up the planet, raise sea level, and have other effects over the span of the next century. Any additional carbon dioxide that we put into the atmosphere is simply an additional factor in that future rise.

- Based on current projections, the global average surface temperature will increase between 1.1°C and 6.4°C by the end of the 21st century—exceeding the total amount of change since the last ice age to the present day.

- GCMs suggest that the rate of warming is likely to be unprecedented. The rates of warming and of sea-level rise are both already increasing faster than the last IPCC median values, or the middle values, of all those computer simulations.

Effects of Sea-Level Changes

- One of the biggest effects of sea-level rise is that low-elevation regions are at risk of losing populated area.

- For coastal regions in a large area such as the United States, people may have to retreat from the coast as the sea continues to encroach upon their homes, or they may be forced to build very expensive seawalls.

- The effects are even more dramatic for countries in the world that have no place to go—no higher ground to go to—including island nations in the Pacific and Indian oceans and Bangladesh.

- For example, Kiribati and the Maldives, which have populations of hundreds of thousands of people, are Pacific atolls that have an elevation of 1.5 to 2 meters above sea level. Projections seem to suggest that in a matter of decades—not centuries—these countries may be uninhabitable.

- In Tuvalu, another Pacific atoll, the highest elevation in the entire country is only 4.5 meters above sea level. A 20- to 30-centimeter sea-level rise would be enough to make the whole country uninhabitable.

- A 1.5-meter sea-level rise—something that we could see in a couple of centuries or maybe even in the next century—would place 16% of Bangladesh under the tidal range and would displace 17 million people.

- According to ocean climatologists, El Niño periods have already become more frequent since the 1970s. There's some evidence that cyclonic storms, hurricanes, and typhoons are becoming more severe—and possibly even the extratropical cyclones, although that's a little less certain. The reason they're becoming more severe, in the case of tropical storms, is that they're fueled by heat.

general circulation models: Supercomputer simulations of the circulation of heat and compounds in the ocean-atmosphere system; used to simulate climate fluctuations and long-term trends.

thermal expansion: The increase in volume of water as it becomes warmer; specifically used to refer to the component of sea-level rise due to this effect as heat content of the ocean changes.

Suggested Reading

Climate Change 2007.

Pilkey and Young, *The Rising Sea*.

Rogers and Laffoley, "International Earth System Expert Workshop."

Questions to Consider

1. If all the ice in the Arctic melts, what effect might that have on North Atlantic Deep Water mass formation?

2. Can you think of other examples (besides sea ice and albedo change) of possible positive or negative feedback in the ocean-climate system?

The Warming, Rising Sea
Lecture 34—Transcript

In the last lecture, we saw that the total heat budget of the planet is changing and has been changing in recent decades. We're going to take a look in this lecture now at the part of the planet that really is going to see that effect first and strongest and that is the ocean. It turns out that the largest effects of the modified heat trapping nature of the atmosphere from the increased carbon dioxide content are already being seen in the ocean and are going to continue probably to be seen in the ocean.

The heat content as we already saw is rising in the ocean at an accelerating pace and that's going to have an effect on all sorts of aspects of the ocean as a whole from sea level to the movement of ocean currents over time. The last few decades have been a period of that change beginning and the future decades are likely to see that change accelerating in nature and in intensity. The first most important change that we're seeing on the planet is that sea level is clearly rising. We already looked at sea level rise when we were talking about beach erosion and things like that so let's return to that for awhile.

Overall when we look at global scale sea level, so the eustatic average, not the local fluctuations in a given place. We have records from tide gauges in various parts of the planet that go back hundreds of years, but in terms of being able to build up a global average we have decent records that give us something back to about 1900 as a reasonable timeframe. If we look at the data that goes back from 1900 all the way up to about 2001 or so, so when we had all these tide gauge records, we see that not much change from 1900 to about 1930. Sea level was globally averaged out pretty much fairly steady, maybe rising very slightly.

From 1930 on the slope of that line on the curve changes and we see an average rate from 1930 all the way up to the turn of the 21st century of about 1.8 millimeters per year, something a little less than 2 millimeters per year. Notice that these tide gauge records have error bars on them and they're larger error bars, there's more uncertainty back in the earlier part of the 20th century and they get smaller as the records get more numerous and better quality as we go to the end of the 20th century. Once there was satellite data that could measure the sea surface height anomalies directly and remember we've used that satellite data time and again to look at very detailed precise measurements of sea level all over the planet, then it became possible to calculate sea level change with even greater precision.

For the period from 1993 to the end of 2008, beginning of 2009, we can see sea level changes with even greater precision. We see some variability. We see the curve fluctuating up and down a little bit mean annual sea level over that window of time, but the slope of that curve gives us about 3, 3.1 millimeters per year of sea level change. It's a much steeper slope, significantly steeper slope, about half again as much as the slope we would take if we take the whole 20th century. Something is accelerating in pace in sea level rise and sea level goes up and down. There are years where sea level actually looks like overall global average is lower than other years. Overall certainly averaged out over this decadal scale it's going up and going up more or less continuously.

That decadal fluctuation is a reflection of large-scale oceanic circulation so for example the dip you see around 2008 is related to that strong development of a La Niña, El Niño oscillation and the ENSO system that we talked about in a previous lecture. Sea level rise closely tracks the overall global average temperature rise over time. We see as we saw in the last lecture, temperatures rising at the surface of Earth and sea level is rising as well and they rise with similar changes in their gradient. If anything sea level is starting to accelerate its rise at a faster pace than the temperature is in the last several decades.

Why do they track each other? Is there an obvious reason why they should? Maybe it is obvious, but sea level rise is due to a combination of two things, one that may be extremely obvious to you and the other that may not be so obvious. The first is that when the global temperature increases, land ice starts to melt. We've probably all heard that the glaciers are in retreat on the planet and that's true. Glaciers are receding up their valleys on average all over the planet. A few glaciers are growing, but most are receding in recent decades. Even more importantly the Greenland Ice Sheet, the major ice caps of the planet, Greenland and Antarctica are losing volume. They're losing land ice and it's turning into water. That water is being introduced into the ocean as new mass and so there's an increase in the volume of water in the ocean. That makes sense. That's part of sea level rise.

The second part though is that the water itself is getting warmer. What's the difference between warm water and cold water? One key difference we've already said is a difference in density, warm water is less dense than cold water and a difference in density implies actually a volume expansion. It means the same mass of water occupies a little bit more space. The sea level rise is also partly due to the thermal expansion of the water. As the water heats up, the water gets a little bit bigger and so it fills the basin a little bit higher than it did before.

Even if there was no introduction of any new melt water whatsoever, sea level would be rising anyway because the water is expanding over time. That expansion is very small. Water doesn't expand a lot. It's a ten thousandth or two of a percent or something like that or fractionally a ten thousandth or two of the volume of the water. It changes with a degree change in temperature and we haven't even seen a degree change in temperature. The oceanic temperature changes in the surface waters are probably down more in the tenth of a degree range. The ocean basin is big. It's a lot of water and even just down to 700 meters. If we take 700 meters of water over the whole planet and we warm it up just a little, we get millimeters and then centimeters of sea level rise out of it.

These two things both contribute and it turns out they contribute in roughly equal amounts that additional melt water and thermal expansion and depending on the given year the thermal expansion comes and goes because we have more heat added to the ocean or less heat added to the ocean, again based on those decade scale oscillations of oceanographic currents and atmospheric redistribution of heat. That one comes and goes a little bit. The melt water input seems to be more steady and also increasing over time. The best available data that we have now in 2010 or up through 2007 was published in 2010 suggests that the overall amount of sea level change is something like from 1993 to 2007; the rate of growth is 3.3 millimeters per year. It actually slowed down if you just take the window 2003 to 2007 to 2.5 millimeters per year, but that's because of those small term fluctuations.

The overall change over that total longer window is at least 3.1 millimeters per year. Of that about two-thirds is land ice melting and about one-third is the thermal expansion and then again in that short window of time. When it went down a little thermal expansion was even less. The thermal expansion fluctuates a little. The input of melted water, fresh water that comes from land ice melting is pretty steady and in fact probably growing over time. That 50–80% of the sea level rise signal comes from added mass from melting and 20–50% come from that thermal expansion.

We already looked at the heat content of the ocean in the last lecture and we said that about 80% of the extra added heat to the atmosphere is stored in the ocean. The ocean is at great heat sink, 80% of the heat comes from the contribution of anthropogenic or carbon dioxide that's added to the atmosphere through human activity makes it into the ocean. This has a number of effects on processes going on in the ocean. Probably the most significant effect, the one that we're seeing most rapidly is the warming of the Arctic region and in particular the annual melting of land ice in the Arctic is rapidly increasing.

It turns out that we expect the warming signal to show up the greatest at the Polar Regions because those are the regions that cool the most seasonally winter to summer relative to the tropics and so the effect of extra added thermal mass can make the Polar Regions see a larger effect from greenhouse warming in general. Certainly what's been going on since the late 1970s is a rapid decrease in the total amount of ice in the Arctic that make it from one season to the next. If we look at a graph of just the monthly average amount of ice in September for each given year and we use September because that's the end of the summer.

The ice that's around in September is the ice that made it through one summer and will probably make it on to continuously being ice in the next year. Those September numbers show a pretty rapid decline even again what has entered annual year to year there's a short-term cycle. Sometimes there's more ice, sometimes there's less, sometimes there's a couple of years in a row with more, but overall there's a huge trend since 1979 to 2010 of decreasing amounts of Arctic sea ice over all that time.

This is going to have a significant effect on the Arctic system in a number of different ways. First of all, just the reduction of sea ice is a problem for a lot of the organisms that live in the Arctic that depend on the sea ice. There are a number of Arctic marine ecosystems that are dependent on sea ice being present on top to provide habitat, to limit the amount of water mixing, wave action, and things like that. Some of the benthic fauna for example would be affected by open water instead of sea ice. We've all heard about the polar bears and the idea that their habitat is critically dependent on being able to hunt for fish by using the sea ice and actually roaming all over what is an ocean after all, not land, the Arctic icepack in general. Remember that the Arctic is an ocean basin. The sea ice that I'm talking about is floating ice sitting on top of the water.

At the current rate of change by 2030 or so, so not that long from now, a few decades in the future, the sea ice is projected to be less than one-third of its average level for the 1979 to 1990 time period. At least seasonally in the summertime, we will have shrunk down the sea ice to a level that is maintained year after year after year and it will open up navigable passages through the Arctic. For hundreds of years now, people have wanted to find a famous northwest passage, a shipping route that goes from Europe or eastern North America to the Pacific without having to go all the way down around the tip of South America or through the Panama Canal.

That is already beginning to happen and in fact in 2007 for the first time ever, navigable waters for ships that were not icebreaker class ships opened up through the Arctic Ocean. This is likely to continue to happen, not necessarily every year, but more and more frequently and persistently by about 2030. That has a secondary affect of also opening up areas for new oil and gas exploration and development as well as mining and there's certainly a land rush on the northern margin of Canada and Alaska and around Siberia to explore areas that might be perspective for either land side or ocean side deposits of petroleum.

We could ask the question then does sea ice melting contribute to sea level rise. It melts all the ice so you have new fresh water and it raises sea level right. Well no, actually that's not true or at least it's not true in the way that you might thing. Think about a glass of ice water filled up with water and ice cubes so that the water is right up to the brim or an iceberg floating in the ocean. When that ice melts does the water overflow the glass? No, of course it doesn't because the ice is floating in buoyant equilibrium. It's Archimedes principle. It displaces its own weight in water.

When the Arctic sea ice melts, the ice will all melt. The fresh water will return to the ocean, but it won't change sea level directly at all. On the other hand, it does actually have some affects on the ocean and there are some indirect ways in which it does create sea level rise. For one thing, if there's that much warming and it's warmer water than it might create additional thermal expansion. More importantly is that the melting of sea ice contributes to a positive feedback as we call it in the ocean climate system and that is the albedo change. Remember what albedo is? It's the reflectivity of the Sunlight so on any surface the Sun shines on it and the energy is either absorbed and turned into heat or reflected back to space.

Sea ice is pretty reflective. It's white and it reflects a good proportion of that incoming solar energy back to space. It has an albedo ratio of .3 to .4, 30 to 40% or so. Open water by contrast absorbs more of the light and converts it into heat. The sun penetrates into the upper waters, the upper few meters of water and turns into heat there. It actually has a lower albedo overall and so the open water albedo ranges depending on a lot of things, how wavy it is, what the solar angle is, how far north you are, but several times smaller than, or a large percentage smaller than the albedo of the ice.

When you melt ice and turn it into open water than more energy is absorbed from the Sun and that warms the water up more which can feed back into melting more ice so there's this positive feedback where melting the ice warms the Arctic Ocean which causes more ice to melt and so on and so on and so on. It's pretty clear this whole process is underway in the Arctic already. This is not speculation about the future. This is what's been going on for the last couple of decades in the Arctic Ocean to cause the rapid change in sea ice melting.

What about the land ice? Land ice really can contribute to sea level rise because it adds water that was on land to the ocean. The land ice change is dominated by Greenland and Antarctica and actually until as recently as 2007, it was thought, by most of the scientists who worked on this, that Antarctica might be gaining ice due to changes in the climate producing increased snowfall there and so as you're adding more mass even though it's overall a global warming system that would increase snowfall on Antarctica. Better satellite data in recent years and multiple independent lines of analysis of that satellite data have shown quite recently that Antarctica is losing ice mass and so therefore that's turning into water that's ending up in the ocean. Most of that, 50 to 80% of the total sea level rise that's coming from ice melting is coming from Antarctica and Greenland together, Antarctica in particular.

What does all this mean for sea level? We've looked at the sea level curves in a lot of detail already. We'll come back to this eustatic sea level curve one more time to remind us that the present day sea level is near the highest it's been over all the glacial and interglacial cycles. There's only been one point in the last 250,000 years where sea level was higher than the present day. That was at the period of the last interglacial period and it was about 6 meters higher than it is at present at a time that was 120-125 thousand years ago or so. The last time that the polar regions were as warm as present or actually a little bit warmer than present, the direction that we thing that they're headed with the increased trapping of heat on the planet then sea level was between 4 and 6 meters higher than it is right now.

Melting of the sea ice and partial, not complete, but just partial melting of some of the polar icepacks could induce and ultimately rise in sea level of 4 to 6 meters or even more if the land ice melting goes even further than that. Remember I said if we melt all the ice caps off of the Antarctic and Greenland Ice Sheets we would see a sea level rise much greater, something on the order of 60 meters. Even if that were to happen that is at least centuries in the future because it's a very slow process to melt all that ice, 4 to 6 meters is also probably well beyond a century in the future as we'll see in terms of the best available models for how much sea level is going to rise. The kind of apocalyptic scenarios of sea level suddenly going up by tens of feet or many meters and flooding coastal cities rapidly is not going to happen. Sea level rise is going to potentially accelerate but be much more slow than that kind of doomsday pace.

Besides sea level, the salinity in the ocean is also starting to be modified by this whole process. The reason for that is linked back up to the North Atlantic deepwater formation. We have the Arctic Ocean covered in sea ice. We're melting that sea ice at an increasing pace. As that happens, it's melting out and adding fresh water back into the sea. Remember I said that the process of North Atlantic deepwater formation was making cold water that was extra salty because it had had ice extracted from it and that's what sinks down to form most of the deep water in the ocean.

The converse is true then also. If you melt the ice and put it back as fresh water it's going to cause the surface waters in the Arctic region and off Greenland and the region that North Atlantic deep water forms to become fresher. There's at least some evidence that since the 1950s when oceanographic salinity measurements start to become available up to near the present day that that salinity has decreased in the far northern regions of the Atlantic and that would suggest that deepwater formation could begin to slow down and could begin to go into a new state where it's not being generated as robustly as it is today.

In fact, that's led to one scenario that had been proposed and was popular in the 1990s that perhaps this influx of fresh water out of the Arctic might shutdown that deepwater formation, pool in the surface, and even shutdown potentially the surface currents like the Gulf Stream. A movie that came out a number of years ago *The Day After Tomorrow* was based on a doomsday scenario like that. One piece perhaps of good news from the climate modelers is that current models suggest really that the likelihood that that effect could be so strong as to significantly impact the Gulfstream and let's say change the climate in Europe and paradoxically throw it into a new ice age looks very unlikely. It seems very unlikely that that can happen on any kind of short-term, and by short-term I mean century's kind of timescale. At least that's one thing that we probably don't have to worry about as much as a scenario in the global warming world.

On the other hand, there are a lot of changes that really are going on and we want to look at what the projections of earth's future climate are. So far, I've talked almost entirely about things that have already happened, the temperature change and heat content change and sea level rise that we've already measured in the ocean. In order to project those into the future, we have to start to speculate more and the way that scientists speculate is to run numerical models, global scale computer simulations of the climate. They use the best available physics and understanding of how the ocean and the atmosphere flow and interact and respond to heat input and all of those things.

They use the biggest computers in the world to run these things that are called circulation models or GCMs. They require the input of not one scientist working on a grant, but many dozens or hundreds even of scientists collaborating to write those computer models and to write the code that they run on these massively parallel computers, the kind of super high-end computing where they're always testing the limits of whatever the latest computer that comes out is.

Those scientists are running those simulations in order to project climate into the future. How can you tell that your simulation is working and that it does what it's supposed to do? It's after all just making a series of mathematical calculations. One of the ways that they test a climate model, I actually alluded to in the last lecture, where they look at testing predicting not the future, but predicting the past. Well that sounds strange. What I mean is you can take as input our best available understanding of the chemistry of the ocean and the atmosphere and the heat content and its flow systems at some point in the past, like 1900 or 1950 or whatever year you choose and then run your computer model based on that input into the future.

Of course, the future is starting from 1950. You run it out to the 21st century and you see how well your model predicts what actually already happened. You don't give it as input, the data from that period up to the present day, you use that as a test and so that's how they calibrate and test these global climate models, global circulation model systems. When these models are run for the future then you also have to try a lot of different scenarios because no one knows how much additional carbon dioxide and methane are going to be put into the atmosphere in the future.

There are various scenarios, the planet as a whole, the collective activity could do business as usual and keep increasing the amounts of fossil fuels going into the atmosphere each year. That's what we're seeing so far. They could all start to agree to reduce the amount of fossil fuels that are used. We could gradually wean ourselves if the economics of different other kinds of energy change. We could have a global economic collapse that would reduce the amount of fossil fuels used. Even in the recessions, we see the amount of fossil fuels goes down and actually CO_2 emissions even go down. Lots of different scenarios are tried and they run these simulations to come up with the heat content of the atmosphere and the ocean into the future.

When we look at those results then we see a warming world. If we project it out 50 years or if we project it out 100 years into the future, all the simulations suggest even based on the idea that what if we stopped emitting carbon dioxide today, not possible, but what if we just said it goes to zero. What's already in the atmosphere and what's already in the ocean in terms of the heat is going to continue to warm up the planet, raise sea level and have other effects over the span of the next century. Any additional CO_2 we put into the atmosphere is simply an additional factor in that future rise.

Some of the basic conclusions from global circulation models today suggests that the global average surface temperature will increase some more. It's already increased at some significant fraction of 1° C since the middle of the 20th century. It will probably increase between 1.1 and 6.4 C by the end of the 21st century, 2099, and more in the Arctic and also over land areas as opposed to over the ocean. The ocean is a heat sink. It soaks up a lot of heat without changing in temperature very much so the areas above the water and also the maritime regions of the coastlines won't see as much change as interiors of the continents or the Arctic regions.

That doesn't sound like a very large number, but remember the difference between an ice age and today is just a few degrees C so 6 would be exceeding the total amount of change since the last ice age to the present day. We'd be into a world that was in a very different condition at that high a change of average global temperatures. We also see from GCMs that the rate of warming is likely to be unprecedented. It already is going very rapidly and unprecedented since the end of the last glacial age, 10,000 years ago. We're entering a new period that over the span of human history we haven't seen before.

For sea level rise, the conclusions are evolving a little bit quickly. In 2007, the conclusion of the IPC, the consensus of climate scientists and oceanographers was that sea level rise by the end of the 21st century would be between 0.18 and 0.59 meters, something maybe up to two-thirds of a meter at the extreme case and probably less than half a meter by 2099. Since 2007, there's been additional much better simulations of what's going on with the dynamics of those ice sheets in Antarctica and Greenland and a better understanding overall of what's happening to sea level rise and so now the consensus is emerging that this is likely to be quite a bit more, 0.85 to 0.12 meters or about some large fraction of a meter of sea level rise by 2099 because the rate of warming and of sea level rise are both already going faster than the last IPCC median values or the middle road values of all those computer simulations.

The effects already underway include sea level rise and the loss of sea ice, but what effect does that have on people on the planet. One of the biggest effects is that low elevation regions are at risk of losing populated area. We talked about that already for coastal regions in a big area like the United States where people may have to retreat from the coast as the sea continues to encroach or build very expensive seawalls and ultimately dike the country up the way The Netherlands are today. Maybe more dramatic are countries in the world that have no place to go, no higher ground to go to and that includes the Pacific and Indian Ocean island nations and Bangladesh.

For example, Kiribati and the Maldives which have populations of hundreds of thousands of people are Pacific atolls. They're atoll islands. They lie at an average elevation. Those two countries, the entire country in both cases has an elevation of 1.5 to 2 meters above sea level, 1.5 to 2 meters. Rising sea level displaces fresh water in the aquifers and it erodes and floods the island so even if the island doesn't actually sink under the waves literally or even before that happens they would be rendered uninhabitable and this is already underway in both of those places. It's looking like in a matter of decades, not centuries, these countries maybe literally uninhabitable. In 2008, the President of Kiribati in the Pacific announced a plan to manage the complete depopulation of his country, everyone moving to Australia, New Zealand, other places in the Pacific Ocean. The country would literally cease to exist if they have to carry this plan out. It's not so far-fetched.

Tuvalu another Pacific atoll, the highest elevation in the entire country is only 4-1/2 meters above sea level. A 20 or 30 centimeter sea level, something that we might see within the next 50 years would be enough to make the whole country uninhabitable. That's a very small country; there are only about 10,000 people there, but the idea that a country would literally go out of business because of sea level rise is not so far in the future. In the Maldives, the President of the country in order to really underscore this whole point in 2009 held an underwater cabinet meeting to sign papers protesting against a lack of response at the Copenhagen Accords to the urgency of the problem. If you live there you really feel it.

In fact, if you live in Bangladesh, you really feel it as well because a 1-1/2 meter sea level rise, something that we could see in a couple of centuries, maybe even in the next century, would place 16% of Bangladesh under the tidal range, displace 17 million people. The impact is wider because first of all salt water encroachment into aquifers spreads the impact farther, but also 17 million displaced people have to go bother other people essentially or they have to be displaced to somewhere. The impacts will be felt all over and especially in the less well-developed regions of the world that are in low-lying coastal areas.

Some additional ocean-related observations of climate change include the change in snow cover and ice extent of land already decreased about 10% since the 1960s; that's adding the net water to the ocean. El Niño periods have already become more frequent since the 1970s according to the ocean climatologists. There's some evidence that the cyclonic storms, the hurricanes and typhoons are becoming more severe and possibly even the extratropical cyclones although that's a little less certain. The reason they're becoming more severe, in the case of tropical storms is they're fueled by heat. If there's more heat in the surface waters of the ocean, that's more energy for them to pick up as they move along.

Computer simulations, by the way, don't show more frequent hurricanes. So far, the general consensus is they just show more severe ones when they do form. That's an area of rapidly changing research so we'll see what happens in the future with that. Ocean temperature is going to continue to rise and accelerate, the heat content will grow, the Arctic sea ice will contract in the 21st century. These are virtually certain. The summer ice may disappear entirely over the span of a number of decades. The Greenland and Antarctic ice sheets will continue to lose ice at an increasing rate so sea level is going to keep rising. The increased risk from the storm surges, the hurricanes themselves because under higher sea level you have less buffer zone and saltwater intrusion are a big secondary, but very important effect of sea level rise overall.

In the future, again according to the simulations we're likely to see an ocean that is both more active in some ways and less active in others. We may see stronger surface heat in the surface water, stronger surface currents, and also as I said stronger storms being fueled by that heat. If the deepwater circulation starts to become slackened or decreased by the lack of that Arctic deepwater formation and perhaps a similar thing going on in the Antarctic. Maybe over time that very slow circulation of all the deep water in the ocean will be modified and we don't know how those effects will play out over a long period of time.

In the next lecture, we're going to take a look at how the oceans will become more acidic as well because of CO_2. That's essentially kind of a completely different effect of the release of CO_2 in the ocean atmosphere system because that's like a pollution effect of the ocean. It causes stress to coral reefs and other ecosystems.

Marine Pollution—The Impact of Toxins
Lecture 35

Human activity is so pervasive that it increasingly has impacts that can be seen all over the world ocean. Oil spills can be locally devastating but tend to be of limited extent and are now much less frequent. Plastic garbage in the sea has become pervasive and can be disruptive to marine life. Ocean acidification from the carbon dioxide humans add to the atmosphere is a form of pollution that has the potential to greatly alter marine ecosystems. Heavy metals and chemical pollution are increasingly problems from industrial runoff, and bioaccumulation causes a health risk to humans.

Human Impact on the World's Ocean

- Marine pollution is the introduction into the ocean by humans of any kind of substances—or even energy—that changes the quality of the water or affects the physical and biological environment.

- Pollutants, by definition, interfere in some way with reproductive, metabolic, or other biochemical processes of life in the sea.

- Solid waste that is dumped at sea still occurs to a great extent, both from sources on land and also from marine dumping from ships.

- Runoff of agricultural waste and industrial waste come through the air in the form of particulates from burning coal that land on the surface of the ocean. These occurrences are introduced less intentionally but are still a result of ordinary practices. Oil spills at sea are another example.

Carbon Dioxide as a Toxic Compound

- One of the fundamental stresses on the planet is energy pollution. The warming of the water can be heat pollution that causes higher water temperatures, which has a toxic effect on many of the different organisms in the sea.

- Coral reefs are the most specific example of energy pollution. When the sea-surface temperatures exceed normal high temperatures for summer by only about 1°C, the corals respond by expelling symbiotic algae that live within the coral polyps, the zooxanthellae, which leads to a process called coral bleaching.

- The worldwide coral population for the number of coral reefs that are healthy today is only about 50% of what it was 50 years ago.

- The introduction of carbon dioxide into the environment creates another form of pollution called **ocean acidification**, in which most of the carbon dioxide that has been introduced into the atmosphere has been exchanged with the ocean and has become dissolved carbon dioxide in the water of the ocean. Dissolved carbon dioxide makes water more acidic because it reacts with the water to form something called carbonic acid.

- A small change in the alkalinity of the water—from a pH of 8 down toward the direction of more acidic—interferes with the corals' ability to make their shells.

- The pH of the ocean today in the tropical regions is about 8.1, and its preindustrial level was about 8.2, which is known from old water samples. If the pH of the ocean changes to 7.9—which is not a huge change, but a pH scale is a logarithmic scale—it's possible that the corals will cease to be able to make their skeletons, causing them to be unable to build a reef at all.

- At present rates, the pH of the ocean is projected to drop to 7.9 in the next 40 years. A near-extinction of many or even nearly all reef-building corals is considered a real possibility by marine biologists.

- Other organisms are at risk, too, as a result of acidification because there are many organisms that make their shells or skeletons out of calcium carbonate.

- More generally, it's simply not known how the larval stages of many organisms will respond to a changing pH balance of the water in which they live. This could interfere with a number of metabolic processes, so changing the fundamental acid chemistry of the ocean has a huge effect on oceanic life.

Toxic Marine Pollution

- There are many examples of the introduction of toxic materials—toxic to life in one way or another—into the sea, including point sources of sewage outfall. For a long time, raw sewage from all over the United States and, certainly, the rest of the world was simply dumped into the ocean.

- The key characteristics of any pollutant in the marine environment are the concentration of that pollutant, or the amount that's present; the **toxicity**, or the degree to which that particular pollutant is damaging; and the **persistence**, or the length of time that pollutant lasts in the environment.

- Runoff from land and the direct introduction of sewage outfall and of solid-waste dumping introduce a number of fairly toxic materials into the ocean.

- Examples of toxic materials include PCBs and heavy metals like mercury and lead, which are organic compounds that are used in industrial practices or in the dry-cleaning industry that interfere with various kinds of biological metabolic processes.

For a long time, raw sewage all over the world was dumped into the ocean, which was viewed as the ultimate drain and sewer.

- Pesticides are delivered primarily from rivers and streams because they're put onto agricultural fields, end up in the hydrologic system, and flow down to the ocean.

- Very small concentrations of heavy metals can cause toxic damage to organisms. Among others, important heavy metals are lead, mercury, and copper.

- Chemical pollution by toxic heavy metals and organic compounds like PCBs has affected virtually all the urbanized coastal areas of North America and, in fact, such areas around the world.

- As a result of chemical pollution, shellfish have too much of the toxic compounds to even be consumed, and fisheries are banned for shellfish in many estuaries that were formerly highly productive.

- Mercury comes from the burning of coal and is a teratogen, meaning it causes genetic damage. Women who are pregnant are advised not to eat too much tuna because of the examples of the acute mercury toxicity that unfortunately have been seen in the world. Minamata disease is essentially acute mercury poisoning.

- In addition to tuna, the FDA recommends children and women of childbearing age to avoid swordfish, shark, king mackerel, altogether and to limit their intake of many other fish. These are all large fish that consume other fish; they're living at a high trophic level as consumers in the ocean.

Biomagnification

- In the late 1950s and early 1960s, DDT was being used very heavily to control mosquitoes and all sorts of pests. The problem is that DDT gets into ocean water at very low concentrations—approximately 3 parts per trillion—and is taken up from the water by plankton, which are then eaten by small fish.

- The amount of food that needs to be eaten at each trophic level is magnified by a factor of 10, beginning with the small fish, where the concentration of DDT is at 0.5 parts per million, all the way up to the larger fish and, ultimately, the birds that were consuming those fish at the fourth or fifth trophic level.

- In pelicans and cormorants, DDT concentration is at 25 parts per million. It's toxic to human beings if we consume animals in high trophic levels, such as tuna and swordfish.

- **Biomagnification** applies to many pollutants, not just to DDT; it applies to mercury, PCBs, and other chlorinated hydrocarbons.

- Dolphins off U.S. coasts have been found to have flesh that had 6900 parts per million PCBs. The human safe limit set by the FDA is 5 parts per million, so those dolphins are essentially toxic substances because of PCB dumping in the ocean.

- Lead is another substance that becomes concentrated through biomagnification.

- There is some good news on these kinds of toxic substances because the recognition of their toxicity and accumulation in ocean water, sediments, and organisms has led to real action.

- In other parts of the world, toxic substances may not be controlled as well. In many developing countries, what goes into the ocean is virtually unknown and uncontrolled.

- Nutrient runoff into the ocean is a form of pollution that can be too much of a good thing. **Eutrophication** is the result of putting excess nutrients in the water, and it causes too much to grow in the water.

- Nutrients enter the water from either sewage outfall or agricultural runoff of fertilizers, causing massive booms of algal plankton such as red tide and yellow foams.

- Red tide is the massive bloom of dinoflagellates, which are photosynthesizing phytoplankton. In high concentrations in the water, they become very toxic to marine life. They can kill a lot of marine life and can sicken or even kill human beings who consume that marine life. Red tide can get so bad that it can even be seen from space, as in satellite images of the Florida peninsula.

- Black tide is a massive bloom of algae in the water that is fed by nutrients from runoff in eutrophication. It's not directly toxic itself, but it uses up the available oxygen.

- The effect of hypoxia, or low levels of oxygen, is that the large fish and shrimp that can move will leave the area and go to where there's more oxygen. Other organisms that can't leave the area or that don't move as fast, such as crabs and shellfish, will suffocate.

- In the Gulf of Mexico, there's something called the dead zone. From February through late summer every year, a huge **hypoxic zone**, or low-oxygen zone, appears in the Gulf of Mexico off the mouth of the Mississippi River.

- One of the maybe positive aspects of the dead zone—in terms of the eutrophication problem at least—is that it's pretty reversible because of the direct influx seasonally of this essentially toxic nutrient load into the water.

Solid Waste in the Sea

- Another form of direct dumping into the water is solid waste. The sea is a dump for trash and garbage all over the world. Restrictions are growing on this kind of dumping, but it's still a big problem.

- Military dumping of solid waste has been going on for a very long time and is restricted now. At the end of World War II, the navy had large stores, many barrels, of mustard gas that had been stockpiled during the war and never used, and they dumped these into the deep water of the ocean. There are huge dumps like these all over the world's ocean.

When garbage is incinerated, chemicals are released into the atmosphere that often end up on the land or in the sea.

- Plastic garbage and particles in the sea have become pervasive. Every year, 135,000 tons of plastic are dumped by ships at sea, including fishing gear that cripples or kills marine mammals. These are very real and growing problems.

- The Great Pacific Garbage Patch is a region of the North Pacific Ocean within the big gyre in which there is an estimated 1 million pieces of plastic per square kilometer over an area that in aggregate might be as large as the continental United States.

- One sampling study of the water in the Great Pacific Garbage Patch showed that the actual plastic particles outweighed the zooplankton in that region by a factor of 6.

- Plastic ingestion by pelagic birds is a major problem. Pelagic birds such as albatrosses and fulmars are found in recent years to have up to 20 or more pieces of indigestible plastic in their stomachs, interfering with their digestive systems.

- These conditions have been found in organisms living in the Pacific and Atlantic oceans and have recently been discovered in fulmars living in the Arctic Ocean region.

Sound Pollution in the Sea

- The industrialized ocean is a very noisy place. Ships use sonar, and seismic reflection exploration below the ocean floor uses air guns that emit loud booms into the water. Most of all, everyday shipping is a constant source of noise from propellers.

- The potential impacts are large for animals that use echolocation and sound to communicate, such as whales and dolphins.

- For the strongest sounds, there is possible damage to internal organs of mammals that use echolocation. Maybe only high-powered navy sonar can do this, but the research is ongoing.

biomagnification: The exponential increase in the concentration of toxic compounds in animal tissues at successively higher trophic levels.

eutrophication: Conditions of overabundance of nutrients in the water usually due to fertilizer runoff, leading to harmful algal blooms and hypoxia.

hypoxic zone: Any region in the ocean of extremely low oxygen availability due to fertilizer runoff; an example is in the Gulf of Mexico off the mouth of the Mississippi River.

ocean acidification: The increase in acidity of seawater that is developing as a result of increased dissolved carbon dioxide.

persistence: The length of time a pollutant lasts in an environment.

toxicity: The amount of a pollutant necessary to cause some form of damage in an ecosystem or organism.

Suggested Reading

Clark, *Marine Pollution.*

Ebbesmeyer, *Flotsametrics and the Floating World.*

Questions to Consider

1. How is ocean acidification connected to—but a completely different effect from—ocean warming?

2. It was often said in past decades that "the solution to pollution is dilution," and the ocean is very big, so it could dilute toxic compounds. Why does this not work for many compounds, such as mercury or PCBs?

Marine Pollution—The Impact of Toxins
Lecture 35—Transcript

In several of the previous lectures, we've examined a number of different major human impacts on the world's ocean ecosystems. We've looked at fishing and whaling and other extraction of resources. We've even seen that human impacts have been going on for a very long time. For example, remember the story of the discovery and then extinction of the Steller's Sea Cow in only 20 some years because of hunting and the demise of that organism. We've looked at sea level rise and changing temperature in the ocean and we've talked about things that are introduced into the sea as well, in particular oil spills, such as the Gulf oil disaster.

What I'd like to do in this lecture now is take up the topic of what we put into this sea in a lot more detail. We're going to look at toxins and pollution in the ocean. Well marine pollution would be defined as the introduction into the ocean by humans of any kind of substances or even energy that changes the quality of the water or affects the physical and biological environment. Pollutants, by definition, interfere in some way with reproductive, metabolic, or other biochemical processes of life in the sea. Some of what's introduced into the ocean is done essentially quite intentionally. For example, we have outfall, we have sewage treated in many cases, not treated in other cases, but it's dumped directly into the sea, quite intentionally or solid waste that's dumped at sea which still goes on to a great extent both from on land sources and also from marine dumping from ships that are travelling at sea.

Other things are introduced less intentionally, but still as a result of ordinary business as usual practices like the runoff of agricultural waste down the rives and into the ocean or other kinds of industrial waste that have made it into the terrestrial ecosystem and getting to the sea or coming through the air in the form of particulates from burning of coal that land on the surface of the ocean. These are major inputs of material into the sea. There are also much more minor inputs, just maybe 10 or so% of all inputs are things like oil spills at sea, direct spills that are accidental introduction of pollutants into the environment.

Let's take a look at a number of these one at a time. I'm going to examine different environmental impacts on the ocean's ecosystems from stuff we're putting into the sea. Some are familiar forms of pollution and others are not actually. Some are effects that worsened until they were recognized as threats to the health of animals or people and then have been mitigated for us. Things are getting better; others are just now worsening or maybe even just being discovered in the past decade or so. The first one I want to look at is actually one that you might not think of as a pollutant at all. It might seem a little bit of a novel concept to you, but the effect of the introduction of carbon dioxide into the atmosphere and the ocean and its effect as a toxic compound.

I talked about the coral reefs already and I talked about some of the stresses on the coral reefs. One of the fundamental stresses is from something we could think of as energy pollution and that is the warming of the water can be heat pollution that causes higher water temperatures. Why is that pollution? Well because it has a toxic effect directly on many of the different organisms in the sea and the coral reefs are the most specific example. Remember coral bleaching. What happens to corals is that when the sea surface temperatures exceed normal summer high temperatures by only about 1 degree or so. The corals respond by expelling those symbiotic algae that live within the coral polyps, the zooxanthellae. That's called coral bleaching.

It can recover if it's a brief episode and the water temperature returns to normal. They repopulate with the zooxanthellae, but if it goes over a month or so remember the corals essentially die off and it doesn't recover. New reef building corals can build structures, but they won't re-inhabit the same coral skeleton.

Well this temperature change in the water can be a semi-naturally occurring even like for example in 1998, the El Niño, La Niña combination caused changes in water temperature in tropical regions around the world and it's estimated to have killed 16% of corals worldwide. That's a natural event, but the corals were right at the edge of their temperature range in part because the ocean is getting warmer and the warmer it gets the closer they'll be and the more vulnerable to meteorological events like that affecting them. Direct introduction of warmer water at coastlines is also causing coral bleaching in many different places. The worldwide coral population for the number of coral reefs that are healthy today is only about 50% of what it was 50 years ago or so.

A different form of pollution comes from carbon dioxide introduction into the environment and that is something called ocean acidification and that is potentially an even greater effect from the coral reefs overall. We've said that there's more carbon dioxide in the atmosphere than there was in the pre-industrial era and most of that carbon dioxide that has been introduced into the atmosphere has been exchanged with the ocean and become dissolved CO_2 in the water of the ocean. Dissolved CO_2 makes water more acidic because it reacts with the water to form something called carbonic acid. The oceans normal pH level is about 8. The ocean's a little bit alkaline; remember 7 is neutral on the pH scale between alkalinity and acidity.

Just a small change in that alkalinity in that pH of 8 down towards the direction of more acid interferes with the corals ability to make their shells. They make their coral skeleton, the reef itself from calcium carbonate, also known as limestone, and if there's more carbonic acid in the water it dissolves the limestone or more directly interferes with their ability to secrete the limestone and make the hard reef structure. Specifically the pH of the ocean today in the tropical regions is about 8.1 and its preindustrial level was about 8.2 known from old water samples. If it gets to 7.9, not a big change, but remember a pH scale is a logarithmic scale, 7.9, which is projected at present rates to happen in the next 40 years or so.

It's possible that the corals will literally cease to be able to make their skeletons; that is build the reef at all. In a near extinction of many or even nearly all reef-building corals is considered a real possibility by marine biologists. This was only recognized over the course of the past less than 10 years really and it's a very new area of study. It's a very new area of major concern among marine biologists that the reef-building corals as we know them could cease to exist within coming decades.

Other organisms are actually at risk too from the acidification because remember there's lots of things that make their shells or their skeletons out of calcium carbonate. Phytoplankton, the coccolithophorids, remember the great white cliffs of Dover and the zillions of dead phytoplankton that make it up; that's all calcium carbonate, limestone, that was secreted by those organisms. If they can't make that calcium carbonate anymore then they won't bloom in the ocean in the perfusion that they have today. Foraminifera and pteropods are other organisms that make carbonate shells. The effect of acidification on all these organisms is really unknown at this time in our major area of current research.

More generally, it's simply not known how the larval stages of many organisms are going to respond to a changing pH balance of the water in which they live. This could interfere with a number of metabolic processes and so changing the fundamental acid chemistry of the ocean is a big effect and it's a big effect that's just beginning and we don't know where it's going, but we do know that it's certainly going to happen because CO_2 is getting into the water and that's some of the most basic chemistry of all. That just simply makes it more acidic than it is today.

That brings us into the whole concept of toxic marine pollution and the introduction of toxic materials, toxic to life in one way or another into the sea. We have all kinds of examples, including point sources of sewage outfall. For a long time raw sewage all over the USA and certainly the rest of the world as well was simply dumped into the ocean. The ocean was the ultimate drain and sewer and you put it there and you assumed that the solution to pollution is dilutions. As is often said, the sea is big so put it out there and everything is fine. It turns out everything is not fine because a lot of the material that goes out in that sewage outfall ends up deposited in the sediments near the outfall source, near where the pipes go into the ocean, or even buried in the sediments around that area. That's a real significant problem.

Solid waste in the ocean is another problem. Let's talk about the key characteristics of any pollutant in the marine environment. There are sort of 3. First of all the concentration of that pollutant, the amount that's present, a trace amount of some pollutants is really not toxic to anything around if the toxicity is relatively low. For some things, we really genuinely don't have to worry about them. The toxicity, the actual degree to which that particular pollutant is damaging, the amount of it ingested by an organism required to cause damage is a major factor. Then finally the persistence, meaning the length of time that pollutant lasts in the environment.

Many pollutants are broken down by organic processes or by ultraviolet sunlight relatively quickly so they make it into the water, but then they break down. They have low persistence. They have short persistence time. That makes them less of a problem than the ones that have very long persistence in the ocean. Runoff from land and direct introduction of sewage outfall and sometimes of solid waste dumping all introduce a number of really fairly toxic materials into the ocean. That includes heavy metals like mercury and lead, PCBs, various kinds of organic compounds that are used in industrial practices or used in a dry cleaning industry and interfere with various kinds of biological metabolic processes.

These are significant problems when they go into the ocean and enter the food chain, the food web that we see in the sea and we'll see examples of that in a few minutes. Those are delivered primarily from urban runoff and sewers and urban activities including industrial manufacture and driving of cars, all that sort of thing. Some other examples are pesticides. Pesticides are delivered primarily from rivers and streams because they're put on to agricultural fields end up in the hydrologic system and flow down to the ocean.

Pesticides when they get into the ocean do exactly what they're meant to do which is kill organisms or hurt organisms, but they're doing it in the wrong place. Instead of doing it to keep down pests on the agricultural fields they're now doing it in the ocean where we don't want them to. Agricultural fields are also treated with fertilizers all the time and so those agricultural fertilizers are nutrients and when they go into the ocean, you might think well nutrients are good right, we want nutrients so that there'll be blooms. Sometimes there's too much of a good thing as we'll see.

The really toxic compounds, the heavy metals, let's talk about them for a second. Very small concentrations of these heavy metals can cause toxic damage to organisms. Important among others, are lead, mercury, and copper. Some of the sources of heavy metal pollution include particular coal combustion, because coal contains significant amounts of these heavy metals and they don't burn up the way the carbon does; they go out the smokestack. They end up in the ocean through particulate outfall into the ocean. Electric power generation, steel and iron manufacturing, from fuel oils, all of these things included, and one major area is actually the incineration of urban trash because when we burn garbage we put things that are in the garbage that we don't want to bury in the ground into the atmosphere instead. A lot of that comes back down on the land or on the sea.

Chemical pollution by toxic heavy metals and organic compounds like PCBs has affected virtually all the urbanized coastal areas of North America and, in fact, all around the world. Shellfish for example have too much of the toxic compounds to even consume and fisheries are banned for them in many estuaries that were formerly highly productive, San Francisco Bay, the region around New York City, the region around Galveston, and Houston, Texas, Southern California, these are all areas where things have too much of toxic compounds for humans to consume. Those are also then in the marine food chain, organic compounds as well and all over the world the problem is essentially the same. Some places they're banned, some places they're not and some places of shellfish fisheries are going on even though there's known to be high toxicity in the material that's fueling the shellfish.

Why does that become a problem? What happens in the marine ecosystem that causes this to become an issue both for the marine life and for human beings? You've probably heard that children and pregnant women are advised to limit their intake of tuna fish. Why is that? Well, it's mercury, and mercury is concentrated in the flesh of the tuna fish. We'll take a look at that concentration in just a second, but the mercury comes from the burning of coal and it's what we call a teratogen meaning it's something that actually causes genetic damage. That's the specific reason why people who are pregnant or might become pregnant are advised not to eat too much tuna because of the examples of the really acute mercury toxicity that unfortunately have been seen in the world.

One of those examples is a famous story of Minamata, Japan, an area that between the 1950s and 1960s was a town, there was an industrial source of really heavy loads of mercury going into a shallow bay, an estuarine environment in the town and the people who live there consumed huge amounts of shellfish that were coming out of that same bay. It caused the most acute probably mass scale mercury toxicity and many, many children were born with genetic defects. It's a very sad story, went on for a very long time before the specific toxicity of the mercury was recognized and steps were taken to mitigate against it. This has been given a name, Minamata disease, which is essentially just acute mercury poisoning.

It's not just tuna. The FDA recommends children and women of childbearing age avoid swordfish, sharks, king mackerel, altogether and many other fish to limit their intake. Why is that? Well what all of them share is they're the big fish that consume other fish. They're living at a high trophic level as consumers in the ocean. The shellfish are concentrating it more or less directly. They're filter feeding right out of the water where the mercury or the other compounds are put directly into the water. These other large fish are way out in the middle of the sea. We talk about tuna, they're swimming around in the ocean, but they're living at a high trophic level. Because of that then, they're susceptible to what's called biomagnifications. This was made famous by Rachel Carson *Silent Spring*, way back in the early 1960s, late 1950s.

The example that really made biomagnifications clear was DDT. In the early 1960s, late 1950s, it was being used very heavily applied to control mosquitoes, to control all sorts of pests. It's a very good pesticide in fact, insecticide. The problem is that DDT gets into the water at very low concentrations, something like 3 parts per trillion in this classic study from Long Island Sound. The DDT is consumed by the plankton. It's taken up from the water by the plankton. It's consumed by the small zooplankton and concentrated there eaten by the small fish. Remember the amount of food you need to eat at each trophic level is a factor of 10 at least magnification.

You go up through the small fish where now it's at half a part per million instead of measured in parts per trillion all the way up to the larger fish and ultimately the birds that were consuming those fish at the fourth trophic level up or the fifth trophic level up. In pelicans and cormorants and things is at 25 parts per million, 10 million fold increase in concentration of that toxin up the food chain. Of course, that's toxic to the animals that are consuming it and it's toxic to human beings if we consume those animals like the high trophic level tuna and swordfish.

Biomagnifications applies to lots of pollutants, not just DDT. Fortunately DDT is mostly out of our environment and those levels have actually declined greatly since it was banned in North America. Biomagnifications applies to mercury, which is the reason for the FDA recommendation. It applies to PCBs and other chlorinated hydrocarbons and dolphins off the U.S. coast have been found to have levels of PCBs, chlorinated hydrocarbons that are many, many times what we consider a safe level on land. Dolphins with flesh that had 6900 parts per million PCBs, the human safe limit set by the FDA is 5 parts per million, 6900, so that dolphin is essentially a toxic substance all by itself and that's because of PCB dumping in the ocean. Lead is another one of course that becomes concentrated through biomagnifications.

There is some good news on these kinds of toxic substances because the recognition of their toxicity and accumulation in ocean water, sediments, and organisms has led to real action. We know DDT use was banned in the U.S. in the 1970s, leaded gas was phased out from 1975 or so and it turns out that the near shore environment shows rapidly declining or showed rapidly declining amounts of these really, really bad substances till by the 1990s heavy metal disposal was greatly tightened up at least here and accumulations have fallen to tiny fractions of the peak levels of the `60s and `70s and `80s. In other parts of the world, they may not be controlled as well and certainly a lot of developing countries what goes into the ocean is virtually unknown and uncontrolled.

On the other hand, the news is not all good because the accumulation of these substances in organisms and in sediments means that many of those compounds are still hanging around. They got taken up by organisms and buried in the sediments. The estuarine shellfish in particular still have large toxicity associated with that runoff from several decades ago. That's why virtually all the urbanized areas the estuarine environments are still off-limits to shellfish fishing.

Another form of pollution, as I said, can be too much of a good thing, which means nutrient runoff into the ocean. I mentioned this once before. The process called eutrophication; the result of putting excess nutrients in the water can be a bad thing because it causes too much to grow in the water. Nutrients go into the water from either sewage outfall or agricultural runoff of fertilizers. Both are major sources, depending on where you are in the coastal regions of the ocean, they're both potentially big problems.

The reason is because the same nitrogen and phosphorus that helps plants grow in agricultural fields, once it gets into the water off shore or the extra organic water that comes from sewage outfall fuels organisms. They're happy, they have lots of nutrients in the shallow water off shore so it causes massive booms of algal plankton or the thing called red tide and even causes some of these other odd things you sometimes see like yellow foams. Now normal sea foam you see at the coast is often not the product of any kind of human introduction of material. It's just part of the marine process in the organic matter, but sometimes when it gets really extreme it's because of excess eutrophication.

We already talked about red tide a little bit. Remember what that is. It's the massive boom of those dinoflagellates, particular kinds of phytoplankton that are photosynthesizers and once they get all those nutrients they can bloom in great perfusion, but many of the dinoflagellates as a defense mechanism have toxic compounds in their body so that they're not good to eat. In high concentration In the water then they become very toxic to marine life, can kill a lot of marine life and can sicken or even kill human beings who consume that marine life and in some cases of allergies even people who live nearby and the wind just blows from the dinoflagellates, the red tide that's all washed up on to the beach. Red tide can get so bad that it can even be seen from space as in satellite images of the Florida peninsula where the red tides form around the coastline.

Another one, the so-called black tide, is a different story because black tide as we see in this image from near the coast of beautiful otherwise pristine waters in New Zealand is a massive bloom of algae in the water, again fed by nutrients from runoff in eutrophication. It's not directly toxic itself, but what it does is it uses up the available oxygen. Algae and other photosynthesizers make oxygen right. What they do is during the day they make oxygen. At night they respire and burn the fuel and they use up some oxygen and then all the zooplankton bloom and larger fish bloom, use up the oxygen that those algae are making and eventually cause the water to become hypoxic or too low in oxygen.

The effect of hypoxia is that the big fish and shrimp and things like that can move will leave the area. They go to where there's more oxygen. They need oxygen to respire. Other organisms that can't get out of the area that don't move as fast, like crabs and things like that, will just suffocate, shellfish as well. In the Gulf of Mexico, there's something called the dead zone, maybe you've heard of it. From February through late summer every year a huge hypoxic, low oxygen zone appears in the Gulf of Mexico off the mouth of the Mississippi River. It's produced by the agricultural runoff that's coming down the Mississippi and causing eutrophication of the shallow near shore waters there.

Nothing is living on the bottom or in the water column above the bottom in this vast plume of nutrients that we call the dead Zone. It varies in size from year to year depending on oceanographic conditions and storms and waves and things, but up to 8500 square miles of area can participate in the dead zone and basically getting worse as the years and decades go by. The Gulf of Mexico dead zone is also only one of many around the world. Anywhere where there's large runoff into the sea from big rivers that drain agricultural areas and especially when they go into very shallow water basins.

One of the maybe positive aspects of the dead zone in the eutrophication problem at least is that it's pretty reversible. It's because of the direct influx seasonally of this essentially toxic nutrient load into the water. For example, there was a very bad dead zone forming in the Black Sea off of the coast of the former Soviet Union and during that period when the former Soviet Union existed, fertilizer runoff ran into the Black Sea in just the way we're talking about the Gulf of Mexico dead zone. After the collapse of the USSR, then the government support of fertilizers and the government support of agriculture dropped precipitously in that area, fertilizer usage dropped and the dead zone actually recovered. That region of the Black Sea has become much healthier since the end of the Soviet Union than it was before.

Another form of direct dumping into the water is solid waste. The sea is a dump for trash and garbage all over the world to this day. Fortunately it's not as much so from the USA as it was in the past, but it isn't over here and it's certainly not over in much of the world. Starting from 1890 basically all of New York City's trash, for example, went into the New York byte, the water just off the mouth of the Hudson River. Garbage of every type, all the urban trash went into the sea. Floating garbage ended up on beaches all over New Jersey and all over the Long Island region and really caused public outcry. Eventually from the 1930s on, floating garbage, at least, was banned or restricted.

It wasn't until 1986 that they actually stopped that dumping and moved to a different dumpsite called the 106 Mile Site because it was 106 miles off shore where they dumped sewage sludge and other solid waste only between 1986 and 1992 actually was that used. Finally ocean dumping from the city was restricted. In that time, that short period of time, 42 million tons of sewage sludge were dumped out there and actually became a study site for growth of benthic organisms because it was in very deep water based on the introduction of extra organic matter, stuff to eat.

Restrictions are growing on this kind of dumping, but it's still a big problem. One kind of problem from that actually is that military dumping of solid waste has been going for a very long time and is restricted now, but there's a legacy of it out there in the ocean that's phenomenal. One of the expeditions that I went out on to go out off shore, the Pacific Northwest, we were intending to go down and take core samples of the sea bottom. The area that we were coring in was a zone that was restricted because according to the information we had gotten, at the end of World War II the Navy had dumped large stores, whole barrels, many barrels of mustard gas that had been stockpiled during the war and never used and so they just went out there and dumped it in the deepwater.

There are huge dumps like that in the Atlantic, in the Pacific, and all over the world's ocean of pretty toxic compounds. We were afraid we might core through an actual old rusting oil drum of mustard gas and get one of our cores back. We had to get clearance on the exact location, but this was done in the 1940s. Records weren't kept particularly well. They just went out to sea and dumped the stuff. There wasn't a record of the exact location and we had to do a camera survey on the sea bottom first to make sure the area was actually clear.

Finally I want to talk about plastics in the ocean. Plastic garbage and particles in the sea have become pervasive and they've become pervasive pretty recently as society has just greatly increased its use of plastics. They come from both land sources in terms of dumping and from marine dumping from ships, in fact. There's an estimate that every year 135,000 tons of plastic are dumped by ships at sea, including fishing gear that cripples or kills marine mammals. We've all seen photos of seals and dolphins wrapped up in plastic or birds caught in the

355

6-pack rings. These are all very real problems and very growing problems. They're kind of exemplified by something in the news lately, the recently discovered Great Pacific Garbage Patch, which highlights the problem.

The Pacific Garbage Patch is a region of the North Pacific Ocean within the big gyre. Remember the oceanic gyre is the currents and in the center of the gyre is areas of water that's relatively calm. It's in the doldrums, the winds don't blow a whole lot, but water doesn't move around a lot and the currents have swept bits of plastic that are entering the marine world into a couple of different concentrated zones within the Pacific gyre. It's not the whole Pacific gyre, which covers an enormous region of the Pacific Ocean, but a couple of specific spots, one near the North Atlantic side of the gyre, one near Japan, and also what's called a convergence zone in the north side of the gyre where the waters are downwelling somewhat in the sea north of Hawaii.

There's an estimated something like 1 million pieces of plastic per square kilometer over an area that in aggregate it might be as big as the continental US, but it's not exactly what maybe the news has pictured as being. Most of that plastic is in the form of very, very small suspended pieces in the water. If you look at the water you wouldn't even see them. If you sample the water you find that there are microscopic bits of plastic everywhere concentrated in this Great Pacific Garbage Patch.

One sampling study of the water showed that the actual plastic particles outweighed the zooplankton in that region by a factor of 6. Now that doesn't mean they do for the whole ocean fortunately. This is a concentrated plastic zone and zooplankton are actually pretty rare. It's a relative biological desert. It's possible though that toxins like PCB and dioxin accumulate on the surface of these plastic and are consumed by various organisms. It's really unknown to what extent the plastic mimics the plankton and is therefore consumed by all form of marine fish and mammals and other organisms with unknown effect.

One effect we do know is that plastic ingestion by birds, by pelagic birds is a major problem for those birds. The pelagic birds are the ones that fly all over the ocean and live basically at sea, albatrosses and related birds called fulmars fly around at sea and they feed. When they see a bit of plastic, not a microscopic bit anymore, but an actual chunk of plastic of some sort, a discarded bottle cap for example, they see it floating in the water; they're going to consume it. They think it's something good to eat.

Those organisms, albatrosses and fulmars, are found in recent years to have up to 20 or more pieces of indigestible plastic in their stomachs interfering with their digestive systems in the Pacific, in the Atlantic, and now even recently discovered for fulmars living in the Arctic Ocean region. The study of diet in these birds back in the 1970s where lots of them were dissected to see what was in their digestive tract reported no plastic particles so no plastic pieces. From the 1970s to today, this has become an enormous problem and may be interfering with these words lifestyle very much.

The last thing I want to mention briefly is sound pollution in the ocean. The industrialized ocean is a very noisy place. We may not think of sound as pollution, but it is in the sea in that it interferes with organisms. Ships use sonar, the seismic reflection exploration below the sea floor uses these air guns that emit loud booms into the water, but probably most of all just everyday shipping is a constant source of noise from propellers and things like that. The potential impacts are large for animals that use echolocation and sound to communicate like whales and dolphins. We don't really know what the effect is on them of all of these sounds.

For the strongest sounds mostly emitted by almost classified are new Navy sonar that's very high powered. It's possible there's direct damage to the internal organs of some of these echolocating mammals. Some have claimed they've actually caused death or beaching of whales, but that's not exactly clear today. It may be true. Research is ongoing on that. Certainly just the noisy marine environment maybe interfering with the long distance communication of the humpback whales and other organism which may be affecting their entire lifestyle and certainly has to at least be annoying them.

On many different fronts, the marine environment is challenged as never before. There are some success stories with respect to point sources, but less so with the broad based runoff and plastics, things that are entering from everywhere and are rapidly growing problem. Awareness of these problems presumably though is the first step to finding solutions to them.

The Future Ocean
Lecture 36

The ocean is constantly changing, and human activity is accelerating those changes. Recognition of human impacts has led to important steps to maintain the long-term chemical and physical balance, stability, and ecosystem health in the ocean, but challenges abound. Marine conservation areas permit refugia for fish to spawn and populations to recover. Increased international agreement on what should be done in the open ocean away from territorial boundaries may help in achieving sustainable yield levels. Heat input from global warming, rising sea levels, and acidification from carbon dioxide will modify the ocean environment in specific ways, presenting challenges for societal interaction with the global ocean.

Change Is Constant

- The ocean is changing over so many different timescales—from human timescales and seasonal cycles of phytoplankton to geological timescales of plate tectonics. Human activity is accelerating those changes, possibly even on those much longer timescales.

- Approximately 41% of ocean areas are strongly affected by multiple impacts, especially overfishing, toxicity, and coral bleaching. That's a huge area of the surface of Earth.

- The activities of human beings are pushing the ocean environment to change more rapidly. Ecosystems are changing much more rapidly than they should naturally because human beings are fishing out lots of the top predators, for example. Coastlines are changing more rapidly because of warming and rising seas.

- It's more difficult for the natural ecosystems to respond in an environment where human beings are trying to maintain certain aspects of the environment.

- Today, there are ongoing studies of coral reefs that look at how they're colonizing areas farther and farther north as the water begins to get warmer. In some cases, they seem to be successful, but in other cases, they don't seem to be keeping up.

- Human beings are removing the top predators and are causing pollution and other upsets to ecosystems that can cause whole systemic collapses of these ecosystems.

- Today, the rate of species extinction appears to exceed anything since the last of the great mass extinctions.

- In a book called *A Sea in Flames*, marine ecologist Carl Safina draws some really interesting conclusions one year after the 2010 Deepwater Horizon oil spill in the Gulf of Mexico.

- For example, Safina saw that when the spill occurred, fishing and shrimping were banned for a period of time. This action likely helped the wildlife in the Gulf more than the spill hurt it because without the shrimping, there was more food in the food chain for all organisms, giving them a chance for their populations to recover. Paradoxically, it was a good year for growth for the marine wildlife in the Gulf.

- The chronic and systemic effects human beings have on the marine ecosystem far outweigh the damage done by singular events like the oil spill in the Gulf of Mexico. Fertilizer runoff in the dead zone, for example, does far more harm than one oil spill.

- Even compared to 50, 70, or 100 years ago, our impact on the ocean is fundamentally different because there are so many more people trying to derive food from the ocean; having an impact in terms of what is put into the sea; pulling oil and gas out of the ocean floor; and driving ships around on the surface, putting sound pollution into the water and affecting marine ecosystems.

Human Impact

- The impact of human beings is pervasive because we've become pervasive, and we've only become pervasive in the most recent times in both human and geological history. We dominate the planet now, including the ocean.

- We've eaten 90% of the large fish in the sea in 50 years. We've lost nearly 1/2 of the coral reefs on the planet, and we don't know whether they can come back or whether they will continue to perish.

- In about 150 years, we've built up the coastlines all around the world—rich and poor countries alike—and we've impacted all those coastal marine ecosystems and the physical environment of the coastlines in enormous ways.

- In 1960, aquanauts Jacques Piccard and Don Walsh went down in the bathyscaphe *Trieste* and visited the bottom of the Mariana Trench, the deepest place in the ocean—11,000 meters below the surface of the water—and stayed there for 20 minutes.

- Since 1960, no human being has ever been back down there. In fact, no human being has ever been back down anywhere in the bottom of the deepest regions of the ocean. It's the most unexplored part of the planet; 95% of the ocean floor has never been seen by human eyes directly.

- The great depths are still great unexplored environments, and at least on a relative scale, they're the places where we're having the least impact. Deep marine ecosystems are largely untouched and unaffected by human activities.

The Coming Decades

- In the coming decades in the ocean, the temperature and heat content of the water are going to increase, and sea level is going to continue to rise—perhaps at an accelerating pace. There's also going to continue to be the chemical change of the entire surface of the ocean in the form of acidification.

- With the input of freshwater in the Arctic and Antarctic regions from the melting of sea ice, there's a possibility that we may even modify the great oceanic conveyor belt.

- As terrestrial resources become increasingly stretched, we're going to see more utilization of the ocean. There's certainly going to be increased aquaculture of freshwater species and mariculture off shore. Therefore, the kinds of fish that we eat will become more and more fish that are farmed instead of fish that are wild caught.

- The industry pertaining to offshore oil and gas drilling—spills notwithstanding—is likely to continue. Probably, mining in the ocean will begin. New energy from the ocean may be a really important source.

- Wind power seems to be involved in the future of energy; windmills are already being placed off shore.

- Another new technique in the realm of energy is the use of tidal energy, or wave energy, which involves the placing of some sort of fixed structures mounted to the ocean floor—or perhaps even floating—that have turbines on them that will turn as ocean currents or tidal rush comes in and out of coastal environments.

- Wave energy, the ups and downs of the waves, is a form of energy that can be potentially tapped to generate electricity as well.

- Another interesting form of energy is called **ocean thermal energy conversion (OTEC)**. If you have an area where you can tap the deep water of the deep-sea environment, you can draw cold water up to the surface. Because of its temperature difference with shallow surface waters, you can drive heat exchangers, or turbines, that will allow you to pull the energy out of a difference in temperature between the surface and the deep water to make electricity.

- One more use of the ocean that is going to continue to grow is shipping. Ships, per unit of good, only need **A large cargo ship that burns diesel is actually a very efficient, low-carbon way to move goods around the planet.** to burn incredibly small amounts of fuel for safe transportation from Asia to North America. The carbon footprint of shipping is excellent relative to land transportation and can be even smaller for long-distance transport.

- Vast areas of the ocean have never been sampled to determine what's living out there. Sampling efforts begun by the Census of Marine Life must continue; there are still many tracts that are entirely unsampled. We still have an underexplored ocean.

- The idea of the Ocean Observatories Initiative is to put sensors both at the bottom of the sea and up through the water column and connect them to land with offshore fiber cables so that real-time data can be acquired.

- The Ocean Observatories Initiative includes autonomous underwater vehicles and buoys in various parts of the sea all over the planet. This initiative is going to be the future of oceanography, and in many ways, it's making our presence not just an expedition at a particular time, but all of the time.

The Coming Centuries and Millennia

- The effects of the enormous accidental geophysical experiment—the release of carbon into the atmosphere and ocean—are going to be felt for centuries, guaranteed.

- Plate tectonics will continue. Evolution will continue. The 4-billion-year-old waters will continue to crash on the shoreline. They'll move in currents and in thermohaline convection for many millions of years to come—whether we're here or not, in fact.

- We can come up with increased international agreement on what should be done in the open ocean, such as the efforts by the International Whaling Commission and the International Commission for the Conservation of Atlantic Tunas. There's a lot of controversy, but territorial waters near land and the more recent Exclusive Economic Zones that extend 200 miles from shore are already governed by international law of various kinds.

- We have to strengthen international laws to avoid the kind of tragic overfishing that's causing ecosystem collapse in the sea today, including the tragedy of the commons.

Instead of taking up space on land, wind turbines can be placed in offshore regions as an alternative source of energy.

- Ocean resources, sea level, and general conditions are international goods for us, and they're also international problems.

- In order to protect something, you have to know about it. To avoid a destructive fate for the world's ocean, we have to first know the ocean realm.

- One hopeful sign is the establishment of marine sanctuaries and marine conservation areas by the United States and by many other countries around the world.

- In the oceans today, 0.8% is protected as marine sanctuaries or marine conservation areas. Perhaps that number should be more like 10%, 12% (the percentage of land protected in national parks worldwide), or 20% to provide enough refugia for the fish stocks to recover and for the ecosystems to thrive.

- The ocean is a vast and interconnected frontier; it is not only a food web, but also an interdisciplinary web in which all the sciences meet. To understand it—and to be good stewards—we have to view the ocean as a whole.

Important Term

ocean thermal energy conversion (OTEC): A pilot technology to generate energy by exploiting the temperature difference between warm, near-surface water and cold, deep water drawn up to the surface.

Suggested Reading

Earle, *The World Is Blue*.

Safina, *The View from Lazy Point*.

1. As humans continue to interact with the ocean ecosystem, what are some tenets or principles for more effective stewardship, without shocking economic activity?

2. In what ways is the ocean likely to remain unchanged by human activity (at least the activities we know about in the present) in 1000 years—or in 1,000,000 years?

The Future Ocean
Lecture 36—Transcript

Now we've come to the point where we can ask the question what does the future hold for the ocean. I think everything we've seen in all of these lectures shows us that in some ways the answer is more of the same, which is constant change. The ocean is ever-changing over so many different timescales from human timescales and seasonal cycles of phytoplankton to geological timescales of plate tectonics. Human activity though is accelerating those changes, possibly even at those much longer timescales.

The recognition of human impacts has led to important steps being taken to maintain long-term chemical and physical balance, the stability in ecosystem health in the ocean as we saw in the last lecture. Certainly major challenges still abound. One group of oceanographers and marine biologists attempted a comprehensive global scale study. It was published in 2008 that they mapped out the human impacts on the entire surface of the global ocean and they include all sorts of impacts from local overfishing or toxicity by pollution right up to global scale effects like the introduction of carbon dioxide and acidification.

The map shows that no area of the global ocean is unaffected by human influence at all. That's fortunately for a lot of the ocean that's mainly the influence of the global scale features like acidification and warming of the waters that are not locally acute necessarily, but they are certainly real impacts that can concern us about the whole ocean. But, 41% of ocean areas they found are strongly affected by multiple impacts, especially overfishing, especially toxicity, coral bleaching, et cetera, so 41%. That's a huge area of the surface of Earth.

There are these large areas of relatively little impact mainly in the Polar Regions and in the far more remote corners, there are no corners of course, of the Pacific Ocean and places like that. Really our impacts are being seen on a global scale in a way that was probably unimaginable 50 years ago to Jacques Cousteau and Rachel Carson and the early explorers and advocates for the marine environment. What we've seen in all of this course and all the different ways we've looked at it is that change really is constant in the ocean over geological timescales, sea level rises and falls, coastlines and barrier islands, move and change, ice ages come and go, species rise and become extinct, an they're all natural processes.

Seasonally and decadally animals grown and phytoplankton bloom and all of these different processes go on nested within one another all in an ocean that is continuously present, the tides rising and falling, the waves breaking on the beach. We can ask the question what's different about the present day from all of those other epics before this large-scale human impact that we see today on the ocean had taken place. The answer is that we're the difference. We build on the coastline. We gain food from the sea. We enjoy its beauty and bounty and we've developed a vested interest, a perfectly normal laudable human interest in keeping things more or less the same, meaning allowing change to take place, but in the way it naturally goes on.

Sometimes that comes in conflict. We want to keep things really truly the same like maintain a coastline even though nature wants to move the coastline back and forth or something like that. The problem is kind of exemplified by that, but applies to all sorts of different things in the ocean because the pace of present day change in most cases vastly exceeds the natural pace of change. The things that human beings are doing are pushing the ocean environment to change more rapidly. Ecosystems are changing much more rapidly than naturally because we're fishing out lots of the top predators for example. Coastlines are changing more rapidly because of warming and rising seas.

It's more difficult in an environment where human beings are trying to maintain certain things the same for the natural ecosystems to respond. For example, in climate change over geological time organisms just move their habitat. They slowly migrate to different regions as the planet gets warmer or cooler or something like that. Habitat migration is much more difficult now. Studies are ongoing today of coral reefs and looking at how they're colonizing areas further and further north as the water begins to get warmer. In some cases, that actually seems to be happening successfully, but in other cases they don't seem to be keeping up. It's an active area of research today. Certainly other kinds of organisms can't move in habitat as quickly as they would need to to respond to these kinds of changes in the ocean because they're very slow growing, and it takes a long time for example for a coral reef to build up.

We're removing the top predators. We're causing pollution and other upsets to ecosystems that can cause whole systemic collapse of these ecosystems. We don't fully understand them, but we're certainly seeing the effects of them on the planet. We saw the impact of the asteroid on Earth 65 million years ago that paleontologists and geologists tell us cause the extinction of the dinosaurs and actually less well-known 50% of the species in the ocean itself. The mass extinction went on underwater just as much as on land. I don't think we want to cause the next mass extinction on earth, but in fact we may. Actually it may already be underway. The rate of species extinction today, the pace appears to exceed anything since the last of the great mass extinctions.

Another thing about human beings I think and what we look at is we tend to focus on the big events. Perhaps we focus on the wrong impacts that we're having on the ocean. In a book called the *Sea in Flames*, Carl Safina, a marine ecologist, in fact a MacArthur Genius Award winner drew some really interesting conclusions one year after the 2010 Gulf oil spill. As a marine ecologist, as a marine biologist interested in the health of the ecosystem, he went in and certainly in his book he doesn't pull his punches. He's very critical of the corporate and government entities and their response and the fact that oil drilling on off shore perhaps about enough safeguards to prevent such spills.

He also saw that many of the worst case scenarios for the ecosystem actually hadn't come true fortunately and he also offered us some surprising perspective on what is going on out there in the Gulf of Mexico or in the ocean in general. For example, he saw that when the spill happened fishing and shrimping were banned for a period of time, that likely helped the wildlife in the Gulf more than the spill hurt it because without the shrimping going on, there was more food in the food chain for all of the organisms around and they had a chance for populations to recover. It was a good year for growth for the marine wildlife in the Gulf paradoxically.

His point he makes is that fertilizer runoff in the dead zone do far more harm perhaps than the spill itself. The loss of wetland area from subsidence because channelization of the Mississippi and other rivers has taken sediment away from the wetlands area, sediment deposition away, and so the wetlands are subsiding and we're losing land area to the sea, a very productive rich estuarine land area. That effect may be far worse than the area that was fouled by oil coming into those wetlands. The headlines are the oil coming into the wetlands, but perhaps our focus tends to be misplaced. The chronic and systemic effects we have on the marine ecosystem far outweigh the damage by singular events like the oil spill, bad as it is. I tend to agree with Safina's point there.

One more interesting thought from Carl Safina before we live him behind is he said in his book a whale might think thank god for petroleum. How's that? Well after all if petroleum hadn't come along to replace whale oil as fuel many species of whales would surely have been hunted all the way to extinction a hundred years ago or more. Petroleum replaced whale oil in lighting our cities and that perhaps is one thing that really truly saved the whales.

We've already touched on the fact that we're reaching a point where the human population is just fundamentally different on this planet than it's ever been before. There were very small numbers of people, much less than a billion people throughout almost all of human history. If we look at the overall timescale we see this curve of human population growth which is pretty familiar which just is this enormous exponential only in very recent years; 1930, 2 billion people were on the planet, 1965, 3-1/2 billion people were on the planet, and now in 2011, something like 7 billion people are on the planet. Even compared to 50 or 70 or 100 years ago our impact on the ocean is fundamentally enormously different because there are just so many more people trying to derive food from the ocean, having an impact in terms of what we're putting into the sea, pulling oil and gas out of the sea floor and just simply driving ships around on the surface putting sound pollution into the water and affecting marine ecosystems in that way.

Our impact is pervasive because we've become pervasive and we've only become pervasive in the most recent instant in both human history and even geological history. We dominate the planet now including the ocean. We've eaten 90% of the big fish in the sea in 50 years in terms of the population of large fish, 90% are gone compared to 50 years ago. As I said before, we've lost nearly half of the coral reefs on the planet and we don't know whether they can come back or whether that will continue.

In 150 years or so, we've built up the coastlines all around the world, rich countries, poor countries alike and so we've impacted all those coastal marine ecosystems and the physical environment of the coastlines in enormous ways. We've impacted almost every place in the shallow ocean in some way, even places we haven't explored particularly well. Maybe the deep ocean is still the wilderness.

In 1960, I told you about Jacques Piccard and Don Walsh, the two aquanauts who went down in the Bathyscaphe Trieste and they visited the bottom of the Mariana Trench, the deepest place in the ocean, 11,000 meters below the surface of the water. It stayed there for 20 minutes. They saw a couple of fish out the window so they noted that there was life there at the bottom of the deepest place in the ocean and they came back to the surface. They were actually pretty worried because a crack had developed in the window.

Since 1960, no one, no human being has ever been back down there. In fact, no human being has ever been back down anywhere in the bottom of the *Challenger* deep or any of the other deep trenches in the ocean. It's the most unexplored part of the planet and in some ways it's a more unexplored of even the Solar System. I've told you about how poorly mapped the ocean floor is compared to other planetary bodies; 95% of the ocean floor has never been seen by human eyes directly.

The great deeps are still the great unexplored environment and at least on a relative scale, they're the place where we're having the least impact. Warming of the surface waters is not yet affecting the temperature of the very deep waters at the bottom it seems pretty clear. It may in the future, but it isn't now. Those deep marine ecosystems are largely untouched and unaffected by human activities. Let's try to keep it that way.

What do coming decades hold then for the ocean? Let's talk about the future ocean at a couple of different timescales. First of all, some things are going to continue to happen, more warming of the ocean is certain at the current pace of warming. The temperature of the water is going to go up, the heat content of the water is going to go up and sea level is going to continue to rise, perhaps at an accelerating pace. There's going to continue to be this chemical change of the entire surface water of the ocean in the form of acidification and we just fundamentally don't know what the affects of acidification are on the life forms that live in that shallow water environment.

With the input of fresh water in the Arctic and Antarctic regions from melting of sea ice, there's a possibility that we may even modify that great oceanic conveyor belt, the deepwater formation that moves the water around the entire sea and that really would have an impact potentially on the deep oceans. We don't really know, but that's certainly within the realm of possibility. We're conducting this great geophysical experiment in modifying the environmental surface of Earth and that fundamentally means the ocean. We don't know yet how it's all going to turn out.

More things the coming decades hold as terrestrial resources become ever more stretched we're going to see more utilization of the ocean. There's certainly going to be increased aquaculture of fresh water species and mariculture off shore so the kinds of fish that we eat will go more and more towards fish that are farmed in one way or another than wild caught. That's partly because it's just simply going to have to be that way. There won't be as many wild fish to catch as those resources are used up and also because of a conscious choice that maybe catching wild fish is not the best idea compared to culturing them. We'll see more mariculture in the ocean and we'll see the practice change and evolve over time to be more responsive to the local ecosystems even where the mariculture is going on.

Certainly see more offshore oil and gas drilling, spills notwithstanding, the industry is likely to go on. Probably mining in the ocean will begin. One interesting new area that we really haven't tapped to any significant extent yet is energy from the ocean or energy from off shore. Let's take a look at a few of the examples of things that are currently in development as prices of oil rise as concerns about nuclear energy continue to be there. New energy from the ocean may be a really important source.

One is wind power. Windmills are already being placed off shore. It's nice to give that in an environment where it tends to be windy all the time or a lot of the time. In shallow water, you can mount them on the seabed. They're not without controversy because people standing on the shore maybe don't want to look at windmills on their otherwise pristine horizon environment as they look out at the sea, but on the other hand this is an alternative source of energy that can be placed in the offshore region and generate electricity and doesn't take up land. That's a good thing as well. This is really likely to grow. It's happening more in Europe today than in North America, but in both areas we'll probably see more wind power generated off shore.

Another new one that's been done in a number of pilot projects and even some small-scale projects in Europe is the use of tidal energy or wave energy. This means the placing of some sort of fixed structures mounted to the seabed or perhaps even floating that have turbines on them that will turn as ocean currents or tidal rush comes in and out of coastal environments. There's a lot of energy in that motion of all that water, the volume of water is so great. Those ocean currents and tidal currents can be tapped to generate electricity. Wave energy, the up and down of the wave is a form of energy that can be potentially tapped to generate electricity as well.

Another interesting form of energy is something called ocean thermal energy conversion or OTEC for short. OTEC is a very simple concept that says if you have an area where you can tap the deep water of the deep sea environment, you can draw cold water up to the surface. Because of its temperature difference with shallow surface waters you can drive heat exchangers or turbines that will allow you to pull the energy out of a difference in temperature between the surface and the deep water and again make electricity. It has some secondary values like on the pipes that carry that cold water condenses fresh water out of the air and make desalinated water, fresh water generation as well.

This has been done again on pilot scale projects and if energy becomes significantly expensive and if the will in society is there to do it OTEC is a potential real new energy source that can be done in many places around the world that have access to deep water, like off the Hawaiian Islands for example. One more use of the ocean that is going to continue to grow is shipping. We still transport most goods around the planet and trade around the planet is an increasing thing by ships. We've been doing it since the days of the Phoenicians and we'll still be doing it into the future.

You might be surprised to think that a very large cargo ship, diesel burning, smelly cargo ship is actually a very efficient, low carbon footprint way of moving things around the planet. Ships per unit of good transported have incredibly small amount of fuel that needs to be burned to get things safe from Asia to North America. Shipping is a good thing and certainly the alternative is stuff like flying them, which isn't going to happen. Sometimes the carbon footprint of a good that was brought to the east coast of the U.S., New York, by ship from Asia is smaller than the same thing, say a bottle of wine for example, that's brought over land by truck from California to New York. It seems strange but the carbon footprint can be smaller for much more long distance transport.

Let's look at the future of the ocean in terms of ocean science. We clearly have learned a great deal about the ocean. We've explored various aspects of it to the greatest depths all over the planet from the poles to the equator. Yet, there's so much more that we don't know. I talked about the Census of Marine Life and its 10 year cataloguing of everything about life in the sea. They published a map at the end of the Census of Marine Life that shows the amalgamation of their 30 million different records of individual organisms and species and things like that from that 10 year study. On this map, they colored a dot for every half degree area of latitude placed on the planet; basically a thousand square miles for each dot where they have at least some data and the reds and blues and yellows are just how many measurements they have in each individual area.

What you see is that vast areas of the ocean are white. There's no colored dot so even with a 10-year study, the largest marine biology study that's ever been done, vast areas of the ocean have never been sampled literally for any kind of what's out there, what's living out there. The Census of Marine Life in the broader sense has to continue and we still have an underexplored ocean for sure.

One of the ways that human presence in the ocean is going to increase is by moving off shore with permanent research stations of various kinds. There's a major initiative underway called the Ocean Observatories Initiative. The idea is to put whole sensors, both at the bottom of the sea and up through the water column and connect them back to land with offshore fiber cables, something like our communication cables, so that data is coming in real time. A series of these, first off the northwest coast of the U.S. and the other areas, but in deep water, out in the open ocean to tell us about what's going on in the sea.

The Ocean Observatory Initiative includes autonomous underwater vehicles. It included buoys in various parts of the sea all over the planet. To start putting essentially a set a network of sensors out there that becomes our stethoscope on the entire sea. This is going to be the future of oceanography and in many ways it's making our presence not just an expedition at a time, but all of the time.

What do coming centuries and millennia hold in the ocean? The effects of this enormous accidental geophysical experiment, the release of carbon in the atmosphere and the ocean is going to be felt for centuries guaranteed. The carbon dioxide is gone from the ground to the atmosphere, but actually as we recall mostly into the ocean, most of the excess CO_2 is being taken up by the water, it's making that warmer and higher water, we'll have more acidity and we'll have less ice in the ocean. What kind of state that's going to get to is unclear so far.

We've said that the present day carbon dioxide balance at the surface is different than it's been in at least 10 million years and maybe longer. A few years ago there was an expedition to drill cores in the Arctic Ocean. The very first samples of that paleoceanography, the history of the ocean basin came out of the core samples from ice breaking ships that went up and drilled the first core samples in the Arctic. What they found was that at the time that those sediments were laid down, 55 million years ago, the Arctic Ocean held blooms of tropical algae. It's not just plate tectonic drift; it was high to the northern latitude, so the North Polar Region had an environment that was like the tropics today.

Are those kinds of conditions going to return once all the sea ice melts? We don't really know. It will be a very long process to get there, but maybe over centuries and millennia that may be exactly where the ocean could be going. Eventually some sort of new equilibrium will be reached and if we stretch it out to centuries, millennia, even longer kinds of timescales then the ocean will still be there and the ocean will reach a stability that's in keeping with the environment of that time. Plate tectonics will continue. Evolution will continue. The 4 billion year old waters will continue to crash on the shoreline. They'll move in currents and they'll move in thermohaline convection for many, many millions of years to come whether we're here or not in fact.

One hopeful sign in terms of really back to our impacts in the present day is that we can come up with increased international agreement on what should be done in the open ocean, especially away from territorial boundaries that have been defined and the definition of those is a major international cooperative coup as well so that we can achieve sustainable yields in the open ocean. The International Whaling Commission I talked about is one example. Another thing, that's the Atlantic Tuna Governmental Organization called ICCAT, the Law of the Sea Treaty and Convention itself is a major effort in this direction and it allows countries to decide or to understand that they have a particular zone that they control the waters in and certainly not without controversy. There's lots of controversy, but the rest of the ocean is governed by international law of various kinds.

We have to strengthen those international laws to really avoid the kind of tragic overfishing that we're seeing that's causing ecosystem collapse in the sea today. All of this is because we have a return to what we think of or what I called before the tragedy of the commons; these ocean resources and sea level and these general conditions are international goods for us and they're international problems. The thing is that the tragedy of the commons is not a metaphor, it's really the truth. The commons, just like the sheep pen that those English villagers had is the entire planet. We really do share the open ocean especially away from the exclusive economic zones of the coastline. The challenges had to reasonably balance our competing needs and desires in the open sea.

I'd like to just briefly remind us of a cautionary tale that has been popularly told and you may have heard already before. It was the highlight of Jared

Diamond's book called *Collapse* and that's the story of the Easter Islanders. Just briefly, archaeology tells us that the Polynesian Easter Islanders arrived there, navigated there about 350 BC and they lived in a rich and fertile forested island. Trees were prevalent all over Easter Island and they were used to build oceangoing canoes and to go fishing and everything else. Population rose to 10,000 or more people. As that happened, overfishing grew in the region. Things started to become scarce. More and more trees were cut down just to be burned for cooking or to build more things or just to clear land for agriculture.

At some point, the last tree was cut down. I can't imagine what it was like to cut down that very last tree, but there was no more resource, there were no more canoes for fishing. Resources dwindled. The society literally collapsed and fell apart and when Captain Cook arrived in 1774, less than 200 people were there. They had crude technology, meager canoes that were barely seaworthy at all. The collapse of this happened because of the overuse of a common resource whether it was the fish or the trees that we're talking about, something happened in a limited resource environment of Easter Island and the people were not good stewards of their resources. The entire planet with its bountiful ocean is our common so is it going to be our Easter Island or is this something that we're going to be able to avoid with foresight into the future.

The first thing is in order to protect something you have to know about it. To avoid that fate for the world's ocean first we have to know the ocean realm. We've seen a great deal of how much we know in this course. Perhaps we've also glimpsed a little bit of how much there still is to explore. A really well-known marine biologist, Sylvia Earle has exhorted us in recent books and speeches to explore and protect the wild ocean, explore and protect. You have to know, you have to explore in order to protect. One is equally as important as the other.

One really hopeful sign is the establishment of marine sanctuaries and marine conservation areas by the U.S. and also by many other countries around the world. Areas where fishing is not allowed or is tightly controlled that permit refugia places for fish to spawn and populations to recover. There was a PBS series that called the National Park System America's best idea. Perhaps we can take that best idea off shore to a greater extent because we have marine sanctuaries and marine protected areas since the early 1970s and there's been quite a few named in recent years. On land, globally speaking 12% of the whole land area of the world is protected in national parks.

In the oceans today, 0.8% is protected as marine sanctuaries or marine conservation areas like that. Maybe that number should be more like 10, 12, 20% or more, to provide enough refugia for the fish stocks to recover, for the ecosystems to thrive.

Now that you know much more about the ocean as Sylvia calls it the blue heart of the planet in all its facets, I hope you feel some deeper appreciation for it, both for its vastness and complexity and paradoxically also for its fragility. We each individually have the responsibility to help insure that future generations have a healthy ocean ecosystem. There are things that we individually can do and make choices. One is as simple as being a good advocate, supporting the formation of things like marine sanctuaries. Another is the personal choices that we make. Sylvia Earle takes the position that eating wild seafood, as tasty as it is, is just fundamentally something that's not okay for the ecosystems.

Timeline

4 billion years ago .... By this time, Earth has formed and is partially or completely covered by a liquid water ocean, which it has had ever since.

3.5 billion years ago .... Marine life exists on the young Earth.

c. 2 billion years ago .... Oxygen revolution by photosynthesis creates an oxygenated atmosphere. Ocean salinity and chemistry stabilize to conditions similar to the present.

470 million years ago .... First evidence for land-based life. Life existed solely in the ocean for the vast majority (about 90%) of the planet's history.

210 million years ago .... Birth of the Atlantic Ocean by rifting of North America away from Africa and Europe.

c. 1500 B.C.E. .... Polynesians had begun long-distance ocean voyaging in the southwestern Pacific.

c. 1200 B.C.E. .... Phoenician, Egyptian, and Cretan sailors plied the Mediterranean and into the Atlantic, trading as far away as the British Isles.

c. 200 B.C.E. .... In Alexandria, Egypt, Eratosthenes recognized the spherical nature of Earth and calculated the circumference to be 40,250 km, within 8% of the correct value (and far better than Columbus's estimate more than a millennium later). He also created the first recorded marine charts.

150 B.C.E. .... Ptolemy's map of the region around the Mediterranean includes surrounding ocean areas; this is the first map to put north at the top and include regular lines of latitude and longitude divided into degrees, minutes, and seconds—just as we use today. Lost to European history for almost 1000 years when the library at Alexandria was destroyed in 415 C.E., Ptolemy's map was rediscovered during the later Crusades and was translated into Latin in 1406.

300–600 C.E. .... Polynesian navigators had colonized nearly every inhabitable island in the Polynesian triangle, extending from New Zealand east to Easter Island and north to the extremely remote Hawaiian Islands.

c. 400 .... Magnetic compass is invented in China.

c. 1002 .... Leif Ericsson and Vikings reach the North American mainland. Around the same time, Arab sailors explore and establish trade routes in the Indian Ocean.

1200s .... Magnetic compass is introduced to Europe.

1405 .... Chinese admiral Zheng He commands the world's largest fleet with 317 ships manned by 27,000 voyagers traveling across the Indian Ocean and to Arabia.

1492 .... Columbus sails west across the Atlantic, (re) discovers the island of Hispaniola and the New World accidentally due to his radical underestimate of the size of Earth.

1507..................................... The Waldseemüller map is published, the first to show "America" and the New World as separate from Asia.

1519–1521........................... Magellan's expedition makes the first circumnavigation around the world (Magellan himself dies along the way), ushering in the age of exploration and conquest.

1674..................................... British chemist Robert Boyle publishes his studies on salinity, temperature, and pressure with depth in *Observations and Experiments on the Saltiness of the Sea.*

1687..................................... Isaac Newton's *Principia Mathematica* is published, including his gravity-based theory of the tides.

1699..................................... Edmond Halley (namesake of the famous comet) commands the Royal Navy vessel *Paramour* on the first purely scientific voyage to the South Atlantic to investigate Earth's magnetic field.

1741..................................... First description of the sea cow, which was hunted to extinction within a generation thereafter, is made by Georg Steller.

1760..................................... First accurate clock at sea, John Harrison's 4th chronometer, allows accurate determination of longitude for the first time.

1768....................................Oceanography as a science begins with the first of 3 expeditions captained by James T. Cook of the British Royal Navy, establishing himself as arguably the first true marine scientist. These expeditions of discovery in the Pacific are the first to include naturalists and systematic botany.

1770....................................Benjamin Franklin and Timothy Folger publish their Gulf Stream chart.

1831–1836...........................Charles Darwin's voyage on the HMS *Beagle*; he identifies 3 types of coral reef and develops a theory of how atolls form (published in 1842). He also makes the fundamental observations in the Galapagos Islands and elsewhere that lead to his theory of evolution by natural selection.

1840....................................Sir James Clark Ross makes the first deepwater sounding in 2425 fathoms (4435 meters) in the North Atlantic.

1872–1876...........................HMS *Challenger* embarks on the first true oceanographic expedition, a 4-year, around-the-world voyage of scientific observation, collection, and measurement. Leads to the publication of the 50-volume *Challenger* report, the basis of modern oceanographic science.

1893–1896...........................Expedition by Fridtjof Nansen in the *Fram*, intentionally frozen into the pack ice, demonstrates that no Arctic continent existed but, rather, that it is an ice-covered ocean; the expedition also pioneers many modern oceanographic techniques of deepwater sampling and sounding.

1903...................................... Scripps Institution of Oceanography
founded, marking the beginning of the era
of dedicated ocean research centers.

1908...................................... Fridtjof Nansen becomes the first
person designated as "Professor of
Oceanography," a post he held at
Christiania University in Norway.

1912...................................... Alfred Wegener publishes his
theory of continental drift.

1925...................................... German research vessel *Meteor* makes
the first large-scale echo soundings.

1930...................................... Beginning of deep-submergence science
with the first bathysphere submersible
to descend more than 1000 feet
(William Beebe and Otis Barton).

1932...................................... International Whaling Commission is
founded to address whaling practices
and endangerment of whale species.

1943...................................... Jacques Cousteau and Emile Gagnan invent the
SCUBA aqualung to allow divers to stay under
water, untethered, for extended periods of time.

1955...................................... First marine magnetometers to measure
strength of magnetic field are used to discover
the magnetic striping of the ocean floor.

1957...................................... First physiographic map of the floor of
the North Atlantic Ocean is published
by Bruce Heezen and Marie Tharp.

1960 .... Don Walsh and Jacques Piccard dive 35,000
feet in the bathyscaphe submersible *Trieste*
to the deepest-known point on Earth in the
Marianas Trench; Harry Hess and Robert Dietz
publish their hypothesis of seafloor spreading.

1961 .... Project Mohole, the first deep-sea drilling
research project, is a pioneering but
ultimately unsuccessful effort to drill down
to Earth's mantle in the Pacific Ocean. Led
to the development of the international
Deep Sea Drilling Project and it's
successors from 1968 to the present day.

1963 .... Vine and Matthews propose that regular
variations in the magnetic field support
the hypothesis of seafloor spreading.

1965 .... Seafloor spreading, continental drift,
and subduction are assembled into the
new theory of plate tectonics by J. Tuzo
Wilson, Jason Morgan, and others.

1968 .... Deep Sea Drilling Project begins with *Glomar
Challenger* carrying out the first extensive
scientific drilling to sample the ocean floor.

1970 .... National Oceanic and Atmospheric
Administration (NOAA) is established in the
United States and takes on the responsibility
for mapping and researching the oceans.

1977................................... During *Alvin* submersible dives to the
Galapagos rift zone, seafloor hydrothermal
vents (black smokers) and associated
chemosynthetic biological communities are
discovered; First physiographic map of the
entire ocean floor is published by Heezen
and Tharp; even at this time, much of it had
to be extrapolated through artistic license.

1978................................... Seasat, the first satellite devoted to
oceanographic observations, is launched.

1983................................... Global Positioning System (GPS) is
first made available for public use,
revolutionizing ocean (and land) navigation.

1985................................... Shipwrecked RMS *Titanic* is found in 3800
meters depth using sidescan sonar and is
photographed using the unmanned deep-
submergence vehicle *Argo* (Robert Ballard
and photographer Emory Kristof).

1994................................... Convention on the Law of the Sea (signed in
1982) comes into effect, defining territorial
waters as a maximum of 12 nautical
miles (22 km) from the coast, Exclusive
Economic Zones (EEZ) for fishing and
construction as no more than 200 nautical
miles (370 km), and a nation's continental
shelf and drilling rights as extending a
maximum of 350 nautical miles (650 km).

1995.....................................Declassification of Geosat satellite radar
altimetry (data gathered starting 1985)
allows David Sandwell and Walter Smith
to map the worldwide ocean bathymetry in
unprecedented detail, producing the first true
global map of the shape of the ocean floor.

2002.....................................End of the first World Ocean Circulation
Experiment (WOCE, began in 1990),
a multinational comprehensive
study of ocean currents and their
interaction with the atmosphere.

2004.....................................Tsunami generated by a subduction earthquake
off the west coast of Sumatra, Indonesia,
causes widespread devastation in the Indian
Ocean basin and the loss of 250,000 lives.

2007.....................................Fourth Intergovernmental Panel on Climate
Change (IPCC) report is issued, which
reports on the increasing heat content of the
ocean, the accelerating pace of sea-level
rise, and progressive ocean acidification as
significant changes in the ocean environment
that are caused by the addition into the
atmosphere of carbon dioxide and other
greenhouse gases from fossil fuels.

2010.....................................Completion of 10-year Census of
Marine Life, involving 2700 scientists
from more than 80 countries and 540
expeditions to comprehensively inventory
the marine biology of the ocean.

Glossary

abyssal: Depth range of 3000–6000 meters in the water or on the bottom of the ocean.

abyssal plain: The vast, open expanse of relatively level bathymetry that comprises most of the ocean floor.

Acoustic Doppler Current Profiler (ADCP): A device that measures current speed by measuring the Doppler frequency shift of sound waves reflected back from particles in the water.

active transport: A process by which cells use energy to move solutes against the concentration gradient across membranes.

ahermatypic coral: Soft coral that makes no hard reef structures.

albedo: The fraction of solar energy reflected by a surface (as opposed to energy absorbed).

amphidromic circulation: Tidal movements as affected by Coriolis forces, causing high water to circulate around a node, or no-tide point.

anadromous fish: Fish that spend part of their life cycle in freshwater and part in the ocean, such as salmon.

Antarctic Bottom Water: The coldest, saltiest, and densest water mass in the ocean that forms off the Antarctic continental shelf and spreads over the base of the entire Atlantic Ocean.

aphotic zone: The range of water depths into which no sunlight penetrates; the dark zone of the ocean.

aqueous solution: A mixture of compounds in water that are dissolved or separated into their charged ionic forms and are bonded to the water molecules through hydrogen bonds.

asthenosphere: The slow-flowing portion of Earth's mantle on which the rigid plates of lithosphere float and move.

atmospheric circulation cells: Large-scale, closed loops of overall mean airflow distributed according to latitude.

atoll: Ring-shaped group of coral islands or reefs formed around a now-submerged volcanic island.

autotroph: Any organism that produces carbohydrate food from primary sources of energy.

azoic zone: Edward Forbes's briefly popular theory of the mid 1800s that no life existed below depths of about 900 meters; the theory was soon disproven by trawls and dredges.

baleen: Horn-like fibrous plates used by Mysticeti whales to strain plankton from seawater.

bathyal: Depth range of 1000–3000 meters in the water or on the bottom of the ocean.

bathymetry: Measurement of water depth below the sea surface; an inverse equivalent to topography on land.

benthic: The environment on or in close proximity to the water on the bottom of the ocean.

berm: The prominent break in slope on many beaches that marks the highest elevation of wave washing.

biogenous sediment: Sediment originating as the hard parts of marine organisms.

bioluminescence: The process of production of light by an organism, used for camouflage, defense, and attraction of prey and mates.

biomagnification: The exponential increase in the concentration of toxic compounds in animal tissues at successively higher trophic levels.

black smoker: One type of hydrothermal vent in which the hot-water plume is laden with mineral particles that give it the appearance of smoke.

blowout: The uncontrolled release of gas, oil, and/or water under pressure from a well.

breakwater: A rocky barrier constructed parallel to shore and just off shore to protect from wave action.

building sea: Area of surface water where wind action is actively creating and growing new waves.

bycatch: Non-targeted fish caught collaterally during commercial fishing; often discarded as noneconomic.

calcite compensation depth (CCD): Depth below which the water will dissolve calcareous shells such that calcareous ooze does not accumulate as a sediment.

capillary waves: Ripples in water defined by the dominance of surface tension as the restoring force.

caprock: Non-permeable marine rock that can trap in petroleum or natural gas that would otherwise buoyantly rise up through denser water and escape to the surface.

celerity: The speed at which a water wave moves; equal to wavelength divided by wave period.

cephalopod: Mollusks including squid, octopus, cuttlefish, and nautilus that are characterized by bilateral symmetry, a prominent head exhibiting many tentacles.

Cetacea: Taxonomic group of marine mammals descended from land ungulates that includes dolphins, porpoises, and whales.

chemical (hydrogenous) sediment: Sediment formed by precipitation of minerals from seawater.

chemical oceanography: Discipline primarily concerning the composition of seawater and distribution of its chemical constituents.

chemoautotroph: Organism that manufactures food (carbohydrates) from the energy of chemical bonds.

chemosynthesis: Production of carbohydrate food energy by extraction from the breaking of chemical bonds.

Chondrichthyes: The taxonomic class comprised of all cartilaginous fish, such as sharks and skates.

chronometer: Precise clock originally used to determine longitude based on timing of local noon.

coccolithophorid: An abundant group of calcareous algal phytoplankton; their remains are responsible for chalk.

continental drift: The early 20th-century theory that the continents had moved with respect to one another over Earth's surface through geologic time; this theory is now superseded by the theory of plate tectonics.

continental margin: The offshore region extending from sea level to the abyssal plain; comprised of the continental shelf, slope, and sometimes rise.

continental rifting: The breaking up of a continent along a narrow zone of faulting and volcanism as a beginning stage of new mid-ocean ridge formation.

continental shelf: The offshore extension of the land of nearly flat average slope, extending to a depth of about 200 meters.

continental slope: The relatively steeply sloping region of the ocean floor that extends downward from the shelf edge to meet the abyssal plain.

copepod: Very small crustacean zooplankton that are widespread in the pelagic ocean.

Coriolis effect: The tendency of any object in motion on Earth to deviate from a straight-line course due to the rotation of the planet.

covalent bond: The strong bond formed when 2 or more atoms share common electrons; for example, the 2 hydrogen atoms and 1 oxygen atom of a water molecule.

CTD: An instrument lowered into the water to make continuous measurements of conductivity (for salinity), temperature, and depth.

ctenophore: Very common pelagic gelatinous organism, also known as comb jellies.

cyanobacteria: The single-celled organisms that carry out photosynthesis; likely the agents of the oxygen revolution.

DART station: Stands for Deep-ocean Assessment and Reporting of Tsunamis. A buoyed transmitter with a seafloor pressure sensor that can detect tsunami waves as they travel across the open ocean, providing early warning information.

deep-sea fan: Accumulation of a wedge- or fan-shaped pile of sediment at the base of continental slopes.

deep-sea trench: Narrow, arcuate features extending thousands of kilometers of especially deep bathymetry that form at subduction zones, where oceanic crust bends to descend into the mantle.

deepwater wave: A wave in water deeper than 1/2 the wavelength.

density stratification: The process by which the early Earth separated into concentric layers with denser iron-rich material sinking to form the core and lighter elements and rock compounds forming the mantle and crust.

desalination: Process of removing salts from seawater by distillation or reverse osmotic pressure.

diatom: A major and abundant group of siliceous single-celled phytoplankton; they produce glassy frustules.

diffusion: The spreading and dilution of solutes by movement from areas of higher concentration to lower concentration.

dinoflagellate: A major and abundant group of siliceous single-celled phytoplankton; they have whip-like flagella.

disphotic zone: The region of the water column in which light is present but insufficient for photosynthesis.

diurnal tide: A single daily cycle of one high and one low tide.

downwelling: The movement of surface water downward, depressing the thermocline due to either high density or Ekman-transport effects.

echo sounding: Determination of bathymetric water depth by precise timing of a sound wave emitted by a ship and reflected from the water bottom.

Ekman transport: The tendency of wind-driven surface currents to move at an oblique angle to the wind direction, caused by the Coriolis effect acting on the water. The effect increases with depth, creating the variation in motion direction known as the Ekman spiral.

epifauna: Benthic organisms that dwell on or above the sea floor.

equatorial divergence: The tendency of wind-driven surface waters to move in opposite directions just across the equator because of the opposite Coriolis effect in the Northern and Southern hemispheres.

estuary: Coastal body of water where seawater and stream- or river-supplied freshwater mix.

euphotic zone: The uppermost portion of the photic zone with sufficient sunlight for net gain in energy through photosynthesis.

eustatic sea level: The globally averaged elevation of the sea surface.

eutrophication: Conditions of overabundance of nutrients in the water usually due to fertilizer runoff, leading to harmful algal blooms and hypoxia.

extraterrestrial (cosmogenous) sediment: Sediments with an extraterrestrial origin that fall into the ocean from space as meteorites or dust.

extratropical cyclone: Rotating mass of air formed by the disturbance of the boundary between polar and Ferrell cells; includes the northeasters.

fetch: Linear distance over which relatively constant wind blows, forming wind waves.

fissipeds: Marine mammal group including sea otters; in the same order as dogs, cats, bears, and weasels.

fjord: Glacially formed deep and steep-walled valley flooded by the sea.

food web: Representation of the feeding relationships and flow of energy through a biological community.

fracture zone: The inactive trace of a past transform fault beyond the overlap of offset ridges; they may extend thousands of kilometers across the ocean floor.

general circulation models: Supercomputer simulations of the circulation of heat and compounds in the ocean-atmosphere system; used to simulate climate fluctuations and long-term trends.

geochemistry: The science that studies the chemical composition of rocks as a clue to past conditions or geologic processes.

geostrophic gyre: The hemisphere-scale surface-current loops set up in each ocean basin that are dynamically balanced by competing effects of Ekman transport and gravity.

greenhouse effect: The physical property of some atmospheric gases to absorb and trap heat from the Sun's radiation shining on Earth.

guyot: A characteristically flat-topped seamount that was once eroded by wave action as an island and is now entirely submerged.

habitat: The physical environment in which an organism lives.

hadal: Depth range greater than 6000 meters in the water or on the bottom of the ocean; the deepest locations in the ocean.

halocline: A strong gradient in salinity with depth; largely coincides with the pycnocline and thermocline.

hard stabilization: Construction of a solid barrier such as a seawall to lessen or delay the effects of beach or sea-cliff erosion.

heat capacity: The amount of heat energy absorbed by a substance to raise its temperature a specified amount, also known as thermal capacity.

hermatypic coral: Coral that secretes carbonate and builds up reefs.

heterotroph: Any organism that consumes organic matter produced by others.

holdfast: The anchor of a kelp seaweed that fixes it to the substrate, as roots do for vascular plants.

holothurian: The sea cucumber or sea pig, a soft benthic echinoderm that scavenges the mud of the sea floor.

hydrogen bond: The weak bond formed when polar ions or molecules are linked by attraction of their oppositely charged regions.

hydrothermal vent: A seafloor hot spring where superheated, chemically laden water is discharged from the oceanic crust.

hypoxic zone: Any region in the ocean of extremely low oxygen availability due to fertilizer runoff; an example is in the Gulf of Mexico off the mouth of the Mississippi River.

hypsometric curve: A graph showing the cumulative area of Earth's surface above any given elevation, above or below sea level.

infauna: Benthic organisms that dwell within the sea floor.

krill: Crustacean zooplankton, very abundant in Antarctic waters in particular.

lagoon: Shallow saltwater region trapped between the beach dune zone and the mainland area.

latent heat: The heat energy that must be absorbed or released to change the state of a material by evaporation or freezing, producing no temperature change.

lithosphere: The rigid outer portion of Earth's crust and uppermost mantle that makes up the tectonic plates.

longshore bar: Sandbar parallel to the coast and just offshore in the tidal range.

longshore drift: Net transport of sediment parallel to the coast due to prevailing wave directions and variable swash and backwash on the beach.

magnetometer: A device that measures the strength and orientation of Earth's magnetic field.

manganese nodule: Roughly spherical particle formed as manganese oxide precipitates from seawater over time.

mariculture: Fish farming, or growing fish for food in ocean-water tanks or pens.

marine snow: Clumps of whitish organic detritus that form a constant "snowfall" to the sea floor in deepwater environments; fuels scavenger ecosystems.

maximum sustainable yield: The amount of a given target species that can be caught each year without long-term depletion of the stock.

mesoglea: Translucent, jellylike gel that makes up the bulk of organisms like jellyfish.

mesopelagic zone: The dimly lit region of the water column; also called the disphotic zone or the twilight zone.

microbial loop: A producer-consumer food web in the ocean consisting entirely of bacteria and largely independent of the conventional ecosystem.

microtektite: Tiny glassy particles produced by impact melting when an asteroid hits Earth.

mid-ocean ridge: The globe-encircling mountain range where seafloor spreading occurs by volcanic activity creating new oceanic crust.

Miller-Urey Experiment: A 1955 laboratory study that demonstrated that organic compounds could be spontaneously generated from inorganic carbon compounds and energy.

mixed tide: Most common type of daily tide cycle, exhibiting 2 tidal cycles per day with differing highs and lows.

monsoon: Seasonal weather pattern typified by heavy rain resulting from onshore flow of warm, humid air drawn in by rising air heated over mountain ranges in the summer, especially in the Indian subcontinent and Himalayan mountain front.

multibeam bathymetry: Bathymetric mapping done by echo sounding using a fan of narrow acoustic beams to image a strip of the ocean floor.

neap tide: The relatively small range between high and low tide at times of quarter Moon due to destructive interference of solar and lunar gravity.

nekton: All organisms that actively swim in the ocean (e.g., fish, marine mammals, cephalopods, and more).

nematocysts: Also known as cnidocytes, the stinging cells of many jellyfish and other cnidarians.

neritic: The region on or over the continental shelf.

Niskin bottle: A device to take a water sample from a specified depth in the water column that has 2 open ends that can be triggered to close and seal in a water sample.

North Atlantic Deep Water: The cold, saline water mass that forms in the North Atlantic and Arctic oceans that is responsible for most of the volume of the deep ocean.

ocean acidification: The increase in acidity of seawater that is developing as a result of increased dissolved carbon dioxide.

ocean basin: The container for the ocean; the region underlain with oceanic crust and bounded by continental slopes.

oceanic crust: The crust of Earth, which is formed at mid-ocean ridges by lava and magma welling up from the mantle that forms the geologic substrate of most of the ocean floor.

oceanography: The scientific study of the oceans, encompassing the application of the disciplines of physics, chemistry, biology, and geology to all aspects of the global ocean.

ocean thermal energy conversion (OTEC): A pilot technology to generate energy by exploiting the temperature difference between warm, near-surface water and cold, deep water drawn up to the surface.

oil boom: A floating curtain of plastic placed into the water to contain spilled oil on the surface of the water.

ooze: Sediment of the deep-sea floor that primarily originated from accumulated shells and skeletons of plankton; can be calcareous (carbonate-based) or siliceous (silica-based) ooze.

orbital motion: The circular path taken by a water particle as a wave passes by, moving it first back and upward then forward and down to return to its starting point.

osmoregulation: Biological process of controlling internal salinity and other chemical balances for optimum metabolism.

osmosis: A passive process causing net movement of solvent (water) across a membrane separating 2 solutions of different concentration level, tending to equalize their concentration.

Osteichthyes: The taxonomic class comprised of all bony fish.

oxygen-minimum zone: Depth range in the ocean where available oxygen is lowest, beneath the photic zone but above the cold, very deep waters.

oxygen revolution: The wholesale modification of Earth's atmosphere from an oxygen-poor one to the present oxygen-rich one between 3.5 and 0.8 billion years ago.

paleoceanography: Discipline that involves studying ancient past currents, climate, and the state of the ocean from thousands to billions of years ago.

Panthalassa: The single large ocean hypothesized by Alfred Wegener that surrounded Pangaea, the unified single continent that has since rifted apart.

pelagic: The open-water environment that is away from coasts and off the continental shelf.

pelagic longline fishing: Fishing method employing baited hooks on a kilometers-long main fishing line, used for fish that have high trophic levels—such as swordfish and tuna.

persistence: The length of time a pollutant lasts in an environment.

photic zone: The sunlit upper layer of ocean water.

photophores: The organs that produce light in bioluminescent organisms.

photosynthesis: The biological process of capturing solar energy by using it to make carbohydrates as food.

physical oceanography: Discipline primarily concerning the movement and physical properties of water in the oceans.

pinnipeds: Marine mammal group including seals, sea lions, and walruses; in the same order as dogs, cats, bears, and weasels.

piston core: A cylindrical sample of the ocean-floor sediments taken by lowering a hydraulically activated, weighted sampling tube from a surface-research ship.

planetesimals: Small asteroid-like clumps of rock orbiting around an early Sun that accreted together by gravity to form Earth and other rocky planets.

plankton: All organisms that drift with water movements and currents passively.

plate tectonics: Scientific theory on the movement and evolution of Earth's outer layers over geologic time.

polyps: The individual coral animals, similar to sea anemones, that collectively make up the colony in a coral head.

primary production: The creation of biomass through photosynthesis or chemosynthesis.

principle of constant proportions: The ratio of major salts in seawater is everywhere the same in the world's ocean—though concentration (salinity) may differ. Also known as Forchhammer's principle.

Project Mohole: The first deep-sea drilling research project; a pioneering but ultimately unsuccessful 1961 effort to drill down to Earth's mantle in the Pacific Ocean.

pycnocline: A strong gradient in density of seawater versus depth.

reservoir rock: Porous marine rock or sediment layers that can hold large amounts of petroleum or natural gas.

residence time: The amount of an element in the ocean divided by the rate at which it is added or removed; a measure of the average time the element stays in seawater.

respiration: Metabolic process of consuming energy by breakdown of carbohydrates with oxygen to fuel activity, releasing carbon dioxide.

river-dominated delta: A river mouth in which the strong flow from land determines the pattern of sediment deposition and channel geometry.

rogue wave: Any wave or short series of waves at least 2 times larger than prevailing waves in the area and time—and larger than the theoretical maximum for a fully developed sea.

salinity: The total amount of dissolved solids in water, expressed by weight per unit volume.

salp: A tubular, gelatinous animal that lives either as an individual or as a colony that is common in equatorial waters.

salt evaporation: Production of sea salt for consumption by evaporation of seawater in open ponds.

satellite altimetry: Measurement of the elevation of the sea (or land) surface precisely using space-based radar-signal reflection timing.

seamount: Volcanic mountain that rises above the surrounding ocean floor but is submerged below sea level.

sea stack: Rocky outcropping near the shore but isolated from the mainland created by erosional retreat of sea cliffs over time.

sediment: Particles of inorganic or organic matter that accumulate in a loose, unconsolidated form.

semidiurnal tide: A daily cycle of 2 high and 2 low tides.

sensible heat: Heat energy that results in a change in temperature.

sessile: Animals unable to move about that are usually permanently fixed to their substrate, such as barnacles or corals.

sextant: Instrument used to measure the angle above the horizon of celestial objects that is used in navigation.

shallow-water waves: Formally, all waves in water shallower than 1/20th of the wavelength.

siphonophore: An order of Cnidaria that are colonial animals; one example is the Portuguese man-of-war.

Sirenia: Taxonomic group of marine mammals that includes manatees and dugongs.

soft stabilization: Addition of sand to a beach through beach replenishment or nourishment to mitigate beach erosion.

solar nebula: The rotating cloud of gases and particles from which the Solar System formed.

spring tide: The relatively large range between low and high tide at times of constructive interference of lunar and solar gravity during full and new moons.

stick chart: Maplike representation of islands, waves, and ocean currents used in navigation by Micronesian and Polynesian seafarers.

subduction zone: Location where oceanic plate lithosphere (the sea floor and its underpinnings) descend into Earth's mantle, consuming the tectonic plate.

submarine canyon: Any offshore canyon on the continental slope that is formed by erosion due to flows of sediment along the bottom in turbidity currents.

substrate: The sediment or rock base forming part of a benthic organism's habitat.

swell: Waves that have left the area of development and are propagating across the sea surface.

swim bladder: Gas-filled chambers many fish have beneath their spine to maintain buoyancy in the water.

terrigenous sediment: Sediment originating from land that is input into the ocean either by water- or wind-borne transport.

thermal expansion: The increase in volume of water as it becomes warmer; specifically used to refer to the component of sea-level rise due to this effect as heat content of the ocean changes.

thermocline: A strong gradient in water temperature versus depth that separates warm surface waters from the vast volume of cold, deep water.

thermohaline circulation: Gravity-driven movement of deepwater masses due to the density differences controlled by salinity and temperature.

tidal bore: An inrushing high-tide wave that funnels up a confined river or estuary.

tide-dominated delta: A river mouth in which the waves and tides determine the pattern of sediment deposition and channel geometry.

toxicity: The amount of a pollutant necessary to cause some form of damage in an ecosystem or organism.

trade winds: Prevailing easterly winds centered on 15° latitude north and south.

tragedy of the commons: Concept articulated by Garrett Hardin that when a resource is available to a large group in common, it benefits each member to maximize his or her use—even if it would be better for everyone to limit their use. Applied to the problem of fishery management.

transform fault: Location where one plate slides past another on Earth's surface—neither creating nor consuming plate area—especially those between offset spreading ridge segments.

transverse current: The generally east-west flowing surface currents that link the boundary currents and also account for the Antarctic Circumpolar Current (also known as the West Wind Drift).

trophic level: A scale of how many steps of consumption an organism is removed from primary production.

tropical cyclone: Rotating mass of tropical, low-pressure air with heavy winds and rainfall fueled by sea-surface heat; includes hurricanes and typhoons.

tsunami: A wave train produced by displacement of water due to sudden mass movement of the sea floor caused by an earthquake or undersea landslide.

tubenose: Taxonomic group of far-traveling marine birds including albatrosses, shearwaters, and petrels.

turbidity current: Flow of suspended sediment-laden water down the ocean floor that is driven by density and gravity.

upwelling: The movement of cold, deeper water upward to the sea surface when surface waters are drawn away by divergence or Ekman-transport effects.

volcanic outgassing: The release of water, carbon dioxide, nitrogen, and other gases from Earth's interior at volcanoes.

Wadati-Benioff zone: The planes of earthquakes extending deep into Earth that mark the location of the consumed plate slab from subduction.

wave-cut platform: A near-flat bedrock plane cut by wave action eroding the coast between high- and low-tide levels.

wave period: The time elapsed from the passage of one wave crest to the next (or any equivalent points on a cyclical wave).

wave refraction: Bending of the orientation of wave crests by differential wave speed caused by local differences in water depth.

wind waves: Waves caused by wind drag on the water surface and defined by the dominance of gravity as the restoring force.

zooxanthellae: Microscopic dinoflagellate photosynthesizers that live symbiotically and are hosted by coral polyps.

Bibliography

Aguado, Edward, and James E. Burt. *Understanding Weather and Climate.* 5th ed. Upper Saddle River, NJ: Prentice Hall, 2009. A comprehensive introductory college textbook on meteorology and climatology.

Atwater, Brian, Satoko Musumi-Rokkaku, Kenji Satake, Yoshinobu Tsuji, Kazue Ueda, and David Yamaguchi. *The Orphan Tsunami of 1700: Japanese Clues to a Parent Earthquake in North America.* Seattle, WA: University of Washington Press, 2005. The amazing story of scientific sleuthing that showed that a massive earthquake in the Pacific Northwest caused a devastating tsunami that struck Japan without warning. Contains an excellent introduction to tsunami science in general.

Berta, Annalisa, James L. Sumich, and Kit M. Kovacs. *Marine Mammals: Evolutionary Biology.* 2nd ed. Burlington, MA: Academic Press, 2005. An advanced and comprehensive textbook and reference with a focus on the evolutionary adaptations of mammals to the marine environment.

Boggs, Sam. *Principles of Sedimentology and Stratigraphy.* 5th ed. Boston: Pearson, 2011. A full-length textbook for those who want to learn about sediments in detail.

Broecker, Wallace S. *How to Build a Habitable Planet.* 4th ed. Palisades, NY: Eldigio Press, 2002. A clear, concise, and relatively jargon-free history of planet Earth and its climate and chemistry. Not dumbed down, but not inaccessible either.

Butt, Tony, Paul Russell, and Rick Grigg. *Surf Science: An Introduction to Waves for Surfing.* Honolulu: University of Hawaii Press, 2004. A very readable popular science book that provides an entry into the physics of waves in the ocean by using the question every surfer wants to know: What makes a good wave?

Carson, Rachel. *The Edge of the Sea.* Boston: Houghton Mifflin, 1955. Wonderfully evocative writing that explores the coastal habitat and ecology of the shore, especially focusing on the Eastern Seaboard of the United States. Her writing is classic and still fresh.

————. *The Sea around Us.* Oxford: Oxford University Press, 2003. An absolute must-read classic of popular science writing, Carson's 1951 best seller remains very fresh and readable. Carson was a marine biologist and painted a broad and beautiful picture of the majesty and power of the ocean and of the fascinating variety of creatures that inhabit it.

Cartwright, David Edgar. *Tides: A Scientific History.* Cambridge: Cambridge University Press, 2000. A historical approach to tidal theory and how it was developed by Newton, Laplace, and others.

Casey, Susan. *The Wave: In Pursuit of the Rogues, Freaks, and Giants of the Ocean.* New York: Doubleday, 2010. A lively exploration of the pathological waves of the ocean with an insider view of the world of big-wave surfing.

Clark, R. B. *Marine Pollution.* 5th ed. Oxford: Oxford University Press, 2001. A thorough textbook on the topic of all forms of toxins and pollution introduced into the ocean.

Climate Change 2007: The Physical Science Basis. Contribution of Working Group I to the Fourth Assessment Report of the Intergovernmental Panel on Climate Change. Technical Summary, edited by Solomon, S., D. Qin, M. Manning, Z. Chen, M. Marquis, K. B. Averyt, M. Tignor and H. L. Miller. Cambridge: Cambridge University Press, 2007. The consensus document of the oceanographic and climatology science community on the present state of global warming; see pages 47–50 in particular for a synthesis of changes in the ocean.

Cone, Joseph. *Fire under the Sea: The Discovery of the Most Extraordinary Environment on Earth—Volcanic Hot Springs on the Ocean Floor.* New York: Quill, 1992. The story of the still-in-progress discovery and exploration of the hydrothermal vents at the mid-ocean ridges and of the scientists who made those paradigm-shifting discoveries.

Cousteau, Jacques. *The Silent World*. London: The Reprint Society, 1954. A classic, Cousteau's evocatively written account of his invention of the SCUBA aqualung and the early days of underwater exploration and life in the reefs he explored.

Darwin, Charles. *The Voyage of the* Beagle: *Charles Darwin's Journal of Researches*. Champaign, IL: Book Jungle, 2009 (originally published 1843). We all tend to have an image of Darwin as an elderly, learned-looking, bearded gentleman. His readable 1839 account of the 5-year expedition on the *Beagle* is a revelation, as he describes both seafaring and overland adventures that would befit Indiana Jones. His dynamic writing puts us right inside the thoughts and adventures of an energetic and brilliant developing naturalist.

Davis, Richard A., and Duncan M. FitzGerald. *Beaches and Coasts*. Malden, MA: Blackwell Publishing, 2004. An overview of the coastal and estuarine environment, including beaches, barrier islands, tidal inlets, estuaries, deltas, and more.

Earle, Sylvia. *The World Is Blue: How Our Fate and the Ocean's Are One*. Washington DC: National Geographic, 2010. Sylvia Earle has been a foremost ocean explorer for decades, and she lays out just how grave the present challenges are and what can be done to better protect the ocean for the future.

Ebbesmeyer, Curtis. *Flotsametrics and the Floating World: How One Man's Obsession with Runaway Sneakers and Rubber Ducks Revolutionized Ocean Science*. New York: Smithsonian Books, 2009. Ebbesmeyer is an oceanographer who used the ordinary trash floating up on beaches to track ocean currents; here, he describes his life's work and makes larger points about the growing environmental threat of all that trash.

Emanuel, Kerry. *Divine Wind: The History and Science of Hurricanes*. Oxford: Oxford University Press, 2005. An entry into the workings of tropical and extratropical cyclones by one of the world's leading experts, spiced with a good deal of social history related to significant storms including the "divine winds" that saved Japan from invasion and gave us the word kamikaze.

Emiliani, Cesare. *Planet Earth: Cosmology, Geology, and the Evolution of Life and Environment.* Rev. ed. New York: Cambridge University Press, 1995. A big-scale, semi-technical overview of the formation of Earth and how it evolved physically and biologically.

Fagan, Brian M. *Floods, Famines, and Emperors: El Niño and the Fate of Civilizations.* Rev. ed. New York: Basic Books, 2009. An interesting look at how El Niño has had far-reaching social and cultural effects as well as meteorological ones.

Fry, Iris. *The Emergence of Life on Earth: A Historical and Scientific Overview.* New Brunswick, NJ: Rutgers University Press, 2000. An exploration of the earliest origins of life (in the sea, of course) from a historical, scientific, and philosophical perspective.

Gage, John D., and Paul A. Tyler. *Deep-Sea Biology: A Natural History of Organisms at the Deep-Sea Floor.* Cambridge: Cambridge University Press, 1991. A comprehensive look, now only slightly dated, at the ecosystems of the ocean floor.

Garrison, Tom. *Essentials of Oceanography.* 5th ed. Pacific Grove, CA: Brooks Cole, 2008. One of several textbooks by Garrison, this condensed and information-packed volume would make an excellent companion to the course (any recent edition would do). It is very useful as a reference and extension of the course material throughout all of the lectures.

Greenberg, Paul. *Four Fish: The Future of the Last Wild Food.* New York: Penguin, 2010. Greenberg's investigation of global fisheries touches on all the topics of overfishing, industrial fish farming, and the ongoing "gold rush" of wild tuna, showing how 4 fish—salmon, tuna, cod, and bass—dominate the seafood world.

Heezen, Bruce, and Charles Hollister. *The Face of the Deep.* New York: Oxford University Press, 1971. Published in 1971, an atlas and gallery of the pioneering photographs of the ocean floor by the scientists who made them.

Hohn, Donovan. *Moby-Duck: The True Story of 28,800 Bath Toys Lost at Sea and of the Beachcombers, Oceanographers, Environmentalists, and Fools, Including the Author, Who Went in Search of Them.* New York: Viking, 2011. The subtitle says it all. A whimsical odyssey exploring the fate of the bath toys and other flotsam lost at sea.

Holthuijsen, Leo H. *Waves in Oceanic and Coastal Waters.* Cambridge: Cambridge University Press, 2010. An advanced treatise on the physics of ocean waves.

Horwitz, Tony. *Blue Latitudes: Boldly Going Where Captain Cook Has Gone Before.* New York: H. Holt, 2002. Equal parts biography of Captain Cook and travel narrative of the Polynesian world today, this volume provides greater insight into Cook as an explorer and as an Enlightenment figure than do many of the more scholarly biographies. Along the way, Horwitz sheds light on the changes Cook's contact wrought on the people of the Pacific islands.

Hsü, Kenneth J. *The Mediterranean Was a Desert: A Voyage of the* Glomar Challenger. Princeton, NJ: Princeton University Press, 1987. An account of one voyage of the *Glomar Challenger*, a deep-sea scientific drilling vessel, by one of the scientists who was there. It provides insight into how sedimentary records tell us about past conditions on Earth and in the sea.

Kaharl, Victoria A. *Water Baby: The Story of* Alvin. New York: Oxford University Press, 1990. A "biography" of the famous deep-diving submarine that made so many of the fundamental discoveries in the abyss from the 1960s into the 21st century, including the wreck of the *Titanic* in 1985.

Kunzig, Robert. *Mapping the Deep: The Extraordinary Story of Ocean Science.* New York: W. W. Norton & Company, 2000. A very readable account of the discovery of the geology and biology of the deep sea, from early explorers to *Alvin* and the hydrothermal vents. Kunzig really captures the wonder of discovery. One of my favorite books.

Lawrence, David M. *Upheaval from the Abyss: Ocean Floor Mapping and the Earth Science Revolution.* 2002. The story of sonar, bathymetry, and the unveiling of the shape of the ocean floor that heralded the plate-tectonic revolution.

Medwin, Herman. *Sounds in the Sea: From Ocean Acoustics to Acoustical Oceanography.* New York: Cambridge University Press, 2005. Comprehensive and technical, this textbook covers the whole field of sound in the ocean.

Melville, Herman. *Moby Dick; or, The Whale.* New York: Harper & Brothers, 1851. Read this odd and amazing novel (again) and discover Melville's amusing and lively description of the characters of the Nantucket whaling community—and of Moby Dick himself. I give you permission to skim or even skip over all the cetacean detail in the middle, but it's worth the effort to get to the end.

Menard, Henry W. *The Ocean of Truth: A Personal History of Global Tectonics.* Princeton, NJ: Princeton University Press, 1986. The story of how the plate-tectonics scientific revolution came to pass by one of the scientists who made it happen.

Miller, Charles B. *Biological Oceanography.* Malden, MA: Blackwell Publishing, 2004. A modern reference and comprehensive textbook on marine biology.

Morrissey, John F., and James L. Sumich. *Introduction to the Biology of Marine Life.* 10th ed. Sudbury, MA: Jones & Bartlett Learning, 2010. A classic and standard text, comprehensively covering in detail the topics of marine life, food webs, ecology, and more.

Murphy, Dallas. *To Follow the Water: Exploring the Ocean to Discover Climate.* New York: Basic Books, 2008. A journalist goes to sea for a month with physical oceanographers and elucidates ocean currents and the link to heat transport on the planet.

Nash, J. Madeleine. *El Niño: Unlocking the Secrets of the Master Weather-Maker*. New York: Warner Books, 2003. A science journalist's investigation of the causes and effects of the gigantic Pacific weather system, using the record-breaking 1998–1999 event as a primary example.

National Oceanic and Atmospheric Administration (NOAA). *Hidden Depths: Atlas of the Oceans*. New York: HarperCollins, 2007. A beautifully illustrated and informative atlas coproduced by the OAA and the Smithsonian as they developed the Sant Hall of Ocean Sciences in the Smithsonian Museum of Natural History, this volume complements the course very well. Highly recommended.

Nouvian, Claire. *The Deep: The Extraordinary Creatures of the Abyss*. Chicago: University of Chicago Press, 2007. This is a bit of a coffee-table book, but the stunning photography of hundreds of only recently discovered organisms makes it well worth a look.

Open University. *Ocean Circulation*. 2nd ed. Oxford: Butterworth-Heinemann, 2001. For those who want to delve deeper into the surface and deep flow in the oceans, this is a physical oceanography text without overreliance on mathematics.

―――. *Seawater: Its Composition, Properties and Behaviour*. 2nd rev. ed. Oxford, UK: Butterworth-Heinemann, 2004. A complete textbook on the properties of ocean water for the seriously interested.

Oreskes, Naomi. *Plate Tectonics: An Insider's History of the Modern Theory of the Earth*. Cambridge, MA: Westview Press, 2003. A collection of essays written by many of the scientists who were there at the birth of plate tectonics that is stitched together by the author, a historian of science.

Parker, Bruce. *The Power of the Sea: Tsunamis, Storm Surges, Rogue Waves, and Our Quest to Predict Disasters*. New York: Palgrave Macmillan, 2010. A more in-depth—but still layperson's—treatment of destructive waves in the ocean.

Philbrick, Nathaniel. *In the Heart of the Sea: The Tragedy of the Whaleship Essex*. New York: Penguin, 2001. The story of the 19th-century Pacific whaling industry told using the device of examining a microcosm—the wreck of the *Essex* that was the inspiration for *Moby Dick*.

Pilkey, Orrin H., William J. Neal, Joseph T. Kelley, and J. Andrew G. Cooper. *The World's Beaches: A Global Guide to the Science of the Shoreline*. Berkeley: University of California Press, 2011. An illustrated introduction to the anatomy of beaches and shorelines and the effects of sea-level rise upon them.

Pilkey, Orrin H., and Rob Young. *The Rising Sea*. Washington DC: Island Press/Shearwater Books, 2009. A brief, clear, and very accessible account of the causes and effects of the accelerating sea-level rise that is now impacting shorelines in the United States and around the world.

Prager, Ellen. *Chasing Science at Sea: Racing Hurricanes, Stalking Sharks, and Living Undersea with Ocean Experts*. Chicago: University of Chicago Press, 2010. An inspirational and lively window to the real life of marine scientists making discoveries and having adventures.

———. *Sex, Drugs, and Sea Slime: The Oceans' Oddest Creatures and Why They Matter*. Chicago: University of Chicago Press, 2011. Wonderfully entertaining and informative look at the life and times of sea cucumbers, octopi, lobsters, and many others. Prager really brings these denizens of the deep to life in an unmatched way.

Pugh, David. *Changing Sea Levels: Effects of Tides, Weather and Climate*. New York: Cambridge University Press, 2004. Textbook-level material for more in-depth examination of tidal theory as well as storm surges, climate, and sea-level rise.

Bibliography

Rogers, A. D., and D.d'A Laffoley. "International Earth System Expert Workshop on Ocean Stresses and Impacts." Summary report. International Programme on the State of the Ocean (IPSO). Oxford, 2011. 18 pp. The current state of knowledge of ocean heat content and temperature change, acidification, and sea level is a rapidly changing target; at the time of this writing, this was an up-to-date and concise summary.

Safina, Carl. *A Sea in Flames: The Deepwater Horizon Oil Blowout*. New York: Crown Publishers, 2011. A marine biologist and conservationist gives his take on the 2010 Gulf of Mexico disaster, arriving at some perhaps counterintuitive conclusions about the nature of society's impact on the Gulf ecosystem.

————. *The View from Lazy Point: A Natural Year in an Unnatural World*. New York: Henry Holt and Company, 2011. A conservationist view of the damage to the ocean environment that modern society is causing, leavened with the author's optimism that the world still contains vast natural beauty and vibrant ecosystems.

Schreiber, Elizabeth A., and Joanna A. Burger, eds. *Biology of Marine Birds*. Boca Raton, FL: CRC Press, 2001. A comprehensive and detailed authoritative source by experts in the field.

Sheets, Bob, and Jack Williams. *Hurricane Watch: Forecasting the Deadliest Storms on Earth*. New York: Vintage, 2001. A history of the scientific progress in predicting and forecasting hurricanes and typhoons.

Sobel, Dava. *Longitude: The True Story of a Lone Genius Who Solved the Greatest Scientific Problem of His Time*. New York: Walker & Company, 1996. A fascinating short account of how the need for navigation at sea led to the development of accurate clocks, providing surprising insights into British class distinctions and science in the 18th century along the way.

Sverdrup, Keith A., and E. Virginia Armbrust. *Introduction to the World's Oceans*. 10th ed. Boston, MA: McGraw-Hill, 2008. A comprehensive textbook that would make a fine companion to the course—either instead of or in addition to Garrison's *Essentials of Oceanography*.

Ulanski, Stan. *The Gulf Stream: Tiny Plankton, Giant Bluefin, and the Amazing Story of the Powerful River in the Atlantic*. Chapel Hill: University of North Carolina Press, 2008. The Gulf Stream, from Franklin to satellites, with lots of marine life thrown in as well.

Van Dover, Cindy Lee. *The Ecology of Deep-Sea Hydrothermal Vents*. Princeton, NJ: Princeton University Press, 2000. An expert writes an accessible text on the unique life at the black smokers and other mid-ocean ridge vents.

Videler, John J. *Fish Swimming*. New York: Chapman & Hall, 1993. A biology textbook on the processes of swimming and hydrodynamics of fin and other fish.

Walker, Gabrielle. *An Ocean of Air: Why the Wind Blows and Other Mysteries of the Atmosphere*. Orlando, FL: Harcourt, 2008. Atmospheric circulation at the level of a popular science account.

Yergin, Daniel. *The Prize: The Epic Quest for Oil, Money, and Power*. New York: Free Press, 2009. A sweeping history of the oil industry and its impact on virtually every aspect of modern life.

Notes

Notes

Notes

Notes